1945

Gift from
Mr. Linn

C0-AOE-409

3 0301 00021751 9

This book may be kept

FOURTEEN DAY

A fine will be c⁻

A. BRAZIER HOWELL

Speed in Animals

their specialization for running and leaping

LIBRARY
College of St. Francis
JOLIET, ILL.

UNIVERSITY OF CHICAGO PRESS · CHICAGO

THE UNIVERSITY OF CHICAGO PRESS · CHICAGO

Agent: THE CAMBRIDGE UNIVERSITY PRESS · LONDON

COPYRIGHT 1944 BY THE UNIVERSITY OF CHICAGO. ALL RIGHTS
RESERVED. PUBLISHED AUGUST 1944. COMPOSED AND PRINTED BY THE
UNIVERSITY OF CHICAGO PRESS, CHICAGO, ILLINOIS, U.S.A.

591.47
H 858

Foreword

THE locomotion of animals has always been of particular interest to me because of its basic importance in influencing form and function and because it is the dynamic expression of bone and muscle anatomy. I have had this book in mind for many years, and during that time I gradually accumulated, as I had the time and opportunity, the information that would enable me to write it. After its completion I am more impressed with the amount still to be ascertained about the subject than with that already known; but this seems to be so of most undertakings of this sort. It is true that the subject could be pursued more exhaustively, to the extent of a lifetime or two, with large sums of money expended upon complicated apparatus for recording this or that. There may be some criticism that I have paid insufficient attention to the mathematical physics of attained speed. Greater excursions into this field were made than the text indicates; but others have done this to a considerable extent, and it is not the approach which has interested me most. The last seven words are perhaps the keynote to the mode of procedure. In pursuing the subject I have followed the method and inquired into the details that proved to be of greatest interest to me individually. Also the presentation reflects my own beliefs. In other words, I have not always presented all sides of long controversial subjects, such as possible evolutionary processes involved, but have merely stated my own convictions.

The number of people with whom I have discussed locomotion is very large, and I am indebted to all of them for helping me to form my ideas. For specific aid, however, I wish to thank Mrs. Carl Akeley, Charles Belden, S. H. Chubb, Mrs. Wilma Dietz, Herbert Friedmann, C. L. Gazin, C. W. Gilmore, W. K. Gregory, E. R. Hall, J. E. Hill, Remington Kellogg, R. L. Law, B. C. Park, H. C. Raven, G. G. Simpson, A. H. Schultz, W. L. Straus, Jr., and S. P. Young. I am under particular obligation to J. M. Sprague for reading manuscript, and to H. B. Dillehunt for the cover and one of the chapter-heading designs. I am also in the debt of the American Museum of Natural History and the United States National Museum for the loan of specimens and free access to their collections.

iii

18857

Table of Contents

List of Illustrations

Introduction

As BERNARD pointed out many years ago, the functioning of a living animal may be divided into two main categories—the purely internal bodily activities, involving integration of individual structures for maintaining health; and those activities of the organism that are directly responsive to the environment. The two, however, are highly interdependent.

Internal bodily activities concern chiefly the vital organs, the assimilation of food, the excretion of waste products, the action of the endocrine glands, and all those complicated processes involving our internal economy. They must be fitted for the usual peak loads imposed by environmental conditions. The respiratory system of the sperm whale must be fitted for prolonged and deep submergence, and the blood-vascular system must be able to supply the extra oxygen and eliminate the extra carbon dioxide incident to the demands that a reasonable maximum of muscular activity imposes. Of what advantage would the legs of a greyhound be if it collapsed from exhaustion in the first 100 yards of a sprint? All these internal activities may be classed under the heading of vital functions, although some of them are not necessarily of vital moment.

Environmental responses fall into three main classifications: those incident to perpetuation of the race, those involved in obtaining food, and those permitting the animal to escape from its usual enemies. All others are basically incidental.

Although mating behavior varies greatly among different animals, it appears to have exerted very little influence upon bodily form. A lethargic species with long body and short legs mates as readily as one that is active, with short body and long legs.

Activities involved in obtaining food and escaping from enemies are extremely variable interdependently. Escape from an enemy may involve dodging into a hole, climbing a tree, or a burst of speed. Recourses of the first two sorts may be adopted by active animals but seldom by those fitted for speedy locomotion. Again, an ungulate may be able to obtain sufficient food without traveling faster than a few miles per hour, but, if the species is to survive, it *must* be able to outrun its usual carnivorous enemies. In the case of a carnivore, such as the lion, it, perhaps, need fear no enemy (except man); but it must be sufficiently speedy to overtake a regular food supply. If it is unable to do so, it must turn to carrion or small game of more sedentary habits, in which case, if it survives, it will in time lose its ability to run with speed. On the other hand, the development of an excess of speed in a large, and particularly in a specialized, carnivore could prove disastrous. If it could secure prey with too much ease, it well might increase numerically to the point where it would destroy its food supply and become starved into extermination. It does not seem unlikely that this was the fate of some of the sabertoothed cats. In their case the predator was not so speedy, but its prey may have been particularly slow and clumsy (like ground sloths), and when the latter were gone the big carnivores were unable to overtake faster food.

So the need for speed, either to secure food or to escape being food for others, is ever present among the phyla of animals, not alone for those that could respond to it, but for those that could not and therefore were obliged to develop resourcefulness, with change of body form in order to take advantage of those niches of environment in which lack of speed would be no insuperable handicap. It is no exaggeration to state that the factor of speed, either defensive or offensive, plus or minus, has been one of the most powerful factors, if not the most powerful, in evolution.

In any sort of study of speedy locomotion, arbitrary standards are necessary. Size and body weight must be considered. Relative to size, a mouse can run faster than a horse, but the former is not a cursorial type and the latter is. A fox can run as fast as a horse; so is the former a more efficient running machine? A mere comparison of relative speeds does not answer the question. Man himself is a cursorial type, yet many quadrupeds but a fraction of his bulk and indifferently fitted for cursorial ability can outrun him.

Speed in reaching a distant objective may be attained by running (cursorial ability), hopping (saltatorial ability), flying (volant ability), or swimming (aquatic ability) on the part of animals fitted for these sorts of locomotion. It is only with the first two of these specializations that this book deals. Obviously, it is impossible for a single individual to experiment with all the speedy mammals in existence; and even in the case of common sorts it is extremely difficult to determine the maximum speed attainable. Hence, one must utilize the types of mammals that prove to be available and the data of others that appear to be most reliable. For an understanding of conditions in mammals it will be necessary to review the locomotor mechanisms of all classes of vertebrates, for cursorial specialization can be built only upon the basic equipment inherited from more generalized ancestors. Fossil forms will be considered only in special cases.

Attention should be called to the fact that during the evolution of the higher types of mammals there has been constant compromise in the response of the organism to environmental stimuli. An animal may attain speed in swimming or flying without limbs, but it must have limbs to run. Only a certain sort of fish could develop into a terrestrial tetrapod. Not alone must it have had fins not too highly specialized as paddles and properly placed, in order to emerge from the water; but it must have had proper respiratory equipment to breath air, and the stimulus, furnished by dwindling pools in a dry climate, so that the fish had to migrate overland to survive; and these had to come at precisely the correct stage in the evolution of the particular sort of fish so that it could respond to the environmental stimuli.

Only those sorts of amphibians—again, perhaps, in a desiccating climate—that had a dermal equipment to withstand drying of the body surface could develop limbs capable of taking them with some degree of speed far from water. Only certain kinds of reptiles, possibly with the ability for developing warm-bloodedness, were capable of developing the mammalian type of limb necessary in a wide-ranging, predaceous vertebrate. And only a fairly open habitat, frequented by a primitive mammal whose bodily equipment was not too highly specialized in other directions (as for digging), could develop a high degree of cursorial ability. So a highly specialized end product in mammals is the result of particular stimuli, usually of a largely necessitous nature, encountered at just the correct stage in the evolution of fairly generalized organisms, whose equipment and ingrained habits did not inhibit responses in the indicated direction and that were not too specialized in other directions.

Almost everyone, at one time or another, has speculated on the question of why we, as mammals, are equipped with certain basic features of form, such as four limbs instead of six, two eyes and two nostrils instead of one, and a single vertebral column. Each of us is composed of thousands of items fitted into a harmonious whole. Some of these details are basic for vertebrates, and others basic for mammals. Some of them are well fitted for particular functions, and others are makeshift, adequate but far from perfect. A few features, such as the vermiform appendix of man, are defective or useless physiologically, a source of danger and hence a handicap to certain individuals but not to the survival of the race.

Hence mammals are imperfect machines, a conglomerate of heritable characteristics handed down from ancestors of a relatively remote period. Some of the details are essential to immediate life, some to the ultimate survival of the individual, and others to the survival of the race. Locomotion is essential, and for this there are usually bilateral limbs that function adequately. Immaterial details are that we have two nostrils instead of one, rounded instead of pointed ears, eyebrows, and a host of other details. They follow a fundamental plan and are fundamentally stable.

So it should be stressed, I think, in this Introduction, that no animal, no matter how highly and curiously specialized, is an end product beautifully and perfectly fitted for its particular existence, but a compromise. Evolution has taken the material at hand and has theoretically done the best she could with it. Sometimes the clay was refractory and at other times plastic; perfection has never been possible, because of imperfections in the ground plan; but always the result, in living animals, has been good enough for the purpose, else the species would have become extinct.

CHAPTER I

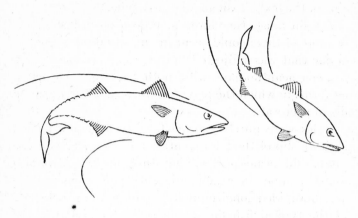

Fishes and Amphibians

THE oldest types of chordates known are the Silurian and Devonian ostracoderms, and this group is believed to have given rise to the vertebrates. Some of them had anterior, some posterior, appendages, and others had none; but the anatomy is too imperfectly known to indicate clearly whether or not these were homologous with the paired appendages of higher vertebrates.

FISHES

Conditions in the very primitive Silurian placoderm fishes, the Acanthodii, however, suggest that there were lines of stress along the body, situated along the midline dorsally, then around the tail and as far forward as the cloaca, and also on paired branchiocloacal lines. Along each of these there developed a series of hypertrophied scales, the particular stimulus for which is unknown. Acanthodians had heterocercal tails, however, probably indicating bottom-feeding ancestors; and in wriggling over the bottom and between stones in the search for food some of the scales along the branchiocloacal line probably encountered a stimulus for still larger size. At any rate, there are remains of acanthodians with scales along this line that have developed into spikes, perhaps in life with membrane between. Theoretically these could occur anywhere from gills to cloaca, and there is evidence that they occupied a variable position in different sorts. That there existed a continuous row of spines of uniform length is unlikely, for continuous paired fins are now known to be not

1

a primitive feature but a specialization that may accompany an extreme lengthening of the body in an anguilliform type.

Primitively, each fin must, therefore, have been of restricted extent, and one or more of them could occur in any situation along the branchiocloacal line that was subjected to the proper stimuli. There appear to have been acanthodians with both pectoral and pelvic "fins" and other forms in which the pelvics were absent but with one or even two pairs of pectorals.

These spiny scales were purely exoskeletal, but each must have been equipped with a slip of the lateroventral musculature, as is the case with the comparable scales of the living sturgeon. The latter also shows the probable manner in which adjacent scales clustered together and then subdivided longitudinally to form the exoskeletal dermotrichia of the typical fish fin. There is little doubt that the paired appendages, at least in bony fish, had a purely exoskeletal derivation and that, although the so-called "fin-fold theory" of the development of the limbs contains basic elements of truth, the details require considerable modification.

Conditions in sharks suggest that, as the adjacent spines clustered together to form a single fin, the muscle slips to these spines likewise fused and that, with increased functioning, the resulting muscle mass experienced fission into a dorsal sheet for elevating the fin, and a ventral sheet for depressing it. Both were innervated by the ventral primary rami of the spinal nerves concerned, and these tended to split into a more dorsal and a more ventral series of branches to the corresponding muscle divisions. The dorsal and ventral primary muscle sheets of the appendage later gave rise to subdivisions with particular functions, such as protraction and retraction.

One naturally thinks of fins in connection with swimming, but it is clear that fins could not be used as oars until finlike form had been attained, and this must have required a very long time. Constantly, throughout evolution, structures are initiated by particular stimuli and develop to the point where they prove to be useful for some entirely unrelated, but more important, purpose. So with the paired appendages. Hypertrophied scales could not function as limbs until of respectable proportions, or as fins until they became paddle-shaped. Accordingly, it seems very likely that enlarged scales along the branchiocloacal line were first of use as a sort of protecting armor where the most stress occurred and then, when they became longer, as crutches or props for aid in wriggling over the bottom and between stones. In this case they were legs of a sort before they were fins.

Only fishes highly specialized in a tangential direction habitually use the paired fins for locomotion. The body is the locomotor organ.

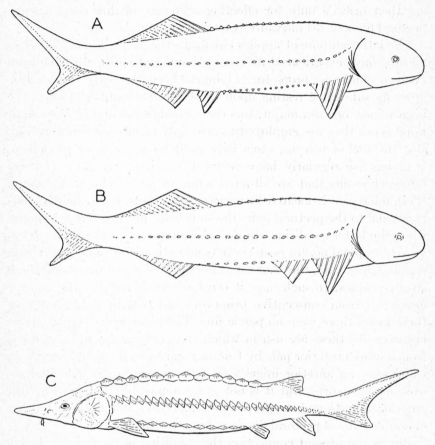

FIG. 1.—*A* and *B:* Hypothetical reconstruction of two ancestral types of acanthodians, with longitudinal series of dermal structures in critical zones; *A*, showing early development of pectoral and pelvic fins; *B*, based on actual conditions in Acanthodes wardi, without pelvics but with double pectorals. *C*, the sturgeon, Acipenser, showing the distribution of longitudinal series of hypertrophied scales.

In the most speedy kinds the body is fusiform, of greatest diameter anteriorly, with large head and trunk that tapers gradually to the laterally compressed tail. Swimming is accomplished by rhythmic transverse oscillations of the entire body, with tail sculling against the water. The fitness for their environment attained by fish is a heritage that has pronouncedly modified the conformation of all terrestrial vertebrates. It is true that while suspended motionless in the water the pectoral fins of a fish may be vibrated for maintaining position and balance and for slow changes of location. But during speedy progression the paired fins are folded against the body and are then utilized only for effecting a change of direction, when a pectoral fin is thrust outward to act as a unilateral brake.

The latter statement applies chiefly to the pectoral pair. The pelvic fins have experienced different stimuli and appear to have been evolved chiefly as props for helping to keep the body from falling upon its side when resting upon the bottom. Doubtless there have been minor, or even major, functions in addition, and in free-swimming types they are employed as accessory agents for equilibration. But the fins of fish are essentially rudders, not oars or propellers.

Living fish regularly have pectoral fins, but only some of them have pelvic fins that are situated adjacent to the cloaca. In many, the hinder pair is located in variable situations, even slightly ventrocranial to the pectoral pair (the so-called "jugular" fins). Usually, when the latter condition obtains, these more ventral fins are innervated by spinal nerves posteriorly consecutive with those to the true pectoral fins, and the skeletal framework of the two constitute a single complex. In such cases it is considered likely that the two are developed from consecutive primordia and that in the ancestry of these kinds there were no pelvic fins. The point is far from certain, however, for there are fish in which the pectoral fins are separated from a more posterior pair by from several to many spinal nerves, in which case an anterior migration of the pelvic fins is indicated, at least in some sorts. But it is not at all impossible that in some fish anterior migration of the pelvics took place to simulate the condition of double pairs of pectoral fins found in other forms.

But in the present connection the condition in most living fish is merely of academic interest, for indicating the possible ways in which limb position might vary. We may be sure that the piscine ancestor of terrestrial vertebrates had a pair of true pectoral fins and a pair of true pelvic ones. It is also certain that the piscine ancestor of terrestrial vertebrates was a crossopterygian, for this is the only group of fossil fishes with basic characters shared with the most primitive of tetrapods. Indeed, in recent years fossils have been discovered that may be called either crossopterygians or amphibians, so well do they blend the characters of each. But there were numerous kinds of crossopterygians, and it is impossible to tell which gave rise to tetrapods or, more specifically, which pattern of fin structure was the truly ancestral one. Although the living Polypterus and Calamoichthys have sometimes been regarded as crossopts, they are specialized Actinopterygii, and the only living representative of the group known is that of the single specimen caught off Africa several years ago, with fin anatomy unknown. Sufficient is known of fossils, however, for a plausible reconstruction of the skeletal features to be attempted.

It is apparent, from a study of living and fossil fish, that the initiation of the paired limbs involved an appendage that outside the body contour was exoskeletal, as already stated. At the base of the fin, inside the body contour, where were located the stresses incident to bending and of muscle pull, hyaline cartilage was formed; and this was the forerunner of the cartilaginous limb girdle. At first it probably had no anchorage to any part of the axial skeleton.

In bony fish (as opposed to the cartilaginous elasmobranchs) the dorsal part of the membranous skull is projected backward, downward, and then forward to form an irregular ring of bone that posteriorly bounds the gill complex, this forming the margin along which fits the edge of the operculum, or gill covering. This bony ring in its entirety is composed of four articulated bones—posttemporal, supracleithrum, cleithrum, and clavicle. In living fish the cleithrum may be absent, and the clavicle is regularly lacking in most sorts. The whole constitutes the membranous girdle; and to it at a relatively early date became attached the beginnings of the cartilaginous pectoral girdle. The latter increased in size, as the pectoral fin gained in strength, to become the scapulocoracoid element.

The fossil record does not show the earliest history of the bony elements of the free part of the pectoral limb. There is little doubt, however, that these first appeared as small nodules of bone, probably with fibrous articulation, in proximal-distal series for giving both stiffness and a degree of mobility to the free part of the appendage. These bones were essentially similar, and fusion or fission was probably easy of accomplishment. They all were short; but all were not of just the same length, so that completely transverse joints did not exist except at the "shoulder" and "elbow" articulations. One "forearm" bone was longer than the other; but which represented radius and which ulna is not known with certainty. More types, with fin plans intermediate between fish and amphibians, must be discovered before this point can be settled.

In modern bony fish the surface of the pectoral fin that fits against the body is that controlled by dorsal muscles—not the reverse, as one might expect. Whether the former condition obtained also in crossopts is not yet known. The implication of this statement is that it is by no means certain that the paired fins of the two groups were strictly comparable in all respects and hence whether or not the paired fins of living teleosts are entirely homologous to the respective limbs of tetrapods.

At any rate, no matter what the precise basic plan, in the change from fish fin to amphibian limb, a wrist joint was required, and radius and ulna came to end at the same point.

Whether the primitive manus basically had but five digits is unknown. Throughout the literature many authors have postulated one or two additional marginal digits, termed "prepollex" and "postminimus." That some tetrapods have marginal bony vestiges that may represent additional "digital" elements of a piscine ancestor may be probable; but there is no evidence that any tetrapod (as contrasted with fish) ever had more than five functional digits.

Naturally, the basic plan of the arm musculature of the ancestral fish-amphibian must remain unknown, but certain inferences may be drawn. It seems certain, from what is known of the crossopt skeleton, that the limb skeleton was asymmetrical in plan, and the same must have been true of the musculature. It is also practically certain that the musculature instrumental in moving the fin involved a set of somatic extrinsic muscle slips, at first from the trunk to the membranous girdle, and from the latter shifting chiefly to the cartilaginous girdle as the latter increased in size; one or more branchiomeric slips, by which the gill complex originally had posterior anchorage to the limb girdle; and a series of intrinsic slips, from girdle to limb bones and between the individual limb bones. Basically, extrinsic and intrinsic muscles were distributed in a dorsal extensor series and a ventral flexor series, innervated by corresponding divisions of the brachial plexus. All dorsal and the more caudal of the ventral nerves to the free fin passed around the axilla, while the more cranial ventral nerves passed to the fin anterior to the girdle or through a "coracoid foramen" in it.

The earliest history of the pelvic fin likewise appears to be even less certain than that of the pectoral member. The stimuli encountered by the two were entirely different. Influencing the pectoral pair were the close proximity of the head, particularly the gills, and the immediate juxtaposition of the membranous girdle. The pectorals, as soon as they could function as limbs, constituted the pair used for pulling the body along, and they were operated chiefly by vigorous lateral oscillations of the entire trunk. The pelvic pair, on the contrary, had none of these influences but, instead, developed independent of any early anchorage to the axial skeleton. They were probably influenced by adjoining cloacal details and by their function as props, for balance, and the stresses that the neighboring tail base imposed. Indications point to the initial form of the pelvic girdle as having comprised a pair of ischiopubic bars, horizontally instead of vertically disposed as in the pectoral pair. They were located ventrally, and the two must early have become articulated along the midline. They were influenced by acting as an anchorage for the cloacal musculature and for the abdominal muscles cranially and the caudal muscles caudally. It is probable that of the muscles acting upon the base of the free fin only the ventral series arose from the girdle, while the dorsal series originated from the surface of the dorsal division of the axial musculature as is still true of some living fish. These dorsal and ventral muscles of the "hip" retained a sheet-like form for a longer phylogenetic period than did the musculature of the shoulder, as is shown by the condition in living examples of the lower tetrapods.

The older morphologists expended an immense amount of effort in the attempt exactly to homologize all the details of the pectoral and pelvic limbs. The results were not only inaccurate but highly misleading and brought considerable ridicule on the science of morphology. Pectoral and pelvic limbs never were the same; they had separate derivations and hence were never homologues. The influences affecting the two girdles were different but with certain points in common, such as functioning as a base for a free limb. The same statement applies to the musculature of shoulder and hip. There are more resemblances in the case of the free limbs. Although used in somewhat different ways, there were certain similarities of function; and the term "quadruped" or "tetrapod" calls to mind the symmetrical use of four appendages in locomotion, with consequent stimuli for at least a considerable degree of resemblance.

Because of the conformation of living forms, one can be sure, in spite of the fact that the fossil record is incomplete, that the early development of the free part of the pelvic appendage was essentially similar to that of the pectoral complement, with a single femoral segment, probably a basically asymmetrical lower leg and pes, which eventually became mostly symmetrical, and digital elements resulting in five toes.

AMPHIBIANS

Amphibians, believed to have evolved from crossopterygian fishes, are the most primitive vertebrates with true limbs, as opposed to fins. In recent years there has been found a great amount of fossil material annectant between these two classes of vertebrates; but the skeleton of the appendages of most of these remains unknown, so that we have no clear picture of the details between the crossopt Sauripterus or Eusthenopteron and the Permo-Carboniferous stegocephalian Amphibia.

An arrangement of the major groups of amphibians is as follows:

AMPHIBIA

ORDER

1. Stegocephali or Labyrinthodonti. Mostly Permo-Carboniferous, but some forms surviving to Triassic. All extinct.

    Suborder A. Embolomeri. Earliest and most primitive of the order; the only group in which 5 digits in the manus is known to have occurred; some still had pectoral girdle anchored to skull by posttemporal; pelvic girdle with iliac process unfused with sacral vertebrae.

    Suborder B. Rhachitomi. Surviving until Lower Triassic; on the main line of tetrapod evolution; mostly large forms lacking posttemporal and with pelvic girdle anchored to a single sacral vertebra.

    Suborder C. Stereospondyli. Small forms, degenerate and quite specialized retrogressively for an aquatic habitat.

2. Lepospondyli. Permo-Carboniferous; small, quite specialized, degenerate and probably exclusively aquatic forms. All extinct.

3. Urodela or Caudata. Includes living salamanders and newts.

4. Salientia or Anura. Includes living frogs and toads.

5. Apoda or Gymnophiona. The living limbless caecilians.

An additional order, the Phyllospondyli, is usually recognized; but Romer (1939) has argued, with much plausibility, that its representatives are merely stegocephalian larvae.

Of the above five orders, embolomerous and rhachitomous Stegocephalia, Urodela, and Salientia are the only ones of interest in the present connection. The Embolomeri are significant as the most primitive amphibians, some of them still with the membranous girdle united to the skull by a posttemporal, without a bony anchorage of the pelvic girdle to the axial skeleton, and clearly with five digits in the manus. In the Rhachitomi the posttemporal had been lost, and the pelvic girdle had come to be articulated with a single sacral vertebra. This group is concededly on the direct line of evolution of terrestrial tetrapods and contains mostly large forms that undoubtedly spent much time on land. The genus Eryops is the one best known. The latter is a rather cumbersome form, with massive bones, and the amphibian that gave rise to the reptiles was probably of a lighter, more agile type.

Living urodeles are rather depauperate amphibians. Although many are not exclusively aquatic, all are highly dependent upon a moist atmosphere, are regressive in skeletal details, and are highly specialized in some parts of their musculature in a direction tangential to what must have characterized the main tetrapod stem. And yet, as the most primitive living amphibian type, they must be extensively utilized in any study of the phylogeny of the soft parts.

Living Salientia are among the most highly specialized of vertebrates, uniquely so in some respects. They attained the characteristic anuran form at least as early as Jurassic times. The frog is of interest as a form that is highly fitted for leaping, and yet not for sustained saltatorial progression. Most toads may be characterized as a sort of frog with decreased saltatorial ability, that relies for protection not upon speed but upon a poisonous secretion of skin glands.

Before considering the details of the primitive amphibian some attention should be given to its general conformation and mode of progression. The ancestral rhachitomous amphibian probably resembled Eryops in most respects but was somewhat less massive, while at the same time more robust and larger than living urodeles. It probably had a rather large head, practically no neck, and a fairly long tail, heavy at the base. The proximal limb segments, or propodials,[1] were directed laterally and horizontal with the ground, fairly at a right angle with the body axis; and the epipodials articulated with the propodials at an angle, the forearm directed forward and the lower leg backward, so that the elbow faced the knee. The manus was directed forward also, but the pes chiefly laterally.

Progression was chiefly by means of lateral oscillations of the entire body, with accompanying diagonal action of the limbs. Twisting to the left advanced the right forelimb and left hind limb, during contraction of their dorsal musculature. The forelimb was advanced

---

[1] The propodials consist of humerus and femur; the epipodials, the bones of the lower arm and lower leg or crus; the mesopodials, the carpal and tarsal elements; and the metapodials, the metacarpal and metatarsal bones.

toward the midline beneath the neck, depressed by the ventral musculature, retracted, and then straightened, thus dragging the animal forward. At the same time the left hind leg was advanced, depressed, and then retracted; but in early stages the action of the hind limb was in the nature of a prop, to keep the body from dragging upon the ground.

One of the earliest amphibians whose pectoral girdle is known is the large embolomere Eogerynus. In this the girdle of the two sides had ventral fusion by means of the interclavicle to form a massive U-shaped structure composed bilaterally of supracleithrum, cleithrum, clavicle, and perhaps posttemporal, with an attached scapulocoracoid (Fig. 12) very much larger than in known crossopterygians. In the rhachitomous stage, represented by Eryops, the supracleithrum, as well as the posttemporal, had disappeared, and the cleithrum

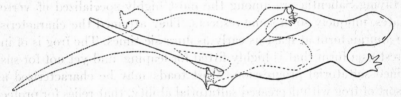

Fig. 2.—The amphibian crawl, adapted from Braus.

and clavicle were reduced to form a narrow cranial border upon the cranial margin of the much enlarged scapulocoracoid. The latter had a very definite coracoid expansion ventrally. In living urodeles the pectoral girdle is very degenerate and specialized retrogressively for a secondarily aquatic existence. Typically only the central part is ossified (in some), and there is here a constriction, dorsal to which is an expanded cartilaginous scapular plate, and ventrally an expanded coracoid plate. Upon the cranial margin of the latter is a process, often long, usually termed the "coracoid process"; but this is a misnomer, for it affords attachment to dorsal muscles, and it should be called the "anterior scapular process."

The humerus of Eryops has contact with the glenoid cavity of the shoulder girdle by a screw-shaped articular facet, of interest in showing that in movement the brachium was obliged to follow a circumscribed, curved pathway. Its humerus was robust and had the form of a tetrahedral prism. Its proximal expansion was attributable largely to the form of the articular surface, and the distal expansion to the extent of the epicondyles, chiefly the medial (ventral), from which arose the flexor musculature of the forearm.

Conditions in lower forms seem to suggest that the crossopts resembled living teleosts in having the pectoral fin with the dorsal musculature pressed against the body, which then necessitated a spiral rotation forward to attain the tetrapod condition. At any rate, there has been a certain twisting of this member which has had a profound effect on its evolution. This is reflected in the tetrahedral shape of the primitive amphibian humerus, and in its articulation with the bones of the forearm. As a result, the musculature of the antebrachium is disposed with an inward twist of 90°, as compared with the corresponding musculature of the brachium.

The old concept that the carpus was basically symmetrical and arranged on the simplified plan illustrated by the tortoise is no longer tenable. The tortoise is a highly specialized reptile, and its limbs are regressively simplified. The primitive carpus must have been asymmetrical in plan, and there is no reason for thinking it much different in arrangement from that of Eryops. It must have involved a proximal radiale or navicular, ulnare or triquetrum, with an intermedium or lunate and a centrale between the two. It appears likely, also, that upon the radial side of the carpus was an extra, partial row of elements that may be termed mediales, as suggested by Schmalhausen (1917). Conditions in Eryops suggest that there were three of these and that distal to them and the ulnare was a row of carpalia, the first one of which became the first metacarpal.

The exact number of carpal elements to be considered as basic is, to my mind, a matter that is not of great importance, for it is abundantly demonstrated in the history of vertebrates that the original elements were capable of fusing or splitting up in a great variety of ways. An investigator may build a plausible argument around any number of theories regarding the carpus, and it is impossible to prove that any one of them is true.

Gregory, Miner, and Noble (1923) have considered that the number of phalanges in the manus of Eryops was 2-2-3-2 (the first digit being considered as absent). This may have been so; but there are grounds for believing that the "ideal" digital formula of the fairly early primitive tetrapod was 2-3-4-5-4 (or 3).

It is believed, as already stated, that the pelvic girdle arose as an ischiopubic bar near the midline, in association with the cloacal as well as the limb muscles. It was unanchored to the axial skeleton. At some stage between fish and the embolomerous amphibians there developed a dorsal process, the ilium, to furnish anchorage for the

extensor musculature of the hip and for the part of the back musculature controlling the girdle. In the rhachitomous amphibians the
ilium became fused with a single vertebra.

The early amphibian femur was not of the tetrahedral pattern
characteristic of the humerus. It was a lighter bone with little of interest with the exception of the slightly underslung head, indicating
a habitually horizontal position of the thigh and the fact that this
segment could not be placed vertical to the ground. Like the forearm,
the skeleton of the lower leg consisted of two bones, probably asymmetrical in basic plan as in the pectoral appendage, but this point is
not so certainly indicated in the case of the pelvic limb.

The tarsus of the rhachitomous amphibian (as in Trematops)
bore a remarkable resemblance, in number of elements and their arrangement, to the manus. It seems, however, that the chief line of
stress or support passed through the postaxial epipodial (fibula) instead of the preaxial unit (tibia), as in the pectoral limb (radius).
The phalangeal formula of the pes in primitive amphibians, so far as
known, appears to have been 2-3-4-4-3, but whether this represents
the basic condition is unknown.

The Salientia or Anura comprise frogs and toads, structurally
more modified for saltation than any other vertebrates. The specialization is, in some respects, unique. It cannot really be regarded as
one involving speedy progression, comparable to the aptitude of
saltatorial rodents, for the frog basically is specialized for making one
mighty leap from a bank into a pool and then swimming into hiding.
On land even the most expert hoppers rely not upon speed but upon
ability to escape a pursuer by instantly attaining high velocity from
a position of immobility and by sudden changes of direction during
progression when encountered away from water. Correlated with
these actions is the fact that the Salientia are the only vertebrates
(with the partial exception of the hares) highly fitted for bidepal
cursorial or saltatorial progression that lack a tail of considerable
weight to act as a counterbalance. As the interrupted and rather
haphazard character of their gait is of survival advantage, a tail
would be more of a handicap than a help.

There is much variation within the order in the degree of ability in
saltation. Some toads are able to hop but a few inches and rely for
survival upon the secretion of their poisonous skin glands. Even the
slowest and most clumsy regularly progress by hops involving the

simultaneous use of both pelvic limbs; but, so far as I know, all Salientia are capable of using the units of this pair of limbs alternately. Toads, particularly, are prone to stalk insect prey by a slow crawl.

The pectoral girdle of the Salientia typically has a partly ossified scapula with a dorsal suprascapula (cartilaginous or partly calcified), and there usually is a vestigial cleithrum upon the anterior border. The remainder of the girdle is quite variable, but most often there is an ossified coracoid bar partly separated by a fenestration from a slender, bony clavicle and cartilaginous or ossified procoracoid. Both clavicle and procoracoid are occasionally absent, or at times the three elements are all fused. The radius and ulna are regularly fused.

In Salientia the number of vertebrae is greatly reduced, in some forms to the minimum of six (Noble, 1931). There is a sacrum, usually comprising a single vertebra, but no caudals; the element projecting posterior to the sacrum of the common frog is the urostyle, formed of the perichordal tube.

The ilium is very long and articulates with the sacrum at its extreme cranial end. The ischium and pubis form only a slight bony expansion around the acetabulum, which latter is thus at the extreme caudal end of the body. The hind legs are much elongated, the femur is rather delicately formed, the tibia and fibula solidly fused, and the length of pes much increased by the elongation of calcaneus and talus (Fig. 33)—not of the metatarsus, as is customary in saltatorial mammals.

An investigation of the musculature of Rana catesbiana, the common bullfrog, shows that the muscles of the pelvic limb have no particular specialization for saltation, other than that of size. In fact, the reverse might be inferred, because of the short ischium, providing a reduced amount of leverage for the muscles retracting the thigh. The leaping ability of frogs is due in major part to increased relative size of the hind legs, to co-ordination of the musculature with a high twitch potential, and in minor part to refinements of body form, such as shortening of the trunk, and character of lumbosacral joint.

Curiously, it is found that the musculature of the pectoral limb in Salientia is more tangetially specialized than that of the posterior member. This fact, doubtless, is attributable to the circumstance that the pectoral limb has largely abandoned its more usual function of aiding forward propulsion of the body and operates as a shock absorber for the body after a long leap. The most noteworthy myological differences, perhaps, concern the deltoid, whose origin has extended onto the medial aspect of the girdle; the fact that a functional "biceps brachii" has been produced from the anterior coracoid matrix (instead of from the ventral elbow matrix); and that the brachialis has a conformation that places it more with the antebrachium than with the brachium.

CHAPTER II

Reptiles and Birds

REPTILES

REPTILES have occurred from Lower Permian to Recent times. It is difficult to distinguish fossil remains of the earliest reptiles from those of ancestral amphibians, for the former were derived from the latter. The crucial difference is that in some manner the eggs of reptiles developed an amnion, so that they could be laid away from the water. It was only thus that vertebrates could become completely terrestrial.

Modern reptiles are very different from the ancestral types. They are retrogressive in some respects and useful in any such study as the present one only in illustrating certain principles. No living reptiles are truly cursorial or saltatorial, although some of them can run at great speed relative to their size. Some of the dinosaurs, however, were more exclusively bipedal than any mammal.

In the following synopsis, the bipedal sorts and those giving rise to mammals are stressed. In the past, reptiles developed an amazing number of widely diversified forms, most of which are of no interest to us in this study.

The following synopsis of the Reptilia, based on the temporal vacuities of the skull, is an arrangement that is artificial in some respects, but it is particularly convenient. Anapsids have no temporal fenestration, diapsids have two, parapsids a superior, and synapsids an inferior fenestration. Some of the smaller suborders, of no interest here, are omitted from the list.

REPTILIA

Anapsida

Cotylosauria. Permian to Trias. The earliest and most diversified reptiles, closely related to stegocephalian amphibians; some with cleithrum. Includes pareiasaurs and diadectids.

Chelonia. To Recent. Turtles and tortoises.

Parapsida. Includes a large aggregation of diversified forms not of interest here. Includes ichthyosaurs, mosasaurs, plesiosaurs and other aquatic types, as well as primitive and all Recent lizard-like sorts (except Sphenodon), chameleons, and also serpents.

Diapsida

Rhynchocephalia. Trias to Recent. Primitive lizard-like forms, including Sphenodon.

Archosauria.

Thecodontia. Permian and Trias. A generalized group that gave rise to crocodilians and dinosaurs. Includes phytosaurs.

Crocodilia. Trias to Recent. Crocodiles and alligators.

Pterosauria. Jurassic and Cretaceous. Flying reptiles.

(Dinosaurs)

Saurischia. Pubes diverging from ischia, meeting in midline. Femur either longer or shorter than tibia.

Theropoda. Trias to Cretaceous. Carnivorous dinosaurs, small to very large. Partly or exclusively bipedal. Hind limbs birdlike, often phenomenally longer than forelimbs; femur usually longer than tibia; metatarsus somewhat elongated. Includes birdlike forms, as well as the giant tyrannosaurids.

Sauropoda. Jurassic to Cretaceous. Secondarily herbivorous forms of moderate to colossal size, partly bipedal or regressively quadrupedal. Hind limbs usually slightly longer than forelimbs; femur longer than tibia. Includes the largest dinosaurs.

Ornithischia. Pubes parallel with ischium and with anterior processes not meeting in midline. Herbivorous and usually large forms, chiefly bipedal or regressively quadrupedal, with hind limbs longer than forelimbs.

Orthopoda. Jurassic and Cretaceous. Chiefly bipedal. Femur longer than tibia; digitigrade, but metatarsus not much elongated. Includes iguanodonts and trachodonts.

Stegosauria. Jurassic and Cretaceous. Armored dinosaurs with regressive tendency to quadrupedal posture, but forelegs short.

Ceratopsia. Cretaceous. Horned dinosaurs probably entirely quadrupedal.

Synapsida

Theromorpha. Lower Permian to Trias. Skeleton primitive; not of interest here. Includes ophiacodonts, pelycosaurs.

Therapsida. Anomodont reptiles of more mammal-like limb posture.

Dinocephalia. Permian. Heavy forms with limbs slightly sprawling.

Dromasauria. Permian. Smaller, slenderer forms.

Dicynodontia. Permian and Trias. A rather highly developed tangential group.

Theriodontia. Permian and Trias. The group giving rise to Mammalia; with incisor, canine, premolar, and molar teeth. Limbs with more mammal-like posture. Includes the cynodonts.

Fossil reptiles are of interest to us as pointing to the characteristics of protomammals and as indicating the manner in which they reacted to cursorial stimuli. One must constantly bear in mind the probable propensities and limitations of the order. Variation in neck length (with a maximum of 76 cervical vertebrae) was attained with far greater ease than in mammals. A long, relatively heavy tail was a basic feature, and perhaps one that it was difficult to change, for few reptiles (other than chelonians) dispensed with a tail of this character. This type of tail, acting as a counterbalance to the body, doubtless facilitated bipedalism. One of the chief limitations with which reptiles had to contend concerned limb posture. The amphibian type of posture, which they inherited, was not conducive to a high character of evolution, and only certain reptiles were successful in overcoming it. High speed in reptiles of considerable bulk was accomplished by bipedalism and accompanied quite high specialization in other directions, and these evolutional end products became extinct. The type of reptile that gave rise to the mammals was not in itself very speedy, but it embodied limb changes that were mechanically suited to the development of speed.

Reptiles (and birds) differ from mammals in having, among other things, the ankle joint between the two rows of tarsal bones, rather than between tibia and tarsus. The earliest and most primitive reptiles, the cotylosaurs or stem-reptiles, appeared in the Lower Permian, and their skeletons were not much different from those of rhachitomous amphibians. Some still had a cleithrum, which disappeared very early in reptilian history. There were two sacral vertebrae. The glenoid was screw-shaped, indicating a labored horizontal action of the humerus, with much lateral bending of the body; but this type of glenoid disappeared after the Permian. The hind limb was slightly shorter and lighter than the forelimb, the tibiale tended to vanish, and there was a reduction in the number of carpal and tarsal elements. Both feet were pentadactylate, and the phalangeal formula appears basically to have been 2–3–4–5–3 for the manus and 2–3–4–5–4 for the pes. The posture was a moderately sprawling one, with propodials held horizontally, but it seems to have been essentially dissimilar to anything in existence today.

Concerning parapsids, we are interested only in the light that living lacertilians can throw on reptilian evolution. The posture is probably more squat than it was in cotylosaurs, with different limb posture, but with greater freedom of forelimb movement (as indicated by the absence of a screw-shaped glenoid), and doubtless of

Fig. 3.—Reconstructions of extinct reptiles, bipedal or largely so. Reproduced without regard to size; after Heilmann. *a*, Camptosaurus; *b*, Podokesaurus; *c*, Struthiomimus; *d*, Ceratosaurus; *e*, Compsognathus; *f*, Iguanodon.

hind limb as well. The basis for the latter assertion lies in the fact that cotylosaurs were not only modified from amphibians but many of them seem to have been partially aquatic, with limbs poorly adapted to terrestrial locomotion. Living lacertilians, on the contrary, are the product of many millions of years of evolution, and their limbs have become well adapted to their needs. Their appendages, from the mammalian viewpoint, are not constructed on an efficient principle, for they are poorly adapted for holding the body off the ground and hence are inefficient for effecting speedy locomotion with a heavy body. Yet for animals of but a few ounces or pounds in weight, limbs of this sort have attained a considerable degree of efficiency. Especially under conditions of high temperature, and therefore of high metabolic rate, some desert lizards are phenomenally swift for a short dash. This is the result not of efficiency of limb mechanics but of rapidity of the rhythm of muscular action, facilitated by low inertia.

It is interesting to note that several living lacertilians resort to bipedalism at top speed. Chlamydosaurus, Grammatopora (Heilmann, 1927), and some other small lizards rise upon their hind legs when moving with celerity. The basilisk (Basiliscus) is in the habit of resting on a log or small island well out from shore in a river or lake and, when disturbed, of dashing to the mainland, using only its hind limbs for actually running upon the water. Its forelimbs are relatively feeble. One or two of our swiftest desert lizards (as Crotophytus) also resort to bipedalism at speed.

The Diapsida are of particular interest in that the group contains all the definitely bipedal sorts of reptiles. They may be divided into the rather generalized rhynchocephalians, which includes the living Sphenodon, the archosaurs, saurischian dinosaurs, and ornithischian dinosaurs.

The more typical archosaurs comprise thecodonts, crocodilians, and pterosaurs or flying reptiles. Some thecodonts were aquatic, but others were lightly built leaping or climbing types, some of which are believed to have been ancestral to birds and others to dinosaurs. In the more strictly bipedal sorts the hind limbs were considerably the longer, with tibia elongated and fibula reduced, while the metatarsus at times was longer and the tarsus shorter. It is likely, however, that all archosaurs, possibly excepting the most highly bipedal sorts, were quadrupedal when not running at speed.

Dinosaurs were of extremely diverse types and sizes, varying from a weight of a few pounds to a score of tons. They were divisible into two very distinct groups according to whether the pelvis was triradiate and reptile-like (Saurischia) or tetraradiate and birdlike (Ornithischia). Both lacked the clavicle as well as the cleithrum, and both were basically bipedal; but many herbivorous forms in both groups reverted to a quadrupedal posture, partially or completely.

The Saurischia are divisible into Theropoda and Sauropoda. The former were carnivorous and bipedal, some forms (as Deinodon) with the forelimb so reduced as to be vestigial and utterly useless for support at any time. The hind limbs were long, often lightly proportioned, with femur generally longer than tibia, metatarsus elongated, and lateral digit reduced. The limb bones and vertebrae were hollow, which character points toward cursorial and possibly scansorial (climbing) habits in the lighter, more primitive forms. For the most part they were small, although some of them attained a length exceeding 30 feet. The remarkable degree to which the avian form was at times mimicked (except for the long tail) is indicated by such generic names as Ornithomimus and Struthiomimus. By Jurassic times, however, there had appeared powerful carnivorous theropods, and these developed such forms as megalosaurs, ceratosaurs, tyrannosaurs, gorgosaurs, allosaurs, and many others, some of which must have been appallingly destructive.

Sauropods were mostly very massively built dinosaurs that had reverted to a herbivorous diet and quadrupedal posture. They had small heads, very long necks and tails, and columnar limbs, the pectoral ones of which were slightly bowed outward and slightly shorter than the pelvic pair. The long bones were not hollow, or at least were very incompletely so, the femur was definitely longer than the tibia, the metapodials were short, and all four feet semiplantigrade. Sauropods include the largest land animals that have ever lived, among which were Diplodocus and Brontosaurus, with maximum length exceeding 90 feet. It is generally accepted that they were swamp dwellers; and it is probable that only amid swampy surroundings could they have secured the immense amount of herbage that they needed. Although it is beyond question that their locomotion was quadrupedal, it seems likely that they were capable of elevating the body upon the hind legs for some such intent as browsing among the treetops. That the long neck was for the purpose of allowing the animals to breathe while walking in water of relatively great depth, as suggested by Cope, is hardly a tenable theory. It has been demonstrated with the help of a rubber tube that at atmospheric pressure inspiration is impossible in man when water pressure on the chest is in excess of that encountered in 3 feet of water, and it is not likely that this depth could be multiplied ten times in the case of a reptile.

Ornithischians were herbivorous dinosaurs with a tetraradiate pubis essentially birdlike in pattern but with an anterior pubic process. They were basically bipedal, but never to the degree characteristic of theropods, nor were the anterior limbs as much reduced. The most bipedal were the Orthopoda, including Camptosaurus, Iguanodon, and the trachodonts or duck-billed dinosaurs, the latter being typically semiaquatic. The tibia was shorter than the femur, and the metapodials were not elongated, in spite of the fact that the posture was digitigrade. It seems probable that only the hind limbs were used in running, but all four limbs in slow walking and while feeding on the ground. Other ornithischians comprised highly specialized Stegosauria (armored) and Ceratopsia (horned dinosaurs) that had reverted still more to quadrupedalism. They probably employed all four limbs in locomotion and when standing but frequently arose upon the hind legs for feeding from high branches.

Synapsida were basically carnivorous and a primitive type of reptile that in the Permian shared dominance with the Anapsida. They exhibited no tendency whatever toward bipedalism, but, rather, their evolutionary energies were directed toward the elaboration of speedy quadrupedal progression. They may be divided into the more primitive Theromorpha and the more advanced Therapsida. There were numerous sorts of the latter, the most interesting of which were the Theriodontia of Permian and Triassic times. The limb posture and limb action of the latter approached that characteristic of the Mammalia. The best-known and one of the most advanced of these groups was the Cynodontia. The skull and dentition approached the Mammalia in certain important respects, as did also the limb posture. The elbow was rotated backward and the knee forward to some extent, which progressive alteration was correlated with the reduction of the coracoid and procoracoid and the appearance of an incipient spine of the scapula; the ilium had an anterior as well as a posterior extension; and the pubis was situated somewhat more caudally; the femur had an offset head; and, although the toes retained the typical reptilian formula (2–3–4–5–3), reduction and immobility of some of the phalanges gave them digits of nearly equal length, each with but three functional joints.

By far the greater part of our knowledge of the ancestors of the Mammalia is derived from the paleontological record. Fossil bones tell a story accurate in many respects and suggestive to some extent of the muscle arrangement. So the general form of the mammal-like reptiles may be reconstructed and many of their attributes deduced. It is also certain that they had a reptilian type of brain, and therefore it is probable that they were very definitely reptilian and as yet considerably deficient in those characters that would indubitably label them mammalian, although practically nothing can be told of their soft parts other than some of the muscles.

Between the therapsid reptiles of the Mesozoic and the oldest remains of Cretaceous mammals, all of small size, the paleontologic record is almost blank. Nevertheless, a scrutiny of what appears, in the light of later development, to be the basic scheme of some of the mammalian architectural features suggests certain probabilities which may be discussed here.

It has been, perhaps, generally considered that all mammals are descended from a single kind of reptile. It seems more probable that the borderland between reptiles and mammals was tenanted by a number of different sorts of theriodont, or at least therapsid, derivatives of considerably different characterization, some of which gave rise to monotremes, others to marsupials and placentals, while still other lines became extinct.

At this point there arises the question: What were the general characteristics of the immediate ancestor of placental mammals? As a concomitant to the acquisition of warm-bloodedness and a high rate of metabolism it is generally conceded that the protomammal must have been a rather small and lightly built carnivorous type. An aggressive carnivore needs not only speed for overtaking its prey but endurance for hunting it. Endurance requires an efficient locomotor equipment, and therefore limbs more definitely of mammalian than of typically reptilian specifications. Agility is more easily attained in an animal of light body than in a more ponderous sort; and warm-bloodedness would be highly advantageous in seeking, as well as in overcoming, prey rendered semitorpid by cool weather. Hence the protomammal probably was an inhabitant of a partly temperate, rather than a strictly tropical, habitat. If terrestrial, this direct ancestor of the mammals may have weighed several pounds, but probably not hundreds of pounds.

It is believed by some that the earliest mammals were of arboreal habits. Certainly, they were small insectivore-carnivores, and this arboreal hypothesis is an attractive one, for not only does life in the trees promote agility, and hence warm-bloodedness, but running along the limbs would be the very best sort of stimulus for the fore-and-aft type of limb movement characteristic of mammals. If arboreal, then it is likely that this ancestor of the mammals weighed but

very few pounds, or even ounces. By arboreal is not meant a vertebrate confined to the trees but one, comparable to a squirrel or tree
shrew, equally at home on the ground or in the treetops. It is not unlikely that the ancestor of the marsupials may also have been a
small arboreal vertebrate, but it seems reasonably certain that that
of the monotremes was a creature of a very different sort of bodily
conformation.

BIRDS

Birds are modified reptiles and resemble some of the thecodont
archosaurs to such a remarkable extent as to leave no doubt that
they are descended from this group. The chief skeletal changes involve details concerned with flight, including those of the musculature of the anterior appendages, while changes in the enlarged brain
and the acquirement of warm-bloodedness and feathers (modified
scales) are also correlated with the ability to fly.

The chief avian point of interest in the present connection is the
reason for the development of the typical avian hind limbs, comprising the elongation and consolidation of the metatarsus. These are
features that in mammals are indicative of saltatorial or cursorial
specialization. Were cursorial habits productive of the same development in birds? The indications are not clear and all that is possible
now is to weigh the probabilities.

It is not at all certain that the most cursorial of living birds—the
struthious birds, or ostriches, rheas, emus, and cassowaries—could
ever fly proficiently; but at least their structure indicates, I think,
that the ancestral stock was well on the way toward volant efficiency
and could, at any rate, glide with facility. In other words, the ancestors of ostriches must have been arboreal at one time, as were
those of all other modern birds, for the reason that no existence other
than an arboreal one could have afforded the needed stimulus for the
development of a flying vertebrate ("flying" fish excepted). There
accordingly intrudes the question of whether the protoave was a
cursorial type before it became arboreal, or whether its life in the
trees was productive of hind limbs simulating the cursorial pattern.

Both may possibly have been the case. A sluggish type of reptile
is not one which logically would give rise to a warm-blooded stock
with inordinately high rate of metabolism. It seems safe to postulate
that the protoave, at the time that it took to the trees, was a reptile,
not of lacertilian form, crawling up the tree trunks, and along the
branches, but of a sort that was able to progress terrestrially at

speed in a posture that was bipedal; hence when it found it advantageous to seek refuge or food among low trees it was able to hop briskly from branch to branch, in pursuit of agile prey, rather than to clamber sluggishly about. Doubtless, its forelimbs were used as an aid to feeding, and in part, occasionally, for climbing. That the forelimbs were not used to an extent equal to the hind limbs, as is the case with an arboreal lacertilian, is suggested by the fact that they developed into wings. If the reverse had been the case, then flying, if possible at all, would be accomplished by both pairs of extremities.

According to the above arguments, the largely bipedal, partially cursorial reptile that was ancestral to the birds had doubtless, while yet exclusively terrestrial, developed attributes of a cursorial character, in the reduction of the femur and the elongation and approximation of the metatarsals, which features were carried still farther at a later date, to the point typical of modern birds, by an arboreal life that was essentially saltatorial in so far as concerned the hind limbs. It is not improbable that this was accomplished in advance of the ability really to fly. The earliest birds whose remains are known, Archaeornis and Archaeopteryx, both had this type of saltatorial limb.

In this connection it should be mentioned that in some respects the most primitive living bird—the hoatzin (Opisthocomus)—seems to be a retrogressive form in that its progression among the tree branches is slow and rather labored and is not indicative of the ancestral condition. This is suggested by its vegetable, rather than carnivorous, or insectivorous, diet and by the fact that its fledglings are more active among the branches than the adults.

It is even more difficult to decide what constitutes a cursorial or saltatorial bird than in the case of mammals, for the reason that all birds are bipedal and almost all that spend much time on the ground can move about with considerable celerity. But even those with marked ability in this regard offer difficulties. There are fairly long-limbed scratchers that make a rather poor show at running; and there are such forms as the minute snowy plover (Charadrius nivosa), whose short legs can be more effectively employed for covering ground than those of such a long-limbed wader as the stilt (Himantopus). It is difficult to determine whether these specialized habits of scratchers, waders, long-legged runners, short-legged runners, and hoppers, which may be presumed to promote increased length of limb, have different effects upon the relative lengths of the limb segments. If so, it seems impossible to decide when the scratcher shifts over to the runner class.

Another confusing detail in birds is the impossibility of segregating the cursorial from the saltatorial types according to groups. It may be true that some entire orders run while others hop, but then one recalls that one of the thrushes, the American robin (Planesticus) runs, while its near relatives, the spotted-breasted thrushes, hop exclusively. This appears to prove that at least in these birds the difference between cursorial and saltatorial bipedalism is slight and chiefly, if not exclusively, involves the functioning of the nervous system.

In view of the difficulties mentioned above, it seems wiser to attempt no systematic scrutiny of the limb segments of all birds considered to be cursorial or saltatorial. Rather is it preferable to present the details only for selected genera representative of different groups —as the roadrunner, a speedy quail, snowy plover, a cursorial raptor, several of the struthious birds—and compare these with other long-legged, noncursorial sorts, such as waders; and this will be done in another chapter.

It is obviously impossible to evaluate the relative cursorial speed of birds of very different sizes, especially when reliable figures are lacking for most of them. Martin Johnson (manuscript) has found that for half a mile the ostrich can attain a rate of 50 miles per hour, and this doubtless is the avian maximum.

LIBRARY
College of St. Francis
JOLIET, ILL.

18857

CHAPTER III

Monotremes and Marsupials

Iᴛ ʜᴀs long been recognized (Cope; Parker and Haswell; Gregory; Scott; Osborn) that the class Mammalia consists of the monotremes, on the one hand, and all other mammals, on the other, although there are still those who follow the old classification, with monotremes, marsupials, and placentals accorded equal subclass rank. The true relationship, however, is better expressed by the following treatment:

        Class Mammalia
           Subclass Prototheria (monotremes)
           Subclass Theria
                Infraclass Metatheria or Didelphia (marsupials)
                Infraclass Eutheria or Monodelphia (placentals)

The Prototheria or Monotremata, consisting of the Echidnidae and Ornithorhynchidae, have no members that, by any strength of the imagination, might be considered cursorial. Nevertheless, they are of interest as constituting the only group of mammals having the typical reptilian type of limb suspension, of a character indicating, in my opinion, an origin from a quite different type of theriodont from that giving rise to the Theria.

Some authorities consider that the marsupials are phylogenetically divisible into polyprotodont and diprotodont (kinds having a reduced set of front teeth), while others would divide them into zygodactylous and azygodactylous types. Zygodactylism, more usually but erroneously termed "syndactylism," in marsupials is the condition in which the second and third pedal digits are contained, almost to their tips, in a single envelope of integument, while in azygodactylism, more frequently termed "didactylism," no such union occurs. More desirable, however, is Simpson's (1930) arrangement of the Recent Metatheria, as follows:

Didelphoidea (superfamily)
  Didelphiidae (New World opossums)
Dasyuroidea
  Dasyuridae (native cats, pouched mice, marsupial wolf, Tasmanian devil, banded anteater)
  Notoryctidae (marsupial mole)
*Perameloidea[1]
  *Peramelidae (bandicoots)
Caenolestoidea
  Caenolestidae (New World caenolestids)
*Phalangeroidea
  *Phalangeridae (Australian opossums, phalangers, koala)
  *Phascolomiidae (wombat)
  *Macropodidae (kangaroos)

At a time when the Australian land mass was still connected to Asia by a narrow isthmus, the ancestors of the marsupials invaded the territory, and then it became segregated from the continental division before the placental mammals had arrived upon the scene. Hence the Australian marsupials, here freed from competition with the placentals, which in other parts of the world they were unable, or hardly able, to withstand, accomplished a degree of adaptive radiation that is noteworthy. They successfully invaded a diversity of habitats, otherwise unoccupied by the Mammalia on that continent, and simulated in many respects placental mammals that elsewhere had become adapted to many sorts of specialization.

Thus there is a remarkable degree of convergence of outward form and of many special details of the marsupials to placental insectivores, moles, anteaters, flying squirrels, jerboas, hares, etc. The marsupial stock has not developed a highly cursorial, quadrupedal herbivore, but it has produced a substitute fitted for a plains habitat in the bipedal kangaroos.

A noteworthy detail in regard to the marsupials is the fact that when a mammal of this type becomes highly fitted for escaping from its enemies in fair chase the mode of progression seems invariably to involve the simultaneous action of the hind feet, the gait being bipedal in two speedy groups (pouched mice and kangaroos) and quadrupedal in one (bandicoots).

[1] Those forms marked with an asterisk (*) are zygodactyl or syndactyl.

It will, perhaps, be helpful for an understanding of marsupial conditions if it be explained that Huxley, Dollo, Bensley, and other authorities on this group have been convinced that the Metatheria were derived from an ancestor sufficiently specialized for an arboreal existence for the latter adaptation to have left a lasting impression upon the foot structure. This is in contrast to the protoplacental ancestor, which, although presumably to some extent arboreal in habits, was hardly modified in this direction to a very definite degree. This must have involved (a) a primitive, terrestrial stage for the protomammal, (b) an arboreal phase, with modification of the podials, in the protomarsupial, (c) a second terrestrial stage for the modern saltatorial marsupials, (d) a secondary arboreal existence for the tree kangaroos (Dendrolagus), and (e) a subsequent reversion to a terrestrial, saltatory existence for one of the tree-kangaroo group (Dorcopsis).

The limitations in discussing the actions of marsupials, many of them very rare or extinct, by one who has never visited Australia, will be appreciated. Accordingly, I must rely on statements published by such authorities as Jones; LeSouef and Burrell; and a few others.

The only marsupials well specialized for speed are the pouched mice, marsupial wolf, bandicoots, and kangaroos. Saltatorial specialization in the pouched mice (Phascogalinae) passes through the broad-footed pouched mice, mostly with five digits upon the pes and of generalized or semiarboreal habits, to the terrestrial, narrow-footed members of the genus Sminthopsis, some of which may be regarded as partially saltatorial. This specialization culminates in the didactylous, carnivorous, jerboa pouched mouse Antechinomys (Fig. 5), comparable in conformation to the most advanced jerboas, save that the front limbs are longer. They bear a remarkable similarity to the placental genus Ascopharynx of the same habitat. It is an inhabitant of the arid interior of Australia, and little is recorded of its habits. Spencer (in LeSouef and Burrell) saw one at night, hopping about on its hind legs with tail curved upward; it made leaps of at least 6 feet. And F. Wood Jones (1923) has mentioned the ease with which it leaps vertically. The length of the forelegs would indicate that the genus is bipedal only at speed and that it spends considerable time engaged in slower quadrupedal activity. The long, tufted tail is, however, a definitely saltatorial specialization, and the very large ears and large audital bullae are other correlated features.

The thylacine or marsupial wolf, as its name implies, simulates the conformation of a member of the placental Canidae. I know of no figures comparing its speed with that of a dog of the same size, but the placental must be considerably superior in this regard.

The polyprotodont, zygodactylous marsupials of the family Peramelidae, or bandicoots, comprise the following genera: Thalacomys, Isoodon, Perameles (the rabbit bandicoots), Peroryctes, Echimypera, Suillomelas, and Choeropus (the pig-footed bandicoot). The manus of all but the last has five digits, and all but Choeropus and Thalacomys have five pedal digits, the former having four and the latter but three, although from the locomotor aspect it is monodactyl. Its pes conforms to the perissodactyl plan, and it is exceedingly interesting to note that its forelimb is artiodactylate. As a rule bandicoots have a tail more than half the length of head and body and very long ears, but such is not the case in Isoodon, Perameles, and Choeropus. They are omnivorous, although chiefly carnivorous; and at least the more generalized kinds, like Perameles, are fossorial to the extent of being able to dig for food and shelter. They are of particular interest in the present connection for the reasons that one genus is, perhaps, structurally the most specialized for speedy, quadrupedal progression of any mammal other than ungulates and because of the fact that they are quadrupedal rather than bipedal like the other swift marsupials. Their development in this direction may be judged by the conformation of the pes, as illustrated (Fig. 16). The tail is of very moderate length.

In principle the most advanced of this group are largely comparable, in form and gait, to a hare, as the popular name of "rabbit-bandicoot" would indicate. The ears are long, and the hind legs are longer than the forelegs. Reputedly, the forelimbs are used in alternation and the hinder pair in unison during slow progression, but at speed each pair acts as a single unit to accomplish a rocking bound. Very little is known regarding the gait of Choeropus, the most specialized, although it has been described (Krefft in Wood Jones) as like that of a "broken-down hack in a canter, apparently dragging the hind quarters after it." This I am loath to believe. The specimen in question may have been injured, for no mammal as highly developed for speed would have aught but a graceful gait, and it must be very fleet. Even in the case of the more generalized Perameles, Wood Jones says it is "an animal of astonishing activity, its powers of jumping being all the more remarkable from its habit of rising vertically in the air."

Superficially, the kangaroos are characterized by their disproportionately developed hind limbs and heavy tail, wedge-shaped body tapering to the rather short neck and small head, relative reduction of the forelimbs, and tendency for an increase in the size of the fourth pedal digit at the expense of the other toes. With the exception of the genus Hypsiprymnodon, they constitute a very homogeneous group, for the separation of which into the customary divisions of rat kangaroos, wallabies, and kangaroos it is necessary to employ more or less arbitrary standards. The family is divisible as follows:

Macropodidae
  A. Foot structure intermediate between that of the other kangaroos and the Phalangeridae; first pedal digit present; tail naked and scaly
      Hypsiprymnodontinae
        Hypsiprymnodon
  B. First pedal digit absent; tail hairy
      Potoroinae

Bettongia	Caloprymnus
Aepyprymnus	Potorous

      Macropodinae

Lagostrophus	Macropus
Lagorchestes	Setonyx (tail short)
Paradorcas (tail ending in a tuft)	Dendrolagus (arboreal)
Petrogale	Dorcopsis (secondarily terrestrial)
Onychogale	

The Potoroinae consist of small genera, none larger than a rabbit, termed "rat kangaroos," which are more generalized than the Macropodinae. Some of them have prehensile tails, being the only strictly terrestrial mammals that are so equipped. Most of them, at least, are not very speedy and can quite readily be caught by a good dog, but their leaping ability is of a high order. Bettongia penicillata is said to have been able to negotiate an 8-foot fence (Krefft in Wood Jones).

The Macropodinae consist of the wallabies and kangaroos, the former being the smaller, less specialized on the whole, and inhabitants of forest and scrub; the latter being mostly larger, more specialized for saltation, and dwellers of grassy plains or rocky hills. But it should be understood that an animal called a "wallaby" in one district may be known as a "kangaroo" in another, the terms being largely comparable in significance to those of "horse" and "pony."

The relative saltatorial ability of the Macropodinae genera and species is unrecorded in the literature. Certainly, some of the more agile wallabies are more speedy than the slower kangaroos. Thus in regard to the hare-wallaby (Lagorchestes leporoides), about the size of a common hare, Gould (in Wood Jones) has stated that for a short distance its fleetness is beyond all others of the group and its powers of leaping extraordinary. One individual pursued by dogs leaped directly over his head in preference to deflecting its line of flight. LeSouef and Burrell have stated that the hare-wallaby rivals a hare in speed, and they have elsewhere asserted that a horse can go faster.

Of the rock wallabies (Petrogale), that from Pearson Island is at a disadvantage on level ground and there appears clumsy, carrying its head low and its tail high. But it favors extremely rocky areas and is said to be phenomenally adept at leaping from one boulder to another. Rock wallabies are said (LeSouef and Burrell) to seek refuge in leaning trees and are amazingly accurate in their judgment of distance and balance.

Which of the large kangaroos of the genus Macropus is the fleetest, or just what speed they can attain, seems to be a matter of some controversy. Anatomical features would indicate that they surpass their smaller relatives in this regard; but this may not be dependable, for the intangible powers of speed may be greater in a form that appears less specialized anatomically. The toolach (Macropus greyi), a very light and graceful form, is said to be by far the fleetest of all the wallabies, its gait being unusual in that it takes two short leaps and then a long one. The Kangaroo Island animal (M. fuliginosus) is said to be the slowest of all the large kangaroos. LeSouef and Burrell (1926) have stated that the average large kangaroo covers about 3 feet at each "walking" step, 4–6 feet at each slow hop, and that at speed an active animal may cover a distance of 26 feet, but not every time, for the next hop may be 10 feet shorter. This seems to indicate variation in the ability to recover balance after a leap. A hunted animal has been known to clear a fence 9 feet high.

Perhaps the most curious action of the Macropodinae is the manner in which the tail is used as a crutch. When nuzzling about for food, the animal will progress not only forward but sideways by bracing with forefeet and tail, while moving the hind feet in unison. When progressing more briskly, however, the tail is held aloft so as to act as a counterbalance to the body, while the animal hops with the hind feet only. It is doubtful if it can voluntarily move these members alternately for progression, although they can use one hind limb, clumsily, for scratching the head. The tail may be further employed after the fashion of a fifth limb when the kangaroo is on the

Fig. 4.—Kangaroo postures, drawn from photographs: *a*, two animals on a single plate, by Kilroy Harris, showing difference in posture at different phases of stride; *b*, observation or fighting posture; *c*, while supported by tail, lunging with all four feet toward an adversary; *d*, resting posture.

defensive, supporting the entire weight, briefly, while the animal lunges with both hind feet toward an adversary (Fig. 4).

The tree kangaroos or tree wallabies, more specifically of the genus Dendrolagus, are of interest as constituting the only known instance of a mammal's becoming markedly specialized for terrestrial progression by saltation and then taking to an arboreal existence.

It was stated by LeSouef and Burrell that tree kangaroos descend a tree tail first (save when startled, in which case they will leap to the ground from a great height) and can walk backward along a branch with great facility. What is more remarkable, they are able to climb a pipe or rope. Their arms are larger and legs smaller than is the case with their terrestrial relatives. In addition, their claws are sharper; but still, on the whole, it seems remarkable that they are so adept arboreally with an equipment that to us appears so essentially terrestrial. Curiously enough, the New Guinea genus of "tree kangaroo," Dorcopsis, has once more reverted to a terrestrial existence.

CHAPTER IV

Placental Mammals

THE Eutheria, Monodelphia, or placental mammals comprise the mammalian group that has proved to be most successful in occupying practically all available habitats of Recent times. Except in the case of those groups most highly specialized for aquatic, volant, fossorial, and arboreal lives, all, with negligible exceptions, can run after a fashion and so might be considered as cursorial. Even those quite gifted in this respect are entirely too numerous to be discussed individually and in detail in a contribution of the present scope. Then, too, the theoretical and applied aspects of the question cannot always be reconciled. Anatomical study may indicate a higher cursorial adaptation in one order of mammals than in another—a conclusion that may not be substantiated by performance, for the reason that speed depends upon many factors other than architectural specifications. Finally, many of the most interesting kinds of mammals are unavailable for study in the laboratory and poorly known in the field. Accordingly, it is necessary to select for study those cursorial types that prove to be most feasible. Extinct mammals present such difficulties in this regard that scant attention can be paid to them.

Cursorial ability of high degree is developed only where it is necessary either for an animal to attain a high velocity to escape from speedy enemies or to capture speedy prey, as the case may be, or else to maintain speed for covering relatively long distances in securing sustenance, where water is scarce and food scanty. In other words, the optimum environment for the development of cursorial ability is a rather arid type of plains habitat. Accordingly, definitely cursorial types are to be found among practically all orders whose representatives have inhabited this type of country for a long period of time. A survey of the orders and families of mammals, however, will at once impress the investigator with the immense variation in the degree with which different groups have adapted themselves to such an environment. There are, of course, various factors involved. An animal may have a physical equipment and basic habits of such a nature that its invasion of open country would constitute nothing less than suicide, or it may irremediably require the succulent herbage of a humid climate, or any number of other things may be involved. These may be grouped under the heading of environmental preferences. A second factor, or group of factors, is the inherent ability of the stock to respond to cursorial stimuli, although it is impossible to evaluate this detail satisfactorily. Nevertheless, one cannot help being impressed with the fact that in some groups, such as the ungulates, a host of species, comprising practically all the members of the order, are of the highest cursorial conformation. In other groups, such as the insectivores, only an insignificant proportion of the species has become cursorial or saltatorial. Then among rodents, for instance, there may be one restricted group of species or genera highly modified for saltatorial progression, while coexisting desert forms of rodents, of diverse sorts, remain inappreciably modified.

There is food for much thought in the fact that relatively slow ungulates have greatly elongated, fused metatarsal complexes and that not only these, but perhaps the most speedy, highly developed forms, may be easily overtaken by the hunting leopard (Acinonyx), which is not only digitigrade, supposedly illustrating a far lesser degree of cursorial ability than the unguligrade condition, but with unfused, shorter metatarsals besides. So it is apparent that speed depends not alone on having limbs of the proper length and conformation but on the manner in which those limbs are used. The conformation not only is a consequence of particular environmental stimuli but also is a measure of the degree to which the organism has responded—could respond, undoubtedly—to those stimuli. In the past many groups of mammals have become extinct because they were inherently incapable of developing types sufficiently speedy for survival in their chosen environment or because that environment changed, as by the invasion of a speedy carnivore.

The orders of Recent mammals may be arranged as follows:

Insectivora (moles, shrews, hedgehogs, etc.)
Dermoptera (flying lemurs)
Chiroptera (bats)

Primates (lemurs, tarsier, monkeys, apes, man)
Edentata (manises, anteaters, armadillos, sloths)
Rodentia (true rodents)
Lagomorpha (hares, rabbits, pikas)
Carnivora (terrestrial flesh-eaters; seals, sea lions)
Cetacea (whales, porpoises)
Tubulidentata (aardvarks)
Proboscidea (elephants)
Hyracoidea (hyraces)
Sirenia (manatees, dugongs)
Perissodactyla (tapirs, rhinoceroses, horses)
Artiodactyla (hippos, swine, cattle, goats, sheep, antelopes, deer, camels, giraffes)

The only ones of these of particular concern in the present connection are the Insectivora, Rodentia, Lagomorpha, Carnivora, Perissodactyla, and Artiodactyla, although some others will be discussed.

INSECTIVORA

Living insectivores may most conveniently be divided into the suborders Menotyphla and Lipotyphla, the former including only the Tupaiidae (tree shrews) and Macroscelididae (African elephant shrews), and the latter all other families. The only members of the order that have become definitely adapted to speedy locomotion are the Macroscelididae. These belong to several genera of two subfamilies, Macroscelidinae, with 5 manual and usually 5 (first vestigial in one genus) pedal digits, and Rhynchocyoninae, with 4–4 digits. For insectivores they are of medium to large size, terrestrial, partly diurnal, and modified in a cursorial direction. The tail is of medium length, the hind limbs are much elongated, and the forelimbs moderately so. In the proportions of their limbs they may thus be compared more properly with the hares and with the marsupial Antechinomys than with the jerboas or kangaroos. The genus Macroscelides (not seen) has much inflated audital bullae, and the general appearance of the illustrations of some genera (as Elephantulus) is very suggestive of a kangaroo rat.

At slow speed elephant shrews are quadrupedal, and the length of the forelimbs would indicate a considerable proportion of their time thus spent; but at a faster gait they are said to be bipedal and to progress by long leaps. The common name has been derived from the fact that the snout is long and mobile, a development undoubtedly correlated with the length of the forelegs.

The primates are divisible into the suborders Lemuroidea, Tarsioidea, and Anthropoidea, with the latter containing the superfamily Hominoidea. Some of the monkeys are able to negotiate arboreal leaps of no mean proportions and have considerable speed in running. No primate, however, is considered to be cursorial except possibly man, and only the tarsier and gallagos can lay claim to being saltatorial.

Tarsius is phenomenally proficient in leaping, but in a manner scarcely comparable to most saltators. As in the case of the frog, specialization is for a single sudden, bipedal leap in pursuit of insect prey, an action also useful in escaping—and surprising—an enemy. The natural procedure is for the animal to spring from one upright limb of a tree to another, with astonishing precision and control of balance. At least 8 feet (Lewis, 1939) and possibly considerably more can be covered at a single bound. With the aid of the broad digital disks, the animal can leap from and land in surprising situations, such as the angle between adjoining walls of a room. The propulsive force appears to be applied through the ankle by means of the musculature of the calf, while the remainder of the limb is held relatively static, with thigh considerably protracted and lower leg moderately flexed. Following the major role of the hind limbs in vigorous locomotion, these members have experienced pronounced enlargement as compared with the forelimbs.

Man is a biped and accordingly might lay some claim to being either a saltatorial or a cursorial type; but his bipedalism was developed in connection with the emancipation of his arms from a locomotor function, in order that they might be used as tools, rather than for speed in progression. Man's length of limb has developed chiefly for the proper support of his entire body; and, as a genus, he has escaped from his enemies by his wits rather than by his legs. Except for length of limb he is very poorly equipped for running, and it seems indicated that man did not develop his present form as a dweller of an open-plains habitat but as an inhabitant of a hilly country, in which there were frequent rocky spots for concealment and scattered trees that might be climbed at the approach of danger.

Man's leaping ability averages very poor. It is probable that only the exceptional young man, even of those athletically inclined, can jump farther than 17 feet or higher than 5 feet, although the greatest known distance for these respective feats are 26 feet 8.25 inches, and 6 feet 11 inches, respectively (the latter unofficial). All but exceptional runners tire rapidly after ¼ mile and are unable to outrun any but the smaller, clumsier sorts of mammals. Table 1 gives a list of the present world's running records for men.

The faster speed for 220 than for 100 yards undoubtedly reflects the greater proportion of time occupied in the shorter distance by the static start. These records are from the *World Almanac* for 1941.

RODENTIA

The rodents are herein considered to comprise the infraorders Sciuromorpha, Myomorpha, and Hystricomorpha (Simpson, 1931), but not the hares and their allies. The rodents, however, are an ex-

TABLE 1

Distance	Time (In Seconds)	Speed (M.p h.)	Distance	Time (In Seconds)	Speed (M.p.h.)
100 yards	9.4	21.7	3 miles........	13:50.6	13.0
220	20.3	22.2	4	19:1	12.5
440	46.4	19.4	5	24:6.2	12.4
880	1:49.6	16.4	10	50:15	11.9
1 mile	4:6.4	14.6	20	1:51:54	10.7
2	8:56	13.4	25	2:26:11	10.2

ceedingly heterogeneous aggregation of mammals, and it is probable that no scheme attempting to reduce them to a few groups will ever prove satisfactory from all viewpoints.

A few (mostly burrowing) rodents are very slow, but the majority can move the limbs with such rapidity that they scurry along with quite amazing speed. This ability is markedly advantageous in escaping from predators, but only where there is considerable cover to help confuse or hinder a pursuer. It is obvious that the swiftest mouse or rat traveling in a straight line over terrain devoid of cover could have but little hope of escaping from a fox or a cat. Hence, dodging is at a premium, and the best dodgers are the saltators. Even many unmodified mice (as Peromyscus) that normally scurry over bare ground will bound along when pursued over rough ground. Accordingly, this is the natural mode of progression for small rodents that are well fitted for rapid progression over the steppe or desert type of habitat. Marked adaptation for saltation in rodents is encountered only in plains dwellers with one exception, and that is the jumping mice (Zapodinae), which are dwellers of meadows. The only rodent that may be said to be markedly modified for cursorial (as opposed to saltatorial) progression is the Patagonian cavy (Dolichotis magellanica and its allies).

The Sciuromorpha include the squirrels, beavers, pocket gophers, the largely saltatorial family Heteromyidae, and the saltatorial Pedetidae.

The Myomorpha include the great body of rats and mice, among which are the variously modified Australian genera that culminate in the leaping Ascopharynx, the rare New ,Guinea Lorentzimys and Malagasy Hallomys and Macrotarsomys, the slightly modified Gerbillinae, and the highly modified Dipodidae.

The Hystricomorpha include the porcupines, octodonts, and cavies and their allies, among which is the small group represented by the swift Patagonian cavy.

It may here be stated that saltatorial specialization among the rodents culminates in a disproportionate lengthening of the hind limbs, chiefly the distal elements, reduction in the number of digits, fusion of the metatarsals, some shortening of the body, with lengthening of the tail, which assumes a white terminal tuft. Associated with these specializations are also fusion of some of the cervical vertebrae and either lengthening of the external ear or enlargement of the chambers of the bony ear, but rarely of both together.

The North American family Heteromyidae, of the superfamily Sciuroidea, is a heterogeneous one including the relatively generalized genera Heteromys and Liomys (spiny pocket mice), the slightly saltatorial genus Perognathus (pocket mice), and the quite highly saltatorial Dipodomys and Microdipodops (kangaroo rats and mice). All are characterized by the possession of lateral, external cheek pouches, a feature shared only with the pocket gophers (Geomyidae). As is almost invariably the case with saltatorial rodents, those definitely modified in this direction show a preference for an arid habitat. The genus Perognathus is of interest chiefly because it shows beautifully a progressive enlargement of the mastoid bullae, a feature usually associated in rodents with saltatory specialization. Dipodomys and Microdipodops exhibit this character to a phenomenal degree, although in these also the external ear is short. They also show enlargement of the head; shortening of the neck and trunk; elongation of the tail and the acquisition by this member of a terminal tuft of hair; some relative reduction of the anterior limbs and elongation of the posterior ones, partly by a lengthening of the metatarsals; and a reduction or suppression of the first pedal digit.

Worthy of note is the rather remarkable trend in markings exhibited by highly adapted saltatorial rodents of dissimilar affinities. Such animals are usually inhabitants of pale desert areas, and so their coloration tends to approach a light buff. But in addition there is a tendency for pure white markings on the face, a white band over the lateral thigh, and a bicolored tail with a terminal tuft of long hairs that progressively develops first a black tip, which is abruptly tipped with white in the more specialized sorts. There appears to be but little doubt that this black-and-white pencil pattern has been developed either directively, so that individuals of the same species may more readily distinguish one another, or more probably for the confusion of a pursuer, the latter then endeavoring to pounce upon the tail tip rather than upon the less conspicuous body.

While creeping about, the kangaroo rats and mice employ all four feet, usually in a typical walk but at times with the hind feet acting in unison. At a faster gait, however, the hind feet operate alone, in the bipedal hop, the tail being employed as a balancer. Probably as much as 3, and possibly 4, yards may be covered in a single leap by the larger species, and when closely pressed by a pursuer the course is sharply zigzag. Only one who has watched the confused and ludicrously ineffectual actions of a dog while pursuing a kangaroo rat can appreciate the advantage to them of saltatorial efficiency. This mode of progression does add to their speed, without a doubt, but their skill in employing it is not as yet perfected. They are prone, when in flight, to leap without looking and often to land off balance, owing apparently to clumsy use of the tail.

The Heteromyidae spend the day in burrows that they construct themselves, mostly in sandy soil. Often they live where free water is unobtainable for months at a time and food so scarce that relatively great distances are undoubtedly covered in gaining a livelihood. They conserve moisture by being active only at night, plugging the mouth of the burrow with sand during the day, digging below the layer of hot surface sand, and resorbing an unusually large amount of water from the urine, both in the tubules of the kidneys and in the bladder.

The Peditidae, or African jumping hares, are of the size of a small hare. In conformation they resemble a large and clumsier edition of a jerboa. The external ears are large, although the bullae are not equally modified, the neck is not shortened so much as in the jerboas, nor are any of the bones fused. Neither is the tail as elongated, although it is of generous length and heavily tufted. The hind limbs are long and robust, the development, however, being comparable to that in Dipodomys, with unfused metatarsals, rather than to the jerboas. It occurs in a habitat that is largely of the plains type, and speedy progression is accomplished by saltation.

Many myomorph rodents of the superfamilies Myoidea and Myoxoidea are slightly modified for leaping, particularly the gerbils and their allies. By far the most gifted in this respect of these two groups, however, are the Australian jerboa rats progressively illustrated through the genera Leporillus, with the hind legs rather long but feet short and broad; Laomys and Zyzomys of delicate build and tail lightly penciled; Mesembriomys and Conilurus with longer feet and long tail well tufted; to Notomys, with elongated hind limbs and feet, plantar pads reduced to four, long ears and long, tufted tail. Ascopharynx, the Australian pouched mouse, has much the same conformation as the last; but it is unique among rodents in having an external, unpaired, gular pouch beneath the chin, comparable in situation to the glandular pouch encountered in some bats. Occurring in an arid habitat, they are pale in color and are said to be great leapers, vertically as well as horizontally, and are prone to jump sideways. Presumably they are quadrupedal at a slow gait and bipedally saltatorial when progressing more rapidly. No specimen is available for examination, but presumably Ascopharynx is more developed in a saltatorial direction than Dipodomys, although not as much so as most of the jerboas. It seems that the metatarsals are unfused.

I know nothing of the New Guinea genus Lorentzimys, or of Hallomys and Macrotarsomys from Madagascar, except that they are said to be slightly saltatorial.

The Gerbillinae are found in Africa, India, and southeastern Russia and comprise several genera slightly modified for saltation but with hind limbs not markedly elongated and tail little or no longer than head and body.

The myomorph superfamily Dipodoidea is of particular interest, for it contains rodents of an astonishing degree of saltatorial adaptation. It is made up (according to Vinogradov, 1937) of the five subfamilies Zapodinae, Euchoreutinae, Cardiocraninae, Allactaginae, and Dipodinae, whose characters are briefly summarized in Table 2.

The Zapodinae are good leapers (Eozapus, Zapus, Napaeozapus), except for the more generalized genus Sicista; but they are rodents of marsh and meadowland, fitted for escape by a few erratic hops amid dense cover, and, except for a long, rather bare tail and somewhat elongated hind legs, they are not markedly modified for saltation. Leaping ability is fair, to the extent probably of about 4 feet; but balance and recovery after a leap are poor because of the untufted tail.

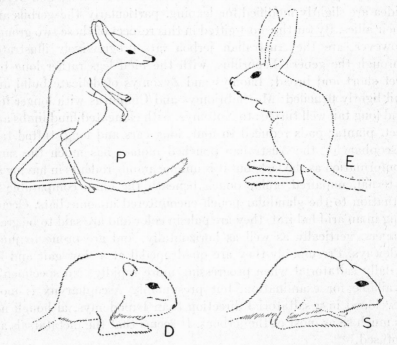

Fig. 5.—P, South Australian jerboa pouched mouse (Antechinomys), after Wood Jones. E, Euchoreutes, after Vinogradov; D, Dipodomys; S, Scirtopoda, after Sowerby.

The remaining four subfamilies are all characteristically inhabitants of plains and deserts. Saltatorial specialization among them varies greatly and doubtless is reflected chiefly in the length of hind leg, particularly of the metatarsals, the degree of fusion of the latter, to a considerable degree in the reduction of the digits, and in length of tail and the development of a terminal tuft. In some of the Dipodinae the pes is much lengthened, particularly the metatarsals, which are fused to form a cannon bone. They have but three pedal digits, except for Scarturus, which has also a very slender fifth digit. The same statements apply to the Allactaginae, except that they also have very slender first and fifth digits. The other three sub-families have unfused metatarsals, five in number except in the genus Salpingotus, which has lost the first and fifth digits. In this genus also, and in the Dipodinae, although to a variable extent, there is an abrupt, dense pad of long hairs growing from the ventral surface of the toes and their bases, forming a digital brush. This undoubtedly aids support in soft sand. In some of the Dipodinae (Paradipus, Scirtopoda, at least) the lateral toes are bordered with a comb of horny bristles, probably for use in cleaning the fur but hardly to be classed as a saltatorial adaptation.

The tail, as an aid to equilibration, is unusually long, but to a variable degree, in all Dipodoidea except the Cardiocraninae, in which it is either shorter or but little longer than head and body. Its effective-

TABLE 2

	No. Toes	Meta-tar. Fused	Tail Long	Tail Tufted	External Ear	Bony Bulla	Cerv. Vert. Fused	Digi-tal Brush	Digi-tal Comb
Zapodinae........	5	No	Yes	No	Short	Small	No	No	No
Euchoreutinae....	5	Yes	Yes	Yes	Huge	Huge	No	No	No
Cardiocraninae....	3–5	No	No	No	Short	Huge	Yes	Yes	......
Allactaginae......	5	Yes	Yes	Yes	Long	Small	No	No	No
Dipodinae........	3	Yes	Yes	Yes	Short	Moderate	Yes	Yes	Yes

ness is increased in the more highly specialized varieties by the acquisition of a terminal tuft or pencil of hair, which tends, in saltatory plains rodents all over the world, to acquire a white tip and a sub-terminal black band. In some of the Allactaginae the proximal part of the tail is swollen by a deposit of fat, which is probably a provision for increasing its weight and hence its effectiveness as an equilibrator.

Small saltatorial rodents show a tendency for reduction in the length of neck and even in the fusion of the cervical vertebrae, and this character undoubtedly is correlated with other details of body form conforming to saltatorial specialization. The first six cervicals only are fused, and with three or four "intervertebral" foramina, in the Dipodinae; but all are firmly fused, with but one foramen, in the Cardiocraninae.

It is interesting that many desert dwellers (such as hares and asses) show an increased length of ear, in spite of the fact that their vision is more unobstructed than animals of most habitats and they might be expected to depend more on sight than on hearing. This tendency is reflected among the Dipodoidea. Some of the Dipodinae have ears but little longer than most rodents, which character is more pronounced in the Allactaginae, some with ears relatively as large as rabbits, and culminates in the Euchoreutinae, in which the immense pinna is proportionately longer than in any living mammal with the exception of certain bats. Another auditory development that is even more remarkable is the phenomenal size of the auditory or of the mastoid bullae, or both, in some Dipodidae. This feature is small in the Zapodinae, only slightly larger in the Allactaginae, moderate to fair in the Dipodinae, very large in Euchoreutes, and truly immense in the Cardiocraninae, in size surpassing the American dipodomyid genus Microdipodops. It appears that this feature of size of middle ear has nothing to do with size of external ear. A large pinna does help to collect air-borne vibrations, but the reception of these can hardly be facilitated by enlargement of the middle ear. On the contrary, it seems probable that enlargement of mastoid and tympanic bullae are for the better detection of vibrations through the ground, such as footfalls, and hence this adaptation is associated with saltation to but a very secondary extent.

Often in the habitat of the Dipodoidea, or jerboas, food is scarce and scattered widely, so that the animals must travel for relatively great distances and swiftly enough to escape from lurking carnivores. Accounts of their actions seldom detail the actual length of their leaps and usually employ such terms as "remarkable." Feniuk and Kazantzeva (1937), however, have stated that at an unhurried pace the hops of Dipus sagitta measure 30, 40, or perhaps even 60 cm., but, when chasing one another, 2 or 3 meters in length. They can also clear an abstruction (leap out of a barrel) 3 feet or more in height. Certainly they should be able to surpass Dipodomys, and it is likely that some of the Dipodidae, of not too light weight, can cover at least 12 and maybe 15 feet at a bound.

Whereas, in the other superfamilies of the Rodentia, adaptation for speed—or, more properly stated, high specialization for a plains habitat—takes the form of development toward a bipedal, saltatory form of progression comparable to that of the kangaroo type, in the Hystricomorpha this specialization follows the path that has been taken by the hares, involving quadrupedal locomotion by the half-bound or bound. This difference is not fortuitous. Saltatory mammals have long tails capable of being used as effective equilibrators, while hares and the speedier types of true hystricomorph rodents, which are quadrupedal, have insignificant tails useless for such a purpose.

Many of the Hystricomorpha are rather large for rodents, a number show digital reduction, and several are quite swift. Cursorial specialization of the feet is progressively shown by the chinchillas, agoutis, and Patagonian cavy, Dolichotis, represented by the species megellanica (often referred to as patachonica), and the smaller D. salinicola of the arid central Argentine. The form of the latter is very harelike, although the ears, long for a genus of this group, are yet shorter than those of a rabbit. The limbs are slender and clean-cut. Captive specimens walk with a crouching, sneaking posture. They also have a slow canter or gallop, and Simpson (1934) has stated that in the wild they bound stiff-legged with all four feet in very peculiar fashion. They must be capable of relatively great speed, possibly as great as a jack rabbit, but reports are lacking. When at rest they are plantigrade but at other times digitigrade.

LAGOMORPHA

The Lagomorpha are classified by some as duplicidentate rodents, but it appears preferable to place them in a separate order. They comprise the families Ochotonidae, the pikas, and the Leporidae. Pikas are shy little beasts, for the most part inhabiting rock slides and broken ground in mountainous country in western North America and Asia. They are entirely unmodified for speed. The Leporidae constitute the hares and rabbits. Broadly speaking, the neck is rather longer than in the majority of rodents, and the tail is insignificant. The forelimbs, although somewhat elongated, are greatly surpassed in this respect by the hind limbs. The pes is elongated also, but the metatarsals are unfused. There is no enlargement of the audital bullae, but the external ear is much enlarged, phenomenally so in the case of the prairie species most modified for speedy locomotion.

There are a number of genera of leporids, varying from the relatively unmodified Pentalagus of the Liu Kiu Islands and Romerolagus of the higher Mexican mountains through the cottontail (Sylvilagus) type of rabbit to the prairie hares. Pentalagus is a remarkable lagomorph with short ears, stout legs, and very short feet. Romerolagus is of largely similar conformation but much smaller, and both represent the most generalized limb structure of existing leporids. I know nothing of the habits of the former, but the latter scurries about through runways in the grass much like a large meadow mouse.

Of the rabbits of the cottontail type, the marsh rabbit, Sylvilagus palustris, of the south Atlantic coast is also in the habit of scurrying rather than bounding along well-beaten runways. And Brachylagus, the Idaho pigmy rabbit, also prefers to scuttle. Other rabbits progress by the bound or half-bound in the manner familiar to all. In the hares this gait is carried to more efficient lengths.

The Leporidae, unlike the kangaroos, can move the hind limbs in alternation; but cottontails proper and hares do this only when creeping about while feeding. Even when progressing at a pace no faster than what would be comparable to a slow walk, both hind feet are used largely in unison. For all practical purposes the gait at speed may be considered as a bound. Actually, however, the forelimbs are placed upon the ground in alternation, so that the gait is a half-bound with the hind footfalls in unison, as is the case with the cottontails and at times with the hares, or else a lateral gallop, with one hind foot placed a bit in advance of the other, but with the interval of transit greatly prolonged. Transit, with body entirely free of the ground, may be for a distance as much as 15 feet in the case of the black-tailed jack (L. californicus), or even as much as 21 feet in the white-tailed prairie hare, L. townsendii (Seton, 1929). One of the prodigious leaps of a L. alleni that I had shot through the abdomen with a .22 rifle covered 23 feet 4 inches.

Many of the hares are in the habit of making occasional bounds that have been termed "spy hops." An animal will travel in an essentially horizontal direction for several strides and then make one stride higher than the others. This may be but a few inches higher, or the animal may leap to a height of 4 feet (Seton). It is an ingrained habit with the black-tailed hares, while it varies to some extent with most of the others. Thus the antelope jack (L. alleni) does not ordinarily make observation hops but will do so if high grass or brush obstructs its sight of possible danger. Clearly, these observation hops are of definite advantage to an agile animal that must escape through dense herbage higher than its head, in order that it may keep informed of the actions of a near-by enemy. I have seen a coyote do precisely the same thing in grass that was 4 feet high. It is a time-consuming habit, for Seton remarks that a spy hop may take three times as long to execute as the other sort. They are not indulged in, however, when the animal is really hard pressed.

The abundance of hares in the northern hemisphere attests to the fact that this prolific animal is a successful type. Not the least of its accomplishments—and one that has added materially to its success—is the remarkable manner in which a hare can abruptly change, at full speed, the direction of its course. A greyhound can capture a hare in fair chase, but this ability to dodge often wins the race.

The fact that lagomorphs have developed quadrupedal cursorial ability rather than bipedal saltatorial conformation is probably due to the fact that the former group has always lacked an effective tail. Saltation in mammals requires a heavy tail as a counterbalance. And yet, under certain conditions, hares have been known to employ the bipedal hop. Swarth (1929) has observed that L. alleni often makes four or five long hops on the hind legs alone, without touching the forelegs to the ground, before settling to the ordinary gait. I am loath, however, to believe this to be a regular habit of the species, for I never observed it during an aggregate of many months spent in its range. It is well known that the Arctic hares do this more regularly. Thus Manniche (1910), in speaking of L. arcticus groenlandicus, stated that "in rapid jumps they hurried up the hillside—never the opposite way—moving on the tip-toes of the hind limbs, while the fore-limbs either dangled in the air or were kept close to the breast." "The vigilant animals danced among each other—still without using their fore-limbs—looking out for the nature of the danger" until their suspicions were allayed, when they dropped upon all fours. They may travel for 100 yards or more on the hind feet, covering 6 or 8 feet at a hop (Greeley, quoted by Seton).

It is tempting to explain this habit by suggesting that the animals found that their smaller forefeet sink in the snow, and therefore it is more convenient to utilize the hind feet alone at certain times. But this does not explain the same action in Arizona jack rabbits. The fact is probably merely that the hind limbs are so much better modified for locomotion than the anterior pair that at times they prefer to use the former only, in spite of the inadequate tail for balance. That hares may become bipedal eventually, just as has man, is a possibility but not so likely as though a heavy tail were present.

Seton has given the maximum speed of the prairie hare as 30 miles per hour and that of the black-tailed jack rabbit as slightly less. But I have paced the latter slightly in excess of 35 miles per hour, and Horace Elmer Wood II (manuscript) has done likewise. My experience with L. alleni convinces me that this animal is capable of 40 miles per hour, while Andrews (1937) has given the maximum speed of the jack rabbit as 45 miles per hour. It is probably only a very exceptional black-tailed jack that could attain the latter speed.

Terres (1941) has recorded the maximum speed of a snowshoe or varying hare as 31 miles per hour, but this was on treacherous footing. Brush-living rabbits are considerably slower.

CARNIVORA

Carnivores, except carrion-feeders, must capture the food upon which they subsist, so, at first thought, it would seem that they must be more speedy than their prey, including the majority of ungulates. Such is not the case, however. Some carnivores are aquatic and others fossorial, some gain their livelihood by stealth and cunning, and the majority feed upon smaller animals that can be secured without any great show of speed. Although, like the rodents, most carnivores can run, some of them quite rapidly for a short distance, many are rather slow. It is only the cats and dogs that can be considered as having definite cursorial modifications. But no carnivore has metapodials fused or greatly elongated, and what would be considered as high cursorial adaptation in this group would be looked upon as exceedingly generalized in the ungulates, for instance.

Living representatives of this order may be arranged as follows (Simpson, 1931).

Order Carnivora
Suborder Fissipedia (terrestrial carnivores)
Superfamily Canoidea
Family Canidae (dogs)
Procyonidae (racoons)
Ursidae (bears)
Mustelidae (weasles and allies)
Superfamily Feloidea
Family Viverridae (viverrids)
Hyaenidae (hyenas)
Felidae (cats)
Suborder Pinnipedia (seals, sea lions, walruses)

Whereas the cats are almost or quite as speedy for short distances as dogs of comparable size, the Canidae as a whole have far more stamina and endurance, surpassing in this respect all other carnivores and, indeed, most other mammals. It is true that the tropical American bush dog, Ictycyon, has legs that are disproportionately short and apparently clumsy, but it is not improbable that this is somewhat in the nature of a genetic freak, comparable to some of the shorter-legged domestic dogs. Neither are the legs of a fox long, but the latter is nevertheless speedy. A gray fox (Urocyon) was forced to a speed of 26 miles per hour along a dirt road (Cottam, 1937) but has been reported (Pack, 1933) as capable of as high a rate as 40. The red fox (Vulpes) has been recorded (Schrenkeisen, 1932) as having done 45 miles per hour in front of a car with a reliable speedometer. This is faster than track records for race horses. I have timed the coyote at 35 miles for a short distance. Andrews (1924) found that the Gobi wolves had a top speed of 36 miles per hour, but this only for a short dash. Stanley P. Young (manuscript) timed a male wolf by automobile in Colorado at 28 miles for a distance of 200 yards, and the same individual informed me of an Alaskan wolf's being chased by an airplane capable of a minimum speed of 50, the animal at times attaining a speed of 40. Young considers the latter estimate as probably too high. It does not seem to me improbable, however, that individual wolves may approach this speed for a short sprint. But it is unlikely that a rate much above 30 miles could be maintained for long. The swiftest of the wild Canidae is probably the wild hunting dog, Lycaon, which is very destructive to game; but its speed has never been reliably reported. The South American fox-wolf, Chrysocyon, is also built for high speed, but I know of no figures on its capabilities.

Several strains of dogs have long been bred for extreme speed, and there are few breeds of dogs whose lines have been kept relatively pure for a longer time. All these may be classed as of the greyhound type, the main variants being the saluki or gazelle hound of Arabia and the closely related Afghan hound, the borzoi or Russian wolfhound, the Scottish deerhound, and the heavier Irish wolfhound. The Italian greyhound, so called, is merely a refined type of toy dog without any definite relationship to its larger counterpart; but in relatively recent times there has been developed a light type of hound for racing, called the whippet, produced by selection from the offspring of greyhound and terrier parents, probably with an Italian greyhound cross as well.

A search through a substantial part of the voluminous literature on the dog fails to indicate the comparative running ability of the various strains of these speedy dogs. The heavier Irish wolfhounds can hardly have the ability of the greyhound. The deerhound must be its inferior as well, else it would have been more popular for coursing hares; and the borzoi, although better for running wolves, has not quite the turn of speed of the greyhound. The latter, however, is probably not quite the equal of the saluki. Ash (1929) stated that this dog is said to travel at 32 yards per second, which is not at the rate of 43 miles per hour, as stated by the author, but of more than 65 miles. It seems incredible that a dog could travel this fast, or so much faster than a greyhound, without long since having entirely supplanted the latter for coursing. In running gazelles with the saluki, a hawk is usually also used to harry the quarry and decelerate it. It is said to take a very good dog to catch a gazelle unaided. But a saluki is reputed to be able to overtake an Arabian horse.

The whippet is now used for track racing to a greater extent than the greyhound. A first-class whippet can cover 200 yards in 12 seconds, which is at the rate of better than 34 miles per hour, and a dog of good size will cover as much as 15 feet at each stride.

The gaits of the Canidae are the walk, the trot, and the lateral gallop. At least the latter is followed by domesticated dogs, and it is assumed that their wild brethren have similar habits. In addition, one occasionally encounters a domesticated dog, usually a setter, that substitutes the pace for the trot. Partly because of its lesser weight a swift whippet is a more effective racing machine than the horse, and yet the latter is far more modified architecturally than any dog. Not only are the metapodials of the Canidae relatively unspecialized, but the digits have only just begun reduction. In most members of the family the digital formula is 5:4, but Lycaon is completely tetradactyl.

No trustworthy figures in miles per hour that the more agile cats can travel are available, and there is almost as much contradictory evidence in this regard as in the case of the ungulates. The common house cat is certainly not built for speed, and yet in a short dash it can outdistance most dogs of equal size. Similarly, such a heavy species as the lion is extremely swift for a short distance and during its initial rush can probably cover ground more rapidly than any but the swiftest antelopes of its habitat. It is a question whether the leopard may not be speedier still for a short dash. At any rate Martin Johnson (manuscript) considered that for 100 feet it is the swiftest living mammal. That such is the case I very much doubt, for the reason that the charge of the leopard is usually through cover of varying density, and a body moving at speed through brush gives the ocular impression of being very much speedier than one in the open.

The fact that cats are more gifted in this regard than their length of limb would suggest is attributable to several factors. They are notoriously limber mammals, have a high proportion of white muscle fibers which permits high twitch action of the muscles, and their vertebral column is extremely mobile, allowing powerful back musculature to bow and straighten the back as an efficient aid to the limbs. In order that the latter may be utilized to the full, the hind limbs, particularly of the smaller cats, act in unison when the animal is traveling at speed, and the half-bound is the result.

Among the Felidae, however, it is the cheetah or hunting leopard, Acinonyx, of Africa and India, that lays chief claim to attention. It has the appearance of a lightly built leopard with small head and extremely long, somewhat doglike limbs. Apparently it is rather loath to exert itself, even when chased, and those who have not been privileged to see it while pursuing game are not impressed with its potentialities. All agree that the cheetah's stamina is extremely poor, for after a quarter or third of a mile a pursued animal will come to bay, apparently exhausted. Martin Johnson (manuscript) had an extremely poor opinion of its speed, as did Selous (1908), the latter having stated that he rode down uninjured cheetahs on two occasions. But it is not unlikely that these conclusions were based on animals satiated with food or out of condition, for those few individuals who have been privileged to observe the cheetah in pursuit of game have found the ease with which it can overhaul a fleet antelope to be perfectly astounding. It seems certain that it can travel at the remarkable speed of 65, and not unlikely that for a short space even 70, miles per hour, but it is soon exhausted.

The Felidae progress by the walk, the trot, and the gallop. It appears that the transverse gallop is the one used, but this detail may vary with the different groups and is often so modified that it becomes the half-bound.

Many of the Viverridae can doubtless run as speedily as cats of similar size, but data are entirely lacking.

For carnivores of such size the hyenas are rather slow, cumbersome beasts. Nevertheless, they are of very real interest in any study of locomotion because of the fact that the forequarters are much heavier than the hinder ones and the former are employed chiefly in progression, while the hind limbs are used chiefly to maintain balance, at least during the low speeds observed in captivity. The proportions of their limb segments are noteworthy among all the carnivores.

The present report does not aim to make more than cursory mention of fossil mammals; yet some consideration must be given to the order Litopterna. Litopterns were a peculiar group of South American ungulates that became extinct in the Pleistocene. They are noteworthy in that one of the two families, the Proterotheridae or pseudo-horses, almost exactly paralleled the Equidae in the development of their limbs. Some of them were three-toed, but one—Thoatherium—was more completely monodactyl than any mammal yet discovered. It was the size of a small dog but as lightly built as an antelope.

PROBOSCIDEA

The elephants, although decidedly not a cursorial type, are of considerable interest as illustrating certain mechanical features that must occur in a quadruped weighing several tons. Or, if one prefers, it may be stated that only a stock having the sort of bodily conformation of the elephant could survive as a giant type. Elephants are descended from a type of ancestor somewhat resembling the subaquatic moeritheres, whose remains occur in the Middle Eocene deposits of Egypt. They were beasts of perhaps one-quarter the size of living elephants; and it is noteworthy that the two, although separated by relatively immense intervals of time, have basic skeletal features that are much the same. These details are excellently fitted for the support of great weight, and this fact undoubtedly has contributed to the development and survival of the proboscideans. Had the ancestors been smaller and more highly specialized in typical ungulate direction, the phylum would doubtless have disappeared long before its representatives had attained their present dimensions.

The skeletal features of the elephants are noteworthy for the excessive shortness of the skull, in this respect surpassing all other living mammals, and the accompanying shortness of the neck. The latter feature is rendered possible only because of the trunk, allowing the animal to feed without moving the head. Relative to height, the body is also short, and the tail is of insignificant bulk. The pelvis is very wide indeed, flaring, and largely vertical as are the legs, for better static support. The femur is very long, placing the knee very low so that, in connection with the short metatarsals, the hind-limb action is more comparable to that of man than of the true ungulates. The two bones in both forearm and lower leg are entire and distinct, and the metapodials are unfused. There are five digits on all feet, and the foot bones are supported by a thick, fibrous heel pad, as is the case in the rhinoceros.

Because of its limb architecture, which in turn was determined by its great weight, an elephant cannot bound along but walks in an essentially stiff-legged manner. It shuffles or glides; and not only is it unable to cross any vertical obstruction that it cannot step over, but this applies to a horizontal obstruction in equal degree. Even if it were physically possible the elephant dare not indulge in any such antics as jumping down from a bank. For this reason it relies exclusively upon the walk or its more speedy equivalent, the running walk, which permits it to keep at least two feet always upon the ground. Not only does the weight make it advisable that this be distributed among each of the four feet when the animal is in motion, but the bulk doubtless requires that the equilibrial stresses be shifted as gradually as possible to each foot, rather than more abruptly as in the trot or gallop.

There are no authentic figures on the maximum speed of an elephant. The African elephant appears to be built upon slightly more rangy lines, and it is likely that it is a bit faster than the Indian animal. Muybridge (1877) stated that the possibility in this regard is 15 miles per hour for 200–300 yards, and then 10 miles per hour. Andrews (1937) has given 24.5 as the speed of a charging African elephant for a distance of 120 yards, based on the experience of one of the American Museum staff. Various African travelers have stated that an elephant can sprint as fast as a fairly good horse and, of course, can readily overtake a man on foot. In this must be figured the element of surprise, on the part of the human, that a beast apparently so sedate can move with celerity, and the disadvantage which a man experiences on a rough terrain. Certainly, however, the proboscideans are not a cursorial type, nor is it likely that they have experienced a need to flee from any enemy save man since they attained their present size, so that their locomotional requirements have been almost exclusively those connected with the necessity of traveling from one feeding ground to another.

UNGULATES

Living members of the true ungulates include artiodactyls and perissodactyls. All except the hippopotamuses are emphatically terrestrial, although some are swamp-dwellers, and none are fossorial. All except the swine may be considered as exclusively herbivorous, and none (save the hippopotamus, if one chooses) is fitted for doing much damage to an adversary by biting. Accordingly, little need is experienced by most of them for offense, and for defense reliance must usually be placed upon kicking or butting. These tactics, except in the case of the very largest forms, are of slight avail when employed against an agile, determined carnivore of large size. So, with the ungulates, discretion has, on the whole, proved to be the better part of valor, and they naturally prefer flight to combat.

Many mammals may substitute stealth for speed, but it is difficult for a large animal to escape in this way from an enemy with a keen nose; and it is difficult for a large animal to give full play to ability for high speed in any but a fairly open, plains habitat. In fact it is a firmly established rule, even although there are occasional seeming exceptions, that the most cursorial types are plains animals and that those less modified in this direction are forest types. In the fossil record of horses and rhinoceroses these two types may often occur contemporaneously.

In the past the perissodactyls developed many and diversified types which numerically reached their zenith during Eocene times and have since declined, until at present they are represented by relatively few forms with rather restricted habitats. On the other hand, the artiodactyls, for some reason, reached the peak of their existence during Recent times. There are too many factors here involved for a ready explanation of this situation to be acceptable. It is clear, of course, that the artiodactyl type has proved to be more adaptable, in the long run, to the conditions that have obtained during the last several million years, but this has depended on many other characteristics, evidently, than cursorial modifications.

It is felt, however, that the fact that two out of the three living families of perissodactyls are essentially noncursorial is of less significance than might appear to be the case at first glance. The existing forms of rhinoceroses have evidently survived largely because they are more ponderous and tougher than any of their enemies; and the survival of the tapirs, as well as of the hippopotamuses, is attributable chiefly to the fact that they find in the water a safe and pleasant sanctuary from their enemies.

The living true ungulates may be arranged as follows:

Order Perissodactyla (Mesaxonia or odd-toed ungulates)
    Superfamily Tapiroidea (tapir)
    Superfamily Rhinocerotoidea (rhinoceros)
    Superfamily Equoidea (horse, zebra, ass)
Order Artiodactyla (Paraxonia or even-toed ungulates)
    Suborder Hyodonta
      Superfamily Suoidea
        Family Suidae (Old World swine)
        Family Tayassuidae (peccary)
        Family Hippopotamidae (hippopotamus)

Suborder Tylopoda
    Family Camelidae (camel, llama, vicuña)
Suborder Tragulina (mouse deer)
Suborder Pecora
  Superfamily Cervicornia (antlered ruminants)
    Family Giraffidae (giraffe, okapi)
    Family Cervidae (muntjac, deer, moose, elk, caribou)
  Superfamily Cavicornia (hollow-horned ruminants)
    Family Antilocapridae (prongbuck)
    Family Bovidae
      Subfamily Oryginae (gemsbok, beisa, oryx, adax, bluebuck, roan and sable antelopes)
      Subfamily Tragelaphinae (bushbuck, nyalla, situtunga, kudu, bongo, eland, nilgae, four-horned antelopes)
      Subfamily Antilopinae (true antelopes, gazelles, black buck, springbuck, gerenuk)
      Subfamily Pantholopinae (chirus)
      Subfamily Saiginae (saiga antelope)
      Subfamily Aepycertinae (impalla)
      Subfamily Reduncinae (reedbuck, waterbuck, nagor, behor, lechwe, kob)
      Subfamily Neotraginae (oribi, steinbok, grysbok, suni)
      Subfamily Rhynchotraginae (dik-dik)
      Subfamily Oreotraginae (klipspringer)
      Subfamily Cephalophinae (duiker)
      Subfamily Bubalinae (hartebeest, bontebok, blesbok, sassaby, gnu)
      Subfamily Rupricaprinae (goat-antelope, chamois, mountain goat)
      Subfamily Caprinae (goats, sheep)
      Subfamily Ovibovinae (musk oxen)
      Subfamily Bovinae (bison, buffalos, cattle)

The above classification of the antelopes is based on Lydekker's (1913–16) arrangement and hence is not strictly up to date, but it is entirely adequate for the present purpose.

For convenience a brief key to the ungulates, including also the subungulate elephants and hyraces, stressing the points of interest in the present connection and largely ignoring dental characters, may be given as follows:

KEY TO THE FAMILIES OF LIVING UNGULATES

Superorder Ungulata. Clavicles absent in postnatal life: humerus without entepicondylar foramen; scaphoid and lunar distinct; ulna and radius often fused; ungues never clawed

Section of Subungulata. Carpale 3 not articulating with radiale; entire fibula always present; upper surface of talus flattened; metapodials never fused

    I. Subungulata

        A. Hyracoidea. Size small; upper incisors rodent-like; dorsolumbar vertebrae not less than 28

B. Proboscidea. An elongated proboscis; dorsolumbar vertebrae less than 28; femur elongated; radius and ulna distinct

Section of Ungulata Vera. Carpale 3 articulating with radiale; never plantigrade or with 5 functional digits; upper surface of talus grooved. Characterized by progressive reduction of distal ulna, proximal fibula, digits 2 and 5, and progressive fusion of metapodials, and of tarsal elements

II. Perissodactyla. Dorsolumbar vertebrae 23 or more; alisphenoid canal present; third trochanter on femur; digit 3 largest; talus articulating chiefly with navicular; calcaneus not articulating with fibula

    A. Tapiroidea. Skull elevated, compressed; orbital and temporal fossae widely confluent; short nasal proboscis; ulna and fibula complete; forefeet with 4 and hind with 3 hoofed digits; metapodials unfused; cuneiforms 1 and 2 free

    B. Rhinocerotoidea. Skull not compressed; orbital and temporal fossae confluent; no proboscis, but with dermal horn(s) in frontal region; ulna and fibula distinct, complete; 3 hoofed digits on each foot; cuneiforms 1 and 2 free

    C. Equoidea. Skull not elevated or compressed; orbital and temporal fossae separated; neither proboscis nor dermal horns; ulna and fibula incomplete; but 1 digit to each foot; cuneiforms 1 and 2 fused

III. Artiodactyla. Dorsolumbar vertebrae 19; no alisphenoid canal; no third femoral trochanter; digits 3 and 4 about equal; talus articulating about equally with navicular and cuboid; calcaneus articulating with fibula

    A. Hyodonta. Premaxillary teeth present; molars bunodont; canines continuously growing; metapodials 3 and 4 never completely fused; tarsals unfused

        1. Suidae. Incisors not continuously growing; nasal ossicle; 4 toes on each foot but only 2 functional

        2. Tagassuidae. Incisors not continuously growing; nasal ossicle; 4 toes on front foot (2 functional) and 3 on hind

        3. Hippopotamidae. Incisors continuously growing; no nasal ossicle; 4 functional digits

    B. Tylopoda. Premaxillary teeth; molars selenodont; audital bullae cancellous, digits 3 and 4 alone present; trapezoid and magnum free; navicular and cuboid free; metapodials fused for most of length

    C. Tragulina. No premaxillary teeth; molars selenodont; audital bullae cancellous; no frontal appendages; odontoid process of axis conical; fibula complete; 4 digits on each foot; middle metapodials usually fused; outer metapodials slender but complete; navicular, cuboid, cuneiforms 2, 3 all fused

    D. Pecora. No premaxillary teeth; molars selenodont; audital bullae hollow; frontal appendages usually present in male; odontoid process of axis crescentric, hollow above; fibula incomplete; lateral digits rudimentary; middle metapodials always fused, outer ones incomplete; navicular and cuboid fused in adult

1. Cervicornia. Solid bony antlers characteristic of males
   a) Giraffidae. No upper canines; molars brachydont; frontal ap-
      pendages skin-covered; lateral digits absent; cuneiform 1 not
      separate
   b) Cervidae. Upper canines usually present; lacrimal not articulat-
      ing with nasal; males with frontal appendages in form of antlers
      or else with enlarged upper canines; lateral digits almost always
      present, frequently with distal ends of their metapodials
2. Cavicornia. Hollow, cored horns characteristic
   c) Antilocapridae. Nearest to Bovidae, but cored horns deciduous;
      lateral digits absent
   d) Bovidae. Horns cored, not deciduous; molars often hypsodont,
      canines absent; lacrimal almost always articulating with nasal;
      lateral digits usually represented by hooves alone, sometimes
      with distal phalanges but never with distal metapodials

Excepting the Hyodonta all the true ungulates have very definite
cursorial modifications, the most apparent features being the elongation and progressive lightening of the limb segments, particularly the
metapodials, which also involves a digitigrade type of support. All
have tails too small to be of consequence as equilibrators, and all,
with the exception of some browsers (such as moose and giraffe),
have heads and necks sufficiently long to reach the ground from the
elevated position of their bodies and always sufficiently long so as
readily to act as balancers during speedy locomotion.

The Hyodonta are digitigrade and so reflect some cursorial modification, but this is chiefly in the nature of an inheritance from ancestors more in the line of cursorial ascent.

PERISSODACTYLA

Perissodactyls are characterized by their teeth, the diagnostic
arrangement of the foramina of the skull, presence of a third trochanter upon the femur, fibula not supported by calcaneus, astragalus with a single pulley and resting solely on the navicular (but en-
croaching slightly upon the cuboid in some of the more ponderous
fossil sorts), mesaxonial with axis of podial passing through third
digit, and usually odd-toed. It should be noted in regard to the number of toes that the digits cannot drop out exclusively in pairs. No
perissodactyl is known with a first digit, and they never have two
digits, but in some stage of evolution they may have four (as in the
tapir manus).

Tapirs are archaic forest mammals that have experienced remarkably slight change since the earliest fossils yet discovered. They
need not concern us here.

Living rhinoceroses are generalized (in progression) remnants of a line that was formerly rich and varied. Some of them were lightly built, as the cursorial rhinoceroses Colodon and Hyracodon, that became extinct in the Oligocene of North America. The features of their limbs were suggestive of an intermediate condition between existing horses and tapirs; and they, as representatives of the upland plains habitat, were paralleled by a contemporaneous forest fauna including less agile types of rhinoceroses.

The living rhinoceroses are thought of as being clumsy, slow beasts. In reality they can move not only with amazing agility but with surprising celerity, and it is regularly stated that an exceptionally good horse is needed to overtake them. Muybridge (1877) claimed that a rhinoceros can equal the speed of a horse for two miles; and Maxwell (1924), who paid considerable attention to the gaits of the African mammals which he encountered, believed that the black rhinoceros (Diceros) can possibly travel at a rate exceeding 20 miles per hour, which appears to be almost a certainty. If it actually can travel for a mile as fast as a fairly good horse encumbered with a rider can manage over uneven ground, it is quite remarkable for a beast so cumbersome and with relatively short legs.

It is of the horse that most of us think when mammals of high speed are mentioned. The limbs of the horse are highly modified in a cursorial direction, and there are few if any living mammals that can go so fast with a man on their backs, and we have been constantly taught to look upon the horse as the personification of quadrupedal speed. In addition he is available for study in life and for comparison of the limb segments after death, so that, by and large, he is a worthy subject for our attention. An additional point of interest is that the fossil record of horses is remarkably complete.

In excess of 250 fossil horses have been named, and among these are a number of tangential lines of specialization. Many are not upon the direct line of ascent, but it is certain that a sufficient number were so close to it that our knowledge of equine evolution is very good. What appears to be the most characteristic and representative genus of each of the main geologic subdivisions will be briefly discussed, but without any attempt at thoroughness. Those interested in pursuing the subject are referred to Scott (1937) and Stirton (1940), who are the latest to have summarized the history of the family.

Equids have varied from the size of a fox terrier (Eohippus) to that exceeding the largest modern draught horse (E. giganteus of the Pleistocene). Before the Middle Pliocene all horses had very slender legs, but in the Pleistocene there was an increase in size and robustness of the limbs. Eocene and Oligocene horses are believed to have been browsers and inhabitants of dense cover. The Miocene horses regarded as close to the main line of ascent tended to be transitional between the smaller forms and the plains horses of later periods. But other sorts of later horses were also of forest types.

Eocene horses were characterized by four functional manual and three pedal digits, although the lateral digit in the manus was reduced. Vestiges of the other three digits were at first present but became smaller with the passage of time. Characteristic of the different parts of the Eocene was Eohippus (or Hyracotherium), the so-called "dawn horse," of the Lower, Orohippus of the Middle, and Epihippus of the Upper Eocene, varying from the size of a small dog to slightly larger.

Oligocene horses had three functional toes on each foot, the manus being but little beyond the stage of evolution of the typical Eocene equid pes, with a vestige of the fifth digit. The middle digits were becoming more robust and the lateral digits smaller. Ulna and fibula tended to fuse partly with the neighboring bones. Mesohippus was characteristic of the Lower, and Miohippus mostly of Middle and Upper Oligocene. They were the size of larger dogs.

In the Miocene there began a differentiation of several rather divergent equid lines that was continued in the Pliocene. Close to the main line was Parahippus of the Lower, and Merychippus of the Middle and Upper Miocene. The former appears to have been closely ancestral to both browsing and grazing types. The side toes were very slender and no longer reached the ground. It was the size of a very large dog, while Merychippus was about 32 inches at the shoulder. The latter genus had teeth transitional between those fitted for soft diet and those specialized for a harsher type of diet—in other words, succulent herbage, on the one hand, and upland grasses, on the other.

Pliohippus, of the Lower Pliocene, was the first truly monodactyl horse, without lateral digits but still with metapodials that were practically full length. It was the size of a pony (45 inches at the shoulder) with slender limbs of deerlike proportions, as was the case with all the older horses. Plesippus, an Upper Pliocene form slightly further advanced, is of chief interest in being the oldest horse with a typically equine, rather than largely antelopine, build.

Equus, of Pliocene, Pleistocene, and Recent times, was distributed throughout all continents except Australia, although it became extinct in North and South America at the end of the Pleistocene.

Among the several groups of Miocene and Pliocene horses that are termed aberrant because of important differences from surviving horses, three genera are represented in my tables of measurements. These are Hypohippus, an arrested forest type of browser that flourished in the Miocene; Neohipparion, a slender Pliocene grazer believed an inhabitant of desert country; and Hippidium, a rather stocky, short-legged horse of the South American Pleistocene. From the viewpoint of its limb proportions Neohipparion was the most highly cursorial horse known, fossil or Recent. Hippidium was anomalous in several respects. Stocky, with short legs, it yet has some of its limb indices highly cursorial, and it may well have been the same sort of aberrant offshoot of the main equine line that the short-legged bush dog is from the canid stock.

The place of origin of the horse phylum is not quite certain, for early Eocene forms are known from both Europe and North America. However, as no other members of the family are known from Europe until Late Oligocene times, one is justified in assuming that the New World was chiefly involved in the development of the horse.

It is remarkable that the origins of a considerable proportion of domesticated animals are shrouded in uncertainty. Such is the case with the horse. Of the undoubtedly large number of subspecies, and even species, of true horses (not zebras or asses) that roamed the world in late Pleistocene times, the only wild representative remaining is the Equus prezewalskii or tarpan of central Asia. The so-called wild horses of other parts of the world are domesticated animals gone feral.

It is, perhaps, popularly considered that the horse is the ideal running machine among mammals. Biologically this is not a fact. The horse was an animal with a temperament to stand domestication, the intelligence to be well taught, of a size to carry a man without experiencing undue fatigue, had stamina, and was sufficiently speedy to be preferable to the ox for riding. These are the reasons for its domestication and also the reasons why man has expended so much time and energy on its improvement.

Living Equidae seem naturally divisible into three groups: the horses, asses, and zebras. Two, and possibly three, types of horses must be considered as having affected the ancestry of the domesticated horse. (1) The E. caballus type, with forelock, relatively long mane and tail, short ears, long limbs, small head, broader hooves, and a gestation period of eleven months. It was probably typically an animal of the southwestern (Arabia, northern Africa) rather than northeastern (Asia) plains habitat. (2) The E. prezewalskii type, with no forelock, a short, erect mane, long hairs absent from the base of the tail, large head, and gestation period said to exceed twelve months. It is now confined to central Asia but typical of the general type of horse so abundant in Europe in late Pleistocene and early Recent times, and enters largely into the ancestry of the large-headed, more coarsely built work horses of Europe. A third type of horse (3) is the so-called E. caballus celticus of North Ireland and the Outer Hebrides, with small head, heavy mane and a fringe of hair at the tail base, slender limbs, and lacking ergots or limb callosities. It has played but little part in the history of the domesticated horse but should be mentioned for completeness.

In the last few hundred years horses of all types have been distributed far and wide; but a thousand and more years ago it appears incontrovertible that the finest, fastest, and most intelligent horses were the Libyan horses of North Africa. Good horses everywhere now carry the blood of this stock.

The asses are more logically divided into those of the hemionus-kiang-onager type and those of the donkey type. The former, ranging from Syria across Persia and through central Asia, is light of build and of color, with a back stripe but no stripe across the withers, and with ears intermediate in size between the donkey and the horse. The larger ones are very fleet, with extraordinary stamina. They are noteworthy for the fact that the limb proportions of my one skeleton of E. hemionus are more highly cursorial in character than those of any other living representative of the genus.

The donkey type of ass is represented by E. asinus and its varieties. It has both a dorsal and a shoulder stripe and typically has the legs distinctly striped. The ears are longer, and the animal is smaller and considerably less fleet than the Asiatic asses. This appears to be the animal from which the domesticated donkey has arisen.

The zebras may be regarded as rather chunkily built asses with stripes. There are considered to be three main sorts—the Grevy,

Burchell, and mountain zebras—with numerous geographical varieties. Their differences need not concern us here.

In cursorial ability the zebra and donkey rank lowest of the Equidae. Selous (1908) considered that a good horse could easily overtake the gemsbok and that the zebra is slower than that animal. Certainly, they are definitely slower than most of the antelopes with which they consort, and a lion has no trouble in overtaking one when it can approach closely enough for a charge.

There are no accounts of the speed of the wild ass of the E. asinus group, but it is surely in excess of the domesticated donkey's. All authorities agree that their larger wild relatives are very swift. The most thorough figures are those of Andrews, who found that a stallion E. hemionus, 13 hands high, could reach a speed of 40 miles per hour for a short dash and traveled 16 miles at the rate of 30 miles per hour. It is doubtful whether any horse living could equal this feat of endurance, and the world's record for a distance of one-half mile by a horse is at a rate no greater than 40 miles per hour, although this rate has been exceeded for $\frac{3}{8}$ mile. It must not be forgotten, too, that these horses were burdened with a rider, although it seems probable that for a short distance an expert jockey can get sufficient added effort from his mount to compensate for the handicap of his weight. (Speed records for horses are given in chap. x.)

There are many historic tales regarding the speed and stamina of horses, including newborn foals. These usually are unsubstantiated and, while undoubtedly based for the most part on some sort of facts, are doubtless considerably embellished with fancy. Even some apparently well-authenticated figures must be discarded. Thus Flying Childers (1721) is alleged to have been able to run 82.5 feet per second, which is at the rate of 56 miles per hour—a speed so greatly in excess of official records that it cannot be seriously considered.

The length of time that the quarter-mile running record and the distance trotting records have remained unbroken is no indication that modern horses are inferior, necessarily, but that these distances have long been in disfavor. The premium now placed on the shorter distances, coupled with the early age at which horses are now raced, have doubtless had an effect in producing thoroughbreds with slightly less stamina than was the rule fifty years ago.

ARTIODACTYLA

Artiodactyls differ from perissodactyls mainly in the unique characteristic that the astragalus has a double pulley, with the inferior surface convex and resting about equally on cuboid and navicular. The calcaneus supports the fibula, there is no third trochanter, the axis of the limbs passes between the third and fourth digits, and the digits occur in pairs (except in the very earliest ancestral forms having 5 digits), so they are thus said to be paraxonial.

The swine are certainly not built for speed, and yet some swine are expert leapers and runners. I have seen a peccary (Pecari) leap with ease an obstruction a bit less than 4 feet high; and the speed of the wart hog (Phacocheirus), as shown by motion pictures, is truly astonishing for a mammal with such short legs. This fact well illustrates the law that any successful herbivore type now found living has the equipment, either in offensive weapons or in speed, to escape from the carnivores of its habitat with critical frequency. The wart hog must so cope with lion, leopard, and hyena. Thus an animal essentially noncursorial, by having the anatomical equipment to move its legs with unusual rapidity, may successfully compete with highly cursorial types of its habitat.

The hippopotamus walks and trots, but there is some doubt as to whether it can gallop: Marius Maxwell (1924) says not. Certainly the latter would be an awkward gait for it, with its rather long body and very short legs and neck. Although it can and does cover miles in traveling from one feeding ground to another, its pace is slow and clumsy.

The Tylopoda, consisting of camels and the South American llamas and their near relatives, are all highly adapted to a cursorial existence, although in length of limb and neck the existing species have been surpassed by some of the extinct giraffe-camels (as Alticamelus of the Miocene). Both these features, however, are better developed in existing species than in all but a very few of the larger ungulates.

The Tylopoda are particularly well fitted to be beasts of burden, and the Asiatic bactrian camel can transport a load as great as 1,500 pounds. In addition to being gifted with singularly evil tempers and gaits that prove particularly distressing to a rider, the group is famous for its endurance, ability to subsist on the poorest fare, and capacity to survive with a minimum of water.

This ability of the camel to get along with little moisture has been greatly exaggerated, and even the reports of trustworthy observers differ to such a degree that one knows not what to believe. Marsh, reporting as long ago as 1856, was conservative in this regard. He stated that in hot weather and on dry fodder the Arabian camel shows distress when it has been working for four days without water but that in the Sahara eight days has been reliably reported as the maximum. He mentioned that in cool weather and on succulent feed a longer period of abstinence is possible.

This ability of the camel to go without water is important in relation to its cursorial capacity, and both have been developed in correlation. Certainly, the Tylopoda are better equipped in the former respect than any other large mammal, for there is particular provision for the storage of a considerable quantity of water, until needed, in the reticulum, or second division of the stomach, as well as in some of the cells of the adjoining rumen, or first division. It appears doubtful, however, whether this ability is very much greater than in some of the other ruminants. Thus I have observed mountain sheep or bighorns on small, desert ranges in northern Mexico many miles from possible water. It was in winter, and they were securing what moisture they needed from the vegetation. I have also known desert cattle to come to water only every third day. Accordingly, one might expect that in cool weather and on food with a fairly high moisture content a camel could go for several weeks, if not indefinitely, without free water, while under a burning midsummer sun, with a heavy load and on very dry food, distress would be experienced in two or three days. It seems also that a camel must be gradually accustomed to a dearth of water if it is not to suffer unduly.

Camels progress by the walk, the pace, and the gallop. Under a load the rate is very slow and scarcely exceeds 2 miles per hour. Their swiftest gait is the gallop, but this is evidently very fatiguing and is adopted only for a short dash or under protest. There seem to be no trustworthy figures regarding the maximum rate that may be so attained, but it appears certain that this is considerably lower than for the horse, in spite of their much longer limbs.

For speedy progression the pace is the mainstay of the camel, and the racing strain of Arabian dromedary that has been developed under domestication is capable of using it to cover immense distances that would be too much for any but an exceptional horse. Accounts vary, of course, with the individual discussed. The distance from Suez to Cairo is 84 miles, and there are many authentic statements of camels having covered the distance in 13 hours, 12 hours, and less. In exceptional cases an animal may average 100 miles per day for a number of days, and Marsh recorded an instance where a camel covered 115 miles within 12 hours. He also stated that a fine racing camel is capable of progressing at the rate of 9 and even 10 miles per hour for a number of consecutive hours. No comparable racing strain has ever been developed from the two-humped, or bactrian, camel which is incapable of such feats of speed.

The above information is suggestive of the fact that the camels are singularly well adapted to a life in the most inhospitable of arid habitats, enabling them readily to travel greater distances between feeding grounds and a water supply than perhaps any other living mammal. It is doubtless chiefly for such purpose that their cursorial ability has been developed rather than directly for the purpose of outdistancing agile carnivores.

The only evidence available regarding the speed of the South American camels is that of Simpson (1934), but he made the somewhat contradictory statement that he has determined with an automobile that a guanaco can run at about 60 km. (37 miles) per hour and that a good dog or horse can easily overtake one in $\frac{1}{2}$ mile. There are few horses outside racing stables that can equal this speed for this distance, particularly in fairly rough going. The discrepancy may lie in a defective speedometer. The guanaco is, however, amazingly efficient in traveling at speed over rough terrain.

In the Tylopoda the femur is relatively longer and is held in a more nearly vertical position than in the majority of ungulates, thus bringing the knee lower. The incomplete ulna, as well as the fibula, are entirely fused with their complements, and the metapodials are fused for most of their length, although the distal extremities diverge. Only two digits are represented on each foot, and in addition the feet have been secondarily modified, having pads instead of hooves.

The Tragulina, or mouse deer and chevrotains, include the smallest existing ungulates, some of them being smaller than a rabbit. Some of the larger forms bear a close superficial resemblance to the musk deer (Moschinae), but these features are merely convergent. They share certain features with, and in this respect are annectant between, the pigs, the camels, and the deer. With the exception of the nonruminants, or Hyodonta, they are the most primitive living ungulates; and the water chevrotain (Dorcatherium), at least, has descended with osteological features virtually unchanged, except in size, from the Lower Pliocene. The ulna and fibula are complete, the middle metapodials often fused, but the lateral ones are complete, while centrale, cuboid, and tarsales 2 and 3 are fused. They are invariably found amid dense brush or grass, through which they dart like rabbits.

The Pecora comprise by far the greatest aggregation of living ungulates. The first group to be considered consists of the giraffes proper and the less specialized okapis. As in the Tylopoda, the lateral digits are entirely lacking, and in the giraffes especially the limb segments are extremely long. The chief feature of the giraffe is its extreme height, occasionally as much as 18 feet. The detail that most readily impresses the observer is the extraordinary elongation of the neck, but this is actually less remarkable than the length of forelimb. The latter feature is more pronounced than length of hind limb; and this, coupled with the conformation of the anterior thorax, makes it difficult for the animal to reach the ground with the mouth, so that for drinking the neck is actually too short, and when so engaged the front legs must be spread.

The length and heaviness of the limbs introduce certain requirements in the locomotion of the giraffe that are unique among living mammals. The stride is long and the rhythm slow, partly because this must correspond to the slow rhythm of a long neck. Hence there is some appearance of clumsiness and of the gait's being labored. Actually, however, slow motion pictures show the giraffe to be one of the most graceful of mammals, surpassing in this respect many of the lighter antelopes.

Apparently the gaits of the giraffe consist only of the walk and a modified gallop (Muybridge, Maxwell). Because of the rather close-coupled body and the extremely long legs the animal must constantly guard against interference of the feet. Maxwell (1924) stated that the walk of the giraffe involves raising the limbs of the same side almost but not quite in unison. In this connection it should be realized that the lateral or transverse inertia of the genus is great because of its height and that some actions can be taken which in a lower body would be too disturbing to its stability in this plane. In the gallop, according to Maxwell, they may lead with either foreleg while the hinder pair move almost in unison, straddling so as to overreach the others without interference. Motion pictures show the correctness of his observations. The same authority timed the speed of giraffes by a motor car and found that they can travel at the rate of 28–32 miles per hour. All those in a position to judge agree that their speed is much greater than the slowness of the rhythm would indicate and that it takes an exceptional horse to overtake them.

Of the Cervidae or ruminants with true antlers, the musk deer and muntjacs may be dismissed with the statement that they are by all odds the most primitive of the family, of small size, dwellers of brushy and often rocky terrain, and undoubtedly less speedy than the majority of true deer. The latter are popularly regarded as the very embodiment of swiftness, partly because they are the speediest mammals of the British Isles and western Europe. Actually, however, they are animals fitted chiefly for life in a broken and brushy, or forested, habitat, and they would be quickly outdistanced by the more highly adapted ungulates of the open plains. One might infer this circumstance from the usual presence of the lateral digits, best developed, I believe, in the reindeer and caribou.

On the whole, the true deer are characterized by their trim and slender lines, especially of the long limbs, and by the fact that the males, and occasionally the females, bear deciduous appendages of a bony nature in the frontal region. These are often of relatively great weight and have doubtless had considerable influence upon the conformation of the neck and character of the gait, even to some extent in the case of the females.

Probably to a very large extent because of the weight of the antlers, those species with the heaviest equipment in this regard favor the trot for speedy progression, this, of course, being a symmetrical gait and so requiring less equilibrational effort than the asymmetrical gallop. But the precise explanation is not simple. It is likely that the inertia of the head with antlers is relatively so great that changes in the cephalic posture, necessary in the gallop, are more difficult than the animal can easily manage. A further element may lie in the fact that a speedy gallop requires extension of the head and neck for proper balance, and this, with the weight of the antlers, may be too tiring for the animal to endure for long. The gallop *can* be accomplished, of course, and the caribou, wapiti, or moose not infrequently progress at this gait. An animal will frequently start off at the gallop when startled, but this is quickly relinquished for the trot if a considerable distance is to be covered. Possibly this preference of gait, located in the central nervous system, is now ingrained in both sexes, or it is conceivable that the females may be more willing to travel by the gallop than are males with antlers. This point can be settled only by extensive observation in the field. But it is also true that moose and caribou have very long legs, and this fact must influence the type of gait.

These, then, are the gaits of the Cervidae: the walk, by all species; the trot, by all, greatly preferred by the larger species or those with heavy antlers, and proportionately less favored by the others; the lateral gallop (by all deer so far as known), especially by the lighter species such as the white-tailed deer (Odocoileus virginianus), whose chief gait it is; and a modification of the gallop consisting almost of quadrupedal saltation, a bound with all four feet leaving the ground at once, and all feet falling upon the ground at practically the same instant. This last is best exemplified by the mule deer (O. hemionus) and to a lesser degree by the black-tailed deer (O. columbianus), both of western North America. It is especially effective in rough and brushy country and is a very spectacular mode of progression, truly astonishing to one who has had no previous experience with it. In this way a party of mule deer will appear to float up the steep and rocky side of a gulch with but instantaneous contact with the ground in an effortless manner that is the personification of grace and ease. But the actual speed of such locomotion is disappointing. Fifteen, 20, and even 25 feet may be covered at a bound (Seton, 1929); but the vertical departure, necessarily subtracted from the horizontal distance covered, slows up the rate of progression. Furthermore, in spite of its effortless appearance, this gait is certainly very laborious to the animal and cannot be maintained for long. Actually, the mule deer are less speedy than the white-tails, but their mode of progression is beautifully fitted for the rough country in which it is most often employed. Newsom (1937) chased a deer on a railway motor handcar at the top speed of the latter, which later was found to be 28 miles per hour. This is in accord with the consensus of opinion of woodsmen that in a short dash the white-tailed deer is capable of 30 miles per hour. But Andrews (1937) quoted Rutledge as having timed a young buck along a country road at 49 miles per hour. This seems excessive, and I should wish to be assured of the accuracy of the speedometer before I accepted that figure.

The wapiti, being a larger animal, more gregarious, and hence better able to take care of itself, might be expected to prove less swift than its smaller relatives, and this appears to be the case. Colonel Dodge (in Seton, 1929) believed that "an elk will trot across ordinary prairie at the rate of about a mile in 3 minutes and 30 seconds," or 17.6 miles per hour. This seems too slow, but there is, of course, in all such cases individual variability. Undoubtedly, they can go considerably faster than this for a short distance.

All the species of deer so far mentioned are phenomenal jumpers. The ability of the mule deer in this regard appears unrecorded but must be very great, while the white-tailed deer and wapiti can easily negotiate an 8-foot fence when pressed.

The moose (Alces) is of particular interest in that it is more essentially a browser than perhaps any other member of the Cervidae and in addition is particularly fond of standing in water up to its belly or deeper and feeding upon aquatic growth. Accompanying these habits is a shorter neck, in comparison to limb length, than in any other genus of the family. As a corollary of its habitat, often palustral or in deep snow, it has large spreading hooves, and it much prefers to trot for any but the most headlong flight. All agree that it can trot very fast, but precise figures seem to be lacking. Seton (1929) says that it can progress at 15 miles per hour through brush, but this surely is not its maximum. I believe it is certain that this, whether by trot or by gallop, must be well in excess of 25 miles per hour.

The caribou of the genus Rangifer are unique in several regards. They are the only arctic deer, and, although some races are confined to regions that are well forested, they are exceptionally well fitted for a life amid the most rigorous surroundings and for traveling vast distances over a country often boggy and covered with snow for much of the time. The hooves of their large feet spread widely to facilitate support on a soft surface, and the lateral toes are better developed than perhaps in any other member of the family. The barren-ground caribou drift back and forth according to season; over the immense distances of the tundra, and especially in late spring and midsummer when their insect foes are numerous, they travel rapidly and almost ceaselessly.

Not only do the males of this genus carry heavy antlers, but these appendages are present in the females, though of smaller size. Partly for this reason, undoubtedly, they much prefer the trot to the gallop; and, although the latter gait is used when the animals bound away in alarm, they soon settle down to an amazingly efficient trot. This may be seen to good advantage in motion pictures of reindeer when hitched to a sled. The action then appears as extreme as in a good standard-bred horse while, with body close to the ground, relatively immense strides are taken. As in a swift trot of the horse, the hind feet must overreach the front ones, being placed to the side of the latter.

In a short dash the caribou or reindeer might be passed by some of the other Cervidae, but in a race of several miles it is very likely that the former would be the winner. Seton (1929) has recorded the instance of a Norwegian driving his reindeer, presumably at the trot, hitched to a sled for a distance over the ice of 2.5 km. in an elapsed time of 7 minutes, which works out not as 1 mile in 3 minutes, as stated by Seton, but in 4.5 minutes, which is a quite ordinary speed of 13.3 miles per hour. Caribou have a rangy build, and moving pictures show that they have a spirited action. It seems certain that an animal in good condition can outdistance a wolf in fair chase, but doubtless not for a short dash. Even more noteworthy is the stamina displayed by the genus. When a herd is thoroughly frightened it often covers immense distances, said by Seton to be as much as 100 miles, before regaining its composure; and the endurance displayed by driven reindeer is said to be remarkable.

The American prongbuck is the only representative of the Antilocapridae, with a combination of some of the characters otherwise distinctive of the other three families of the Pecora, and with one of its own, this being the deciduous character of its cored horns. It has but two digits upon each foot and is the sole species of typical antelopine form and abilities now existing in the open-plains country of North America.

The gaits of the prongbuck consist of the walk, a rather slow trot, which, however, is executed with unusual spirit and action, and the lateral gallop, accomplished not only with grace and ease but with efficiency and swiftness in the typical antelopine manner. Before settling down to real work, accomplished with a minimum of vertical deviation, the prongbuck often indulges in a few bounds with legs held almost rigid, which carry it several feet above the ground (Seton, 1929).

The numerous statements regarding the speed of this animal are illustrative of the difficulties encountered in trying to determine the cursorial ability of any wild animal. There are records of prongbucks having been ridden down by a rider on a good horse and of greyhounds having caught them. George Bird Grinnell (in Seton) has recorded an exceptional hound that was known to have run down twenty-two unwounded individuals in fair chase. Seton has stated that a railway train traveling at 35 miles per hour will forge ahead of a prongbuck, but that the latter will maintain a lead at 30 miles. A bit better is the account of De Vore (1921, quoted by Seton), who had timed prongbuck by motor and claimed that any good doe could do 43 miles per hour. Contrasted to these figures, Stanley Young (manuscript) raced a buck for half a mile along a wire fence at 55 miles per hour, which was as fast as the car would go. And Charles

Belden (manuscript) has checked these animals a number of times for a distance of at least 2 miles at 60 miles per hour. A neighbor of his, circling over flat country in Wyoming, ran a group of young prongbucks by car for a distance of 27 miles in 45 minutes, which averages at 36 miles per hour. The latter figures indicate that the prongbuck can easily win in a fair race with any wild animal of North America.

There should be mentioned the curious natural unwillingness of the prongbuck to negotiate vertical barriers. When fences were first erected in their habitat, a single strand of wire was sufficient to baffle them, and low fences were enough to interrupt their migrations, although they could clear gullies of surprising width. Soon, however, they learned to leap at speed, with limbs closely folded, between strands of wire with amazing precision, and at present they are said regularly to be able to leap a 5-foot fence.

The Bovidae, which includes all cattle, goats, sheep, antelopes, and gazelles, is the group of ungulates that has proved to be best fitted for recent conditions; whether most adaptable or most plastic or best fitted in some other manner remains an unanswered question; but the family has split up into a truly remarkable array of diversified forms that have spread over all possible migration routes. The land bridge to Australia disappeared before the ancestral stock had had opportunity to reach that area; similarly, it was unable to take full advantage of the narrow or otherwise difficult path to the Americas, nor was it able to cross the bridge to South America. The Old World is the stronghold of the family, and the glaciation of much of North America in the Pleistocene introduced difficult conditions that further reduced its representation in that continental area. Although the muskox shares with the caribou the distinction of being the most northern ungulate and the distribution of the mountain sheep or bighorn is essentially boreal, the members of this family occur in greatest number in more temperate regions, and those of highest development are to be found wherever there is a plains type of habitat.

Adeciduate horns of the cored variety are almost invariably present, and in both sexes, although as a rule these are smaller in females. In cursorial specialization, as reflected in the limbs, many of the Bovidae surpass the Cervidae, some of them being equal in this respect to the living Equidae, although some of the goats, for instance, and the heavier, more clumsy oxen are very indifferent runners. Unfortunately, the accomplishments of many of the most interesting species remain undescribed, or else they are vague, and there can be presented only a miscellaneous assemblage of recorded insertions.

The gaits employed consist of the walk; the trot, although the latter is apparently never so strongly preferred as by the heavier Cervidae; and the gallop of both the transverse and the lateral types. There is, however, insufficient information available to determine which of the latter is the more usual, nor will there be until motion pictures accumulate in adequate amount. The gallop, however, has been modified in various details to meet the precise requirements of individual species. Thus a tendency toward the half-bound and the bound is often shown by goats adapted to the most mountainous habitats; and there should also be considered the fact that in some kinds the importance of the anterior limbs has increased at the expense of the hinder pair.

The latter detail is apparently encountered more frequently in the Bovidae than in any other family of mammals, although it also occurs in the hyenas. I regard it as perhaps primarily brought about by vertical locomotional requirements and but secondarily by horizontal progression. Thus it is a feature often present in goats, although perhaps not in very pronounced degree. The American mountain goat (Oreamnos) and Asiatic takin (Budorcas) are thus of heavier conformation in the anterior than in the posterior part of the body, with light hindquarters, high shoulders, and head held low. For an ungulate they are very poor runners on level ground, but the ability to negotiate an almost perpendicular cliff is astounding. The mountain goat is able to pull itself upward to any ledge over which it can hook its front feet and its precision of movement and correlation for balance—or, in other words, its sure-footedness—are developed to a great degree. It will travel without an instant's hesitation up or down declivities that a man would have to scrutinize for footholds with the greatest deliberation, and I have watched bighorns rushing headlong over a terrain of rough lava blocks that would have meant a broken leg for me at a sixth the speed. In the case of ungulates, especially sheep, goats, and ibexes, which spend their lives amid rocky habitats, this facility of instant co-ordination between eye and feet has been developed to the point where it gives the appearance of being automatic—and it has been developed through specialization of the nervous reflex arcs.

In the other groups of the Bovidae the American bison has the forequarters disproportionately most developed, and in this respect it was surpassed by some of its larger, extinct relatives. Clearly, this is a modification not for quite the same purpose as in the mountain goat but for supporting a particularly massive neck and head. The latter is held extremely low, and the whole is very effective in fighting with other individuals or goring and tossing an adversary. Among the other subfamilies of this group perhaps the nilgai (Boselaphus) of India has the forequarters most markedly heavier than the hinder pair, although it can be seen from a skeleton that this is due to axial details and not to the length of the limbs proper. In all such mammals, with heavy forequarters and lighter, if not actually smaller, hind limbs, the former must play a correspondingly important part in locomotion. All ungulates with this conformation are decelerated because of the diminution in relative dynamic ability of the hind limbs, so it is likely that the forward pair then play a correspondingly important role in actual propulsion.

Leaping ability varies so with weight that it is difficult to evaluate properly. Thus it is a matter of personal opinion as to whether a small rodent that leaps for a vertical distance of 4 feet is more gifted in this regard than a buck that clears an 8-foot fence. I should judge, however, that the latter, involving the elevation of a body of considerable weight, is the more difficult for a phylum to accomplish. Many of the antelopes and gazelles are phenomenal horizontal leapers. The genus perhaps most famous for its ability in this line is the impala (Aepyceros). When startled, especially, the individuals of a herd of this genus will bound about in all directions like so many gigantic fleas. According to the motion pictures I have seen, the vertical distance so covered must be as much as 8 feet, and it has been frequently claimed that the horizontal distance is as great as 40 feet. Actual measurements in the neighborhood of 30 feet have been made, and it is easy to appreciate that such actions, erratically executed, would tend to confuse a pursuer. The springbuck (Antidorcas) is also famous for indulging in series of great bounds, often somewhat ludicrously executed. In addition a number of the African Bovidae, particularly the gnus (Connochaetes), often execute a series of antics, leaping and cavorting in a manner suggestive of a bucking horse. Such feats are most often seen when the animals are first startled and would appear to result chiefly as a decelerant, so that one suspects that the habit has its foundation deeper than merely a desire to play or to dodge possible danger.

The vertical leaping ability of the little African klipspringer (Oreotragus) is very remarkable. With head and body length of less than 3 feet and a weight in the neighborhood of 20 pounds, it is more markedly unguligrade than any other mammal, its little hooves being practically vertical instead of sloping at an angle to the limb axis. Mrs. Carl Akeley (1929) has recorded an instance where a female klipspringer and her young one, two-thirds grown, spent the day on a sheer rock pedestal 25 feet high, 20 feet in diameter, and located beneath the edge of a precipitous ridge where a blind, and hidden observation, were possible. Daily, at about 11 o'clock, the two appeared upon the top of the rock, presumably at a single bound. Examination showed that the pedestal was somewhat narrower at base than at top, with no possible avenue of ascent or foothold upon its face, and that the vertical leap necessary to surmount it was 25 feet by actual measurement. Unfortunately, the brush about the base of the rock and the angle from which it was watched made it impossible for the observers to determine whether it was surmounted from a standing or running start (M. J. Akeley, manuscript). This I regard as a most phenomenal performance; but, as the animals were not actually seen to surmount the rock in one leap, it can be accepted only provisionally, for an intermediate foothold may have escaped notice.

Some of the heavier members of the Bovidae seem quite deficient in speed and are supposed to be slower than a good human runner. Thus an Indian afoot often led a charging band of American bison into ambush, although whether the man had a good start I do not know. At any rate Barry C. Park (manuscript) timed a two- or three-year-old bison with a motorcar at 32 miles per hour, which was his top speed. Large bovines have little to fear from predators but are deceptively quick for such large bodies, and most of them are capable of a surprising burst of speed.

The eland (Taurotragus) is certainly one of the slowest of the antelopes, and it has been claimed that an occasional old male may be run down on foot. Some of the goats of the more precipitous type of habitat are not possessed of much speed on the level, and Terhune (in Gordon, 1933) found that a mountain goat (Oreamnos) could not much exceed 20 miles. The waterbucks and reedbucks (Reduncinae) appear not at all built for speed, as compared with some of the more slender antelopes; and yet Martin Johnson (manuscript) considered the reedbucks to be very fast. They lay back their ears and with head held low dart through scattered or dense brush with a combination of running and long, low leaps. The posture, as well as the brushy surroundings, might well lend the appearance of greater speed than the animals possess. Most of the antelopes are among the swiftest of mammals, and it is exasperating to have so few and scattered figures regarding the actual rate at which they progress, and these so contradictory.

Kirby considered that the impala (Aepyceros) is swifter than the sassaby (Damaliscus), while the springbuck (Antidorcas) is more speedy than either. Selous, whose opinion on such matters would gain respect in any company, has claimed that the sassaby is the fleetest, toughest, and most enduring of all South African antelopes, although the wildebeest (Connochaetes) and the sable antelope (Egoceros) are able to press it. Fortunately, we have a yardstick for this matter in the statement of Bonfield (1930) in the case of the roan antelope of the last-mentioned genus (Egoceros). He reported that while driving in a motorcar along a road in northern Rhodesia at a speed of 30 miles per hour he noted an animal of this species running parallel to his course and maintaining the same rate for about a mile, when it put on a burst of speed and dashed across the road in front of the car before disappearing in the brush. It may thus be presumed that these antelopes, which are not of such clean-cut, slender build as some of the others, can attain a speed at least in excess of 35 miles per hour. Selous considered that a good horse should invariably overtake a herd of gemsbok, while the latter is inferior in speed to the sassaby, Cape and Lichtenstein hartebeests, blue and black wildebeests, and blesboks.

Martin Johnson had considerable opportunity for judging the speed of African mammals. He stated (manuscript) that Thompson and Grant gazelles (Gazella thomsonii and G. granti), as well as ostriches, can do better than 50 miles per hour for a half-mile and that wildebeest (Connochaetes) can attain this rate for a quarter-mile, but that the latter soon give up.

The possible speed of the Mongolian gazelle (G. subgutturosa) has been estimated by Andrews (1924) as 60 miles per hour for a short dash. One individual maintained a speed of 40 miles per hour in front of a motorcar for a distance of 10 miles, and even when but a day or two old a speed of 25 miles is possible. It seems not unlikely that some of the longer-limbed gazelles of northern Africa should be able to better these figures. Such rapidity of locomotion in the adult is not needed to escape from any living carnivore except the cheetah, where that occurs, and the ability may have been developed either selectively in the newborn individuals or by the exigencies of feeding conditions. It is true that a speed of 60 miles an hour would hardly be utilized in going to and from distant feeding grounds, but a species that has that rate as the maximum can travel very comfortably at 40 miles and be at an advantage in a sparse and frugal land.

It is thus seen that there is very meager accurate information regarding the maximum speeds of wild animals. Some of the antelopes can exceed 60 miles per hour, while some cannot accomplish 20, except for a short dash, and others vary between these figures. The only general statement that it is safe to make is that every ungulate of large or medium size is sufficiently speedy to escape in fair chase from the predators with which it regularly has to cope, excepting the cheetah. A partial exception is in the case of those forms that escape by climbing over rough terrain. It may also be said that the ungulate inhabitants of arid plains tend to be more speedy than those types characteristic of well-watered terrain, presumably for enabling the former to cover rapidly and with ease great distances between good feeding grounds in areas where these seldom occur, thereby helping by just so much to meet the competition offered them by associated mammals of similar habits.

Brief mention should be made of the propensity of so many ungulates to follow a leader in more or less blind fashion and of the difficulty that they often have in denying an urge to cross in front of a swiftly moving body. The latter feature is commonly described by observers in all parts of the world and seems now to be a firmly intrenched, ungulate character, at least in the more gregarious species.

Save when made inordinately wild by close hunting, most gregarious ungulates, and some occurring singly, show a great fondness for racing parallel with any swiftly moving body, such as a mounted horseman or motorcar, and then, if possible, increasing the speed so as to cross in front of the object, after which the whim is seemingly satisfied, and the animals will then usually go on about their business. In a circumstance of this sort their desire to follow the leader at all costs, so familiar in the case of the domesticated sheep, may prove disastrous. In the case of a large, straggling band the leader often decides to cross the path of the speeding entity that he is racing as soon as he has a lead that he considers safe. This, however, may mean that the last and slowest animal will have a hard time dodging trouble, but he will often maintain the established line of travel at all costs even though he must cross behind the fleeing object while his brothers barely pass in advance of it. This stubbornness—I hesitate to call any such trait "foolish" when it may have had its inception in sound logic—has unquestionably spelled the destruction of a great many individuals.

Before leaving the ungulates, mention should be made of the propensity for the newborn young, especially of the speedier sorts, to exhibit cursorial specialization of a relatively higher order than occurs in the adult. This, to my way of thinking, constitutes a most remarkable character. A gazelle, for instance, is the complicated product of an immense amount of evolutional effort, and that its own young is born better equipped in this regard than its parents is quite astonishing. It is readily seen, however, that this is a feature that may be of vital importance to a species. Of what avail would it be to an antelope to be a bit faster than its most persistent enemies if the young did not also have this safety factor? The species might well be exterminated in one or two generations. So it is possible in the majority of ungulate species for the young, after a preliminary period of hiding lasting for several days, to approximate the speed, if not the degree of stamina, of at least the slower adult members of its race. The limb proportions of young ungulates as compared to adults will be discussed in future chapters.

CHAPTER V

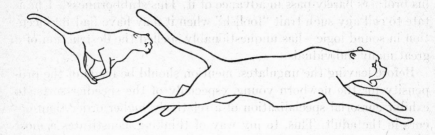

The Muscular System

AMUSCLE is an aggregation of bundles of contractile tissue, anchored at either end. One of these anchorages must be movable in respect to the other. The less movable end, usually the more proximal, is termed the "origin" and the more movable, usually the distal or peripheral end, the "insertion." If both ends are anchored on bone, there will be at least one joint and sometimes several (in feet or hands) between them; but at times muscles end in soft tissue, as on the face and around the pharynx.

Muscles habitually operate as levers, with the joints as axes and the parts to be moved as weights. Levers of the first and third orders only occur in the body. In the former the axis occurs between the power and the weight (as in extension of the forearm by the triceps brachii); in the latter the power occurs between the axis and the weight (as in flexion of the forearm by the biceps brachii).

The work accomplished by a muscle need bear no relationship to resultant movement of the body, e.g., one may exhaust himself by tensing most of the muscles of the body without moving an inch. Certain muscles must work to control the direction and amount of movement without in themselves directly accomplishing such movements. In a generalized animal, with muscles fitted for many sorts of movements, a relatively large proportion have functions for purposes other than progression at speed; or the muscular system may be adapted for strength in such activities as digging. In swift animals all possible muscles contribute as much as practicable to the operation of the limbs in the sagittal plane.

The effectiveness of a muscle depends upon imponderable factors, as later explained; upon its size and form (including arrangement of its fibers); and upon the leverage that it can exert.

Muscle leverage can best be understood by consulting a simple diagram. In Figure 6, *A* represents action at the elbow of a lever of the first (I, m. triceps) and of the third (III, m. biceps) order. If the insertion *B* is moved to the right, the strength of action will be increased but the speed decreased, and vice versa. This principle is illustrated by the parallelograms of forces (Fig. 6, *B*), as presented in every book considering muscle action in much detail. This scheme resolves the pull of a muscle into two forces, one performing useful work at a right angle to a second ineffective force of compression, caused by the rigidity of the bone, which prevents movement in the line of muscle pull. In Figure 6, *FG* may be taken as the upper arm, *GH* as the forearm, and *FH* as a hypothetical muscle longer than the

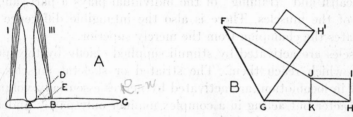

Fig. 6.—*A*, A schematic elbow, illustrating the action of a lever of the first (I, m. triceps) and of the third (III, m. biceps) order. *AB* = power arm; *AC* = resistance arm; *D* = angle of rotation; *E* = angle of pull. *B*, The parallelograms of forces.

biceps. If one selects a point *J* on this muscle and constructs a parallelogram, *JK* will represent the amount of possible useful work in relationship to the amount of ineffectual work, *JI*. Now if the forearm be partly flexed, the proportion of useful work will increase in relationship to the ineffectual work. When the angle *FHG* is 45°, both are equal.

The size and form of a muscle depends upon the sort of work that it performs. A muscle can usually contract to an amount slightly less than one-half the length of its fibers (not one-half the length of the muscle). Obviously, it would be wasteful for a muscle to have fibers 10 mm. long if it was so situated as to be able to contract but 1 mm. in length. A fact of interest in this connection in relation to the development of speedy locomotion is that when a limb segment increases in relative length, during cursorial and saltatorial adaptation, the distal part is rendered lighter and hence more quickly movable, because the length of muscle fibers does not also increase and the fleshy part is prone to be grouped proximally while the distal tendinous part elongates (Fig. 9).

The kind of fiber is also important. A muscle largely composed of so-called "white" fibers can contract faster, but tires sooner, than one with more "red" fibers (contrast the breast muscle in a grouse and a duck).

There are many intangibles concerned with the functioning of muscles. Thus it is believed that the quality of nerve impulse has an important bearing, but this does not mean that the difference in action between the muscles of a sloth and those of a gazelle is due only to the nerve impulse. There are many unknown factors in the pattern of muscle action characteristic of a particular animal, such as the facts that a chimpanzee is stronger than any man and that some small men are much stronger than the majority of large men. The health and "training" of the individual plays a part, and the tonus of the muscles. There is also the intangible difference that segregates the champion from the merely superior.

Muscles are activated by stimuli supplied chiefly by the specific nerves which reach them. The striated or skeletal muscles, employed in locomotion, are activated by nerves essentially voluntary in character but acting in a complex manner only partly under the control of the individual. In more accurate language, co-ordinated action of the skeletal musculature involves series of reflexes, subject to voluntary modification but operating in a pattern that is essentially involuntary. Thus one moves by a series of complicated, rhythmic muscular contractions whose sequence has been established for the species. One runs merely as the result of the will to run, without thought of procedure, although one may start, stop, or avoid obstacles as necessary.

With few exceptions (sphincters), muscles must operate in pairs. Where there is a muscular unit or series for prime movement (usually considered as the ventral or flexor group), there must be a complementary antagonist unit or series for recovery (usually considered as the dorsal or extensor group). Thus when one takes a step, one must have the muscular equipment to bring the leg back to the original position. This pair of complementary movements is termed the "stride," and the sequence of strides, involving all limbs, is termed the "locomotor cycle."

The operation of the locomotor cycle is extremely complex. Not only must the muscles of a single limb function in sequence, but so also must the muscles of the other limb of the pair, of the other pair of limbs, and of the entire body. All the stimuli and their controls are very imperfectly understood; but it is known that impulses originating in the central nervous system (or from sight, sound, smell, taste), stretching and contracting of the proper muscles, position of the joints, and impact of the ground upon the sole of the foot all play their respective parts.

It is seldom that a single muscle acts alone. Usually it contracts with others (called "synergists") as a group to attain particular results. Thus several muscles co-operate to flex the elbow; but if the resistance be great, one may need to brace his legs and back, thus bringing into action almost every muscle in the body. It is probably not the easy movements of everyday life that are chiefly instrumental in shaping the muscular and osseous pattern, but the critical potential that is usually held in reserve. The grazing antelope can usually get along very well without exceeding a speed of 10 miles per hour: it is the sprint which in emergency carries him faster than the charging lion that has been the factor in his development and existence. So it is with a considerable number of individual muscles. One uses the gluteus maximus very little indeed in standing and walking. During such activities a muscle one-tenth the usual size would suffice, but without a gluteus maximus one could arise from a sitting posture or climb steep stairs only with great difficulty. Such muscles are as important to us as a first and second gear is to an automobile.

Another fact that is but poorly understood is that the necessary amount of work will be done by a muscle group to accomplish a particular action and that if one unit is prevented from doing its share, other units participating will take on an added burden. Thus Stewart (1937) found that in cutting the muscles of the leg in rabbits and studying subsequent locomotion it was only after several muscles had been cut that an effect was apparent, indicating that the unaffected muscles automatically assumed an added, compensatory load. How this is accomplished is entirely unknown.

The way in which the muscular system is used during locomotion —the locomotor reflex pattern—doubtless depends on a number of complicated factors. Ease of operation is probably a chief determinant. The caribou with heavy antlers finds it less fatiguing to trot, so it never gallops for long distances; trotting or pacing would doubtless be very awkward for the giraffe, so it always gallops when in a hurry. Why the opossum never gallops (so far as I know) is problematical. The large kangaroos seem too heavy for saltation to be a comfortable mode of progression. This method was probably established as normal by smaller and lighter ancestors and became too firmly fixed for ready change.

The above brief arguments are offered in explanation of the fact that the locomotor behavior pattern for each animal is a firmly established series of reflexes. Most animals have several possible gaits (such as walk, trot, gallop) which can be used selectively as speed and other conditions warrant. A few highly specialized mammals (like kangaroos) have a single locomotion pattern so narrowly and firmly established that only one gait is possible and other sorts of movements (even unilateral scratching) can be made only laboriously or not at all.

AXIAL MUSCLES

The trunk muscles of fish are segmental in arrangement and operate in a bilateral rhythm, resulting in oscillation of the entire body in the horizontal plane. The same basic arrangement of the axial muscles obtains in amphibians and reptiles, for the same movements; but the segmental plan is more modified, particularly in the ventral musculature. In mammals this modification is still more marked. Not only has the segmental plan disappeared in the abdomen and ventrally, but other movements have introduced complicating factors, and many of the units of the back span a number of segments. The axial muscles in mammals are arranged in a dorsal extensor series of back muscles, the erector spinae, and a ventral flexor series. The latter, except in the tail, is secondarily divided into a lateral group (scaleni, intercostals, abdominal muscles), a ventral group (infrahyoids, rectus abdominis), and a minor hypaxial group (deepest neck flexors and quadratus lumborum). Undoubtedly the most primitive reflexes operating these muscles are rhythmically bilateral, as in the lower tetrapods and as used by mammals to some extent in slow walking and trotting. In such gaits as the gallop, the bound, and the half-bound the trunk muscles bend the body in the vertical plane. In such a case they are a definite aid to locomotion, in addition to a role fulfilled in all locomotion of every sort—that of maintaining equilibrium by means of the proper shift of the center of gravity.

The fibers of the back musculature follow an extremely complicated pattern, and the intervertebral movement at any point is very small in amount. As a result, any specialization that it experiences in cursorial adaptation is practically impossible to evaluate. As mentioned elsewhere, animals with very heavy heads (Bison) have powerful dorsal neck muscles, with attachment to especially high spines, and this is true also of many of the runners which throw the head up and down in aid of the asymmetrical gallop; the muscles of the back and lumbar region (particularly quadratus lumborum) must be strong in animals that arch the back to a marked extent in running; the muscles attached to the pelvis must be adequate in those forms with very powerful hind legs, as must also the muscles of the base of the tail in strong leapers. During speedy progression the trunk muscles act largely to maintain equilibrium or, in other words, to shift the center of gravity. A secondary but still very important function of the back musculature is to control the rhythmic swings of the head (in asymmetrical gaits) and of the tail when this member is requisite to balance (as in kangaroos). Saltation can be effected without this provision, but only with difficulty and probably never for a great distance. The abdominal muscles are useful in all strong movements of the body, but in a way that is decidedly insubordinate in so far as locomotion is concerned.

The limb musculature was clearly derived from the lateral body musculature, and the plan of the former that one accepts as basic then depends arbitrarily on the stage that one selects for presentation. In gaining an understanding of the early stages, only generalities are possible, for fish vary greatly among themselves and their limb musculature is rather diffuse.

The basic plan of the muscles of the appendages comprises a ventral set of muscles, innervated by ventral components of the limb plexuses, and a dorsal set, innervated by dorsal components of the plexuses, for prime movement and recovery. Each came to be divided into several subgroups; in addition, a part of the gill arch or branchiomeric musculature (trapezius) reached the pectoral limb. Some of these muscles are extrinsic (extending to limb from trunk) and some intrinsic (confined to the limb). In living fish the pectoral fin is so held that the surface supplied by dorsal muscles is held pressed to the body and the ventral surface is directed laterally. If this was the condition in our piscine ancestor, rotation of the appendage, during evolution, was necessary in order that in tetrapods the palm might be applied to the ground. This plan may have been different in crossopterygians.

A convenient treatment of the muscle groups, reflecting basic conditions, is presented below. This takes into consideration the arrangement in amphibians and reptiles, as applied particularly to mammals, but does not dwell on the amphibians with much detail.

MUSCLES OF THE PECTORAL LIMB

Functionally, the muscles of the pectoral limb include every muscle attached to any part of that extremity. Strictly speaking, however, the group is considered as excluding from the above classification the trapezius and omohyoid muscles, which belong to other, axial matrices but have reached the limb secondarily. The units of the group that I have termed "suprazonal matrix," being extrinsic, belong less intimately to the appendage than do the intrinsic components and so could be considered as comprising a separate category. The limb muscles are innervated by branches of the brachial plexus. Comparative anatomy shows that the limb muscles, and hence the limb, have migrated caudally from a position directly posterior to the head in the Amphibia. In mammals the plexus characteristically is derived from five nerves, from C5 to T1, with axis through C7 and frequently with contributions from C4 or, more rarely, T2. In a few mammals the axis shifts slightly caudally (llama, kinkajou, sloth, and a few others), or more rarely the shift is 'cranial (some cetaceans). There is a slight tendency for contraction of the plexus in the direction of a four-rooted complex in cursorial specialization (ungulates, carnivores), perhaps reflecting a simplification in the kinds of movements of the limb.

The muscles, then, concerned with operation of the pectoral limb comprise the trapezius, plus the muscles of the limb proper, which are divisible into dorsal and ventral groups.

The trapezius is a branchiomeric muscle of the spinal accessory field, to which also belongs m. sternocleidomastoideus. Both originally passed from the last gill arch to the membranous girdle. As the gill apparatus became specialized for a terrestrial existence, the origin of the trapezius settled onto the trunk in the occipital region. In tetrapods the origin is characteristically from the posterior skull and the mid-dorsum of neck and thorax, and insertion is upon the spine of the scapula, acromion, and clavicle. Its action is complex, and it is brought into play in almost all movements of the shoulder. Most often it is used in dorsal movements of the scapula (with rhomboids) and in cranial movements of the shoulder. The latter is employed in advancing the foreleg; hence the part to the clavicle could operate better if its insertion could migrate onto the upper arm. Functionally this can be accomplished by the elimination of the clavicle and the fusion in tandem of the cranial part of the trapezius and adjoining cleidomastoid with the clavicular part of the deltoid to form a cephalohumeral or brachiocephalic muscle. This development probably cannot be regarded as a cursorial specialization, for it is found also in Edentata, Proboscidea, and Hyracoidea. Likely it is associated merely with repression of the clavicle in mammals using the forelimb chiefly for support and is an equipment put to extremely good usage by stocks that have developed highly cursorial forms (carnivores, perissodactyls, artiodactyls). The cephalohumeral gains much effectiveness by a co-ordinated tossing of the head during its contraction, as may be witnessed in any racehorse as it begins to tire.

The remaining muscles of the pectoral limb may be most conveniently discussed by segments—shoulder, upper arm, forearm, and hand—and are divided into a number of natural subgroups, as indicated by the innervations and other criteria of their comparative anatomy.

SHOULDER MUSCLES

The dorsal muscles of the shoulder were probably originally one dense complex of both extrinsic and intrinsic fibers, but in tetrapods one may divide them conveniently into a suprazonal matrix, thoracodorsal matrix, and axillary matrix.

Suprazonal matrix.—This had as its basal unit a serratus anterior, arising from the ribs (or their homologues) throughout the cervical and thoracic regions and inserting upon the vertebral border of the scapula. The origins of the more posterior and medial fibers of this unit appear to have shifted to the midline (reptiles) and later migrated anteriorly even as far as the head to become the rhomboids. In some forms there appeared a hiatus in the inferior cervical part of the serratus, the more cranial portion remaining then being known as the levator scapulae. Not infrequently in mammals the insertion of a part of the latter muscle migrates along the scapular spine toward the acromion and becomes a levator claviculae or omotrachelien.

The functions of all these muscles are to adjust the vertebral border of the scapula, to move it dorsally (rhomboidei), ventrally (serratus), cranially (levatores scapulae, claviculae, and rhomboideus capitis), and to rotate it in a direction that moves the glenoid in the cranial direction (part of serratus inserting upon the caudal or glenovertebral angle). The rhomboideus dorsi is not of great dynamic importance to a strictly quadrupedal mammal but acts mostly in antagonism to the serratus. The latter is essential for cushioning the shock of landing on the forefeet and for thrusting with these members in running. Advancing the scapula toward the head, by the levatores, is obviously of great use in speedy locomotion, and even more so, perhaps, is the rotation of the scapula. The latter action by the posterior part of the serratus is peculiar in several ways. There is no directly antagonistic action on the scapula itself. It can be rotated in one direction (advancing the arm) from a position of rest but not in the other, recovery being attained by the latissimus dorsi (chiefly). Also, this rotating action will not take place until the foreleg is at a right angle to the body. In other words, the muscle will not help in recovery from a retracted position of the limb.

Thoracodorsal matrix.—The basic unit of this group is the latissimus dorsi, from the trunk caudal to the shoulder and inserting upon the upper humerus. It is by all odds the most powerful retractor of the arm; is largely an antagonist to pectorals, anterior deltoid, and posterior serratus anterior; and is one of the oldest units of the arm. Also appearing to belong with this group is the teres major, from caudal scapula to the humerus at the latissimus tendon—a recently formed unit confined to mammals.

Axillary matrix.—Evidently the initiation of this group was as a sheet of muscle passing from the cleithrum and clavicle to the humerus. When the cleithrum disappeared, the part of the muscle originally arising therefrom settled onto the neighboring part of the scapula, to become the dorsalis scapulae of lower tetrapods, while the part from the clavicle was, and is, the deltoid. Later, in mammal-like reptiles and mammals, encroachment of the suprascapular muscle between deltoid and dorsalis scapulae crowded the latter to the caudal edge of the scapula, where it now occurs as the teres minor. Meanwhile, deep fibers arising from the scapula had differentiated slips (proscapulohumeralis and scapulohumeralis of amphibians; proscapulohumeralis and subcoracoideus of reptiles), one of which seems to have migrated around the caudal border of the scapula to become at least the more posterior part of the subscapularis (reptiles, mammals). The anterior part of the subscapularis may possibly have been derived in some animals from the supraspinatus, as suggested by the topography, double innervation, and double motor nucleus of this muscle.

The function of this matrix was originally that of advancing the limb, with some elevation. In reptiles the latter was accentuated. In that class and in mammals a new action was developed, by the sub-scapularis, as an inward rotator and fixer of the joint. Rotation becomes minimized in cursorial types. The anterior part of the muscle can also act with the supraspinatus in advancing the limb. The deltoid in mammals has extended along the acromion and the spine of the scapula, so that it abducts (minimized in cursorial varieties) as well as advances the limb. The anterior part frequently adds to its effectiveness by fusing with the spinal accessory musculature (as explained under trapezius) to form a cephalohumeral. The teres minor is an outward rotator and fixer of the joint.

The ventral muscles of the shoulder, from a phylogenetic viewpoint, may most conveniently be considered as comprising four groups.

Infrazonal matrix.—This group is first encountered in reptiles as slips from the ribs and sternal region to the coracoids. In mammals it is represented by m. subclavius, from the sternal region to the clavicle, and sometimes also by m. sternoscapularis, to the acromion or coracoid. These muscles are used in fixation and are unimportant in the present connection.

Pectoral matrix.—All tetrapods have a true pectoral muscle, which in mammals is represented by the deep pectoral layer with minor, abdominalis and panniculus carnosus divisions. Typically, the first of these arises from the sternal region, the second from the cranial part of the abdomen, and the third from the posterior trunk. The panniculus is subject to extreme specialization, or disappearance, in different forms of mammals. Insertion of this group is upon the upper arm, joint capsule, or coracoid. In mammals action is in conjunction with the pectoralis major of another matrix. The minor portion is chiefly an adductor of the shoulder, and the abdominal and panniculus parts are retractors of the arm from the advanced position and hence are of much importance in running.

Anterior coracoid matrix.—This consisted basically of a sheet of muscle from the anterior coracoid to the humerus, for protraction and ventriflexion of the limb. As the reptilian limb posture changed to that of mammal-like reptiles (as indicated by fossils of the latter), a part of this matrix migrated dorsally to take origin from the scapula and become the supraspinatus and the infraspinatus, and possibly the anterior part of subscapularis. The remainder shifted its origin from procoracoid to sternum, to become the pectoralis major. The latter adducts the arm, and in the retarded position the anterior

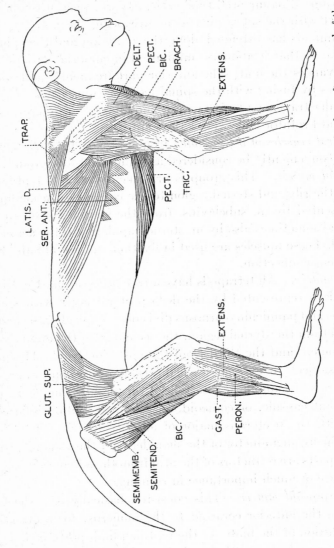

TRAP.

LATIS. D.

SER. ANT.

GLUT. SUP.

SEMIMEMB.

SEMITEND.

BIC.

DELT.

PECT.

BIC.

BRACH.

EXTENS.

PECT.

TRIC.

EXTENS.

GAST.

PERON.

Fig. 7.—The superficial muscles controlling the extremities of the macaque monkey, after removal of the cutaneous musculature.

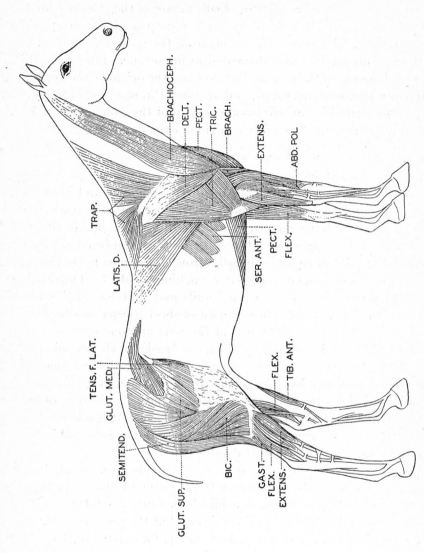

BRACHIOCEPH.

DELT.

PECT.

TRIC.

BRACH.

EXTENS.

ABD. POL

TRAP.

LATIS. D.

SER. ANT.

PECT.

FLEX.

TENS. F. LAT.

GLUT. MED.

FLEX.

TIB. ANT.

SEMITEND.

BIC.

GAST.

FLEX.

EXTENS.

GLUT. SUP.

FIG. 8.—The superficial muscles controlling the extremities of the horse, after removal of the cutaneous musculature. Redrawn from Ellenberger and Baum.

portion advances the member. The supraspinatus is an important protractor, and the infraspinatus chiefly a fixer of the shoulder joint.

Posterior coracoid matrix.—Originally this was also a relatively broad muscle, with several divisions, from the posterior coracoid to the arm. This muscle mass decreased in importance, however, with the development of the mammalian posture; the origin of the muscle, and hence the bone, retreated; and at present in mammals the muscle is represented by m. coracobrachialis and the bony element by the coracoid process. The muscle advances the upper arm.

MUSCLES OF THE BRACHIUM

It is convenient in the arm to recognize as separate groups the muscle elements originally associated with the elbow and with the wrist joint, each with a dorsal and a ventral division. The respective fibers appear to have migrated in both directions, proximally to form units from humerus, and even scapula, to the proximal forearm, and distally to comprise muscles from distal humerus to the region of the wrist, some of these later reaching the digits. Thus there are what may be termed "brachial" units and "antebrachial" units.

Dorsal brachial units.—These consist of short triceps muscles from the humerus to the proximal end of the ulna and one or more long units—a scapulotriceps from the posterior border of the scapula and frequently a dorsoepitrochlearis, usually from the latissimus tendon. Both insert on the elbow. The scapulotriceps, or long triceps, doubtless reached the scapula by proximal migration. The history of the dorsoepitrochlearis is not so clear, and it may be either a derivative of the triceps proper or a distal migration from the latissimus. The function of the group is powerful extension of the lower arm.

Ventral brachial units.—The muscles of this division consist basically of a brachialis, from humerus to radius or to ulna or to both, and its derivative, m. biceps brachii. Apparently the latter muscle was lacking in the fundamental condition; but the need for a muscle of this conformation must have been great, for a functional biceps occurs in all tetrapods, but with different derivation in (*a*) tailed amphibians, (*b*) frogs and toads, and (*c*) reptiles and mammals (Howell, 1935*b*, 1936*a*, 1937). In the last group it appears to have been formed by the proximal migration along a fascial plane of brachialis fibers. In most cases there is a long head from the supraglenoid tubercle and a short head from the coracoid; but not infrequently the element is single.

MUSCLES OF THE ANTEBRACHIUM

These muscles, both dorsally and ventrally, consist of two layers: a more superficial that has migrated distally from the elbow and a deeper that has migrated proximally from the wrist. On each side the former tends to separate into a marginal unit of each border of the forearm, inserting in the vicinity of the wrist, and a central unit to the palmar fascia or the digits.

Superficial antebrachial extensors.—Basically these extensors arise from the lateral epicondyle of the humerus, but a part of the origin sometimes settles upon the forearm. The primitive tetrapod condition appears to have involved a three-group plan, as indicated by both amphibians and reptiles. (1) The extensor humeroradial element extends to the distal radius or to carpus or to both. In mammals it occurs typically as m. brachioradialis, a powerful flexor of the forearm, to distal radius; and mm. extensores carpi radialis longus et brevis, extensors of the wrist, to the metacarpus. (2) The extensor humerocentral element basically extends to the deep fascia of the wrist; but in mammals it is continued to the four lateral digits and has given rise to an extra extensor digiti quinti (and at times also a quarti) proprius. (3) The extensor humeroulnar element, primitively to the distal ulna and ulnare, occurs relatively unmodified in mammals as m. extensor carpi ulnaris.

Superficial antebrachial flexors.—These flexors arise basically from the medial epicondyle of the humerus; but, as in the extensors, some of the fibers of origin settle onto the forearm. In addition there appears to have been a degree of fusion with deeper units in primitive mammals. (1) The flexor humeroradialis element is simple. It goes to the distal radius in tailed amphibians, slips extend to both radius and radiale in some reptiles, and in the latter there also splits off a pronator teres. In mammals there is a flexor carpi radialis, a wrist flexor, to metacarpals 2 and 3; m. pronator teres to the radius; and m. palmaris longus to the palmar fascia. The last of these is often decadent and with little real function. (2) The flexor humerocentral element appears primitively to insert into the palmar fascia, which is attached to the base of the metacarpals, as in Necturus. In reptiles it continues to the digits, with function of flexing the wrist and bases of the fingers, while in mammals it extends to the distal digits as the perforated flexor tendons of m. flexor digitorum sublimis. Windle (1890) and some others have believed that this element basically has five origins—lateral, middle, and medial condylar, radial, and ulnar heads—but this does not seem to me to accord with the evidence. (3) The humeroulnar element remains a simple extensor of the wrist, in mammals inserting through the pisiform onto the fifth metacarpal.

Deep antebrachial extensors.—Judging from amphibians and reptiles, these units basically comprise an element from the distal ulna to the most radial digit—a supinator manus—and a short extensor from the ulnare or its vicinity to each digit (Necturus). In addition it also probably extends to a series of ten dorsometacarpals, present in reptiles but not in amphibians or mammals. In reptiles (Iguana) the origin of the supinator manus, as an abductor pollicis longus, has migrated proximally along the ulna, and it is in sequence with the first of the short extensors, one of which passes to each digit. In mammals the origins of all units have shifted to or toward the ulna, while the insertion of the most proximal fibers appears to have settled upon the radius to became m. supinator. The original supinator occurs as m. abductor pollicis longus, the short extensor to the pollex as m. extensor pollicis longus, and those to the second and third digits as mm. extensores indicis et tertius proprius (where the latter occurs). Deep slips to fourth and fifth digits are absent in mammals.

Deep antebrachial flexors.—This division, like the extensors, is an oblique series from ulna and ulnare to the radial side of the wrist and manus. Basically it appears to have occurred in two layers, the origins of both of which migrated proximally along the ulna. The deeper of these has become m. pronator quadratus, and the more superficial, m. flexor digitorum profundus and its derivative, m. flexor pollicis longus. They have reached the digits by developing perforating tendons from the deep fascia of the hand.

MUSCLES OF THE MANUS

The dorsal muscles belonging to the manus have migrated proximally in mammals, as already discussed. The ventral division is naturally separable into a superficial and a deep series, each of which becomes further subdivisible.

Superficial manual flexors.—In urodele amphibians this layer is probably secondarily simplified. In reptiles (Iguana) there is a parafascial (Howell, 1935b) sheet, associated with the palmar fascia, and a deeper series of paratendinous slips from the common flexor tendon to the digits. In mammals the former is no longer sheetlike; but the marginal fibers have persisted and settled to the bone, to become, on one side, m. abductor pollicis brevis and the superficial head of m. flexor pollicis brevis, and, on the other, m. abductor digiti quinti and m. flexor digiti quinti, while the central part of the sheet sometimes persists as m. palmaris brevis. The paratendinous slips of reptiles become in mammals mm. lumbricales.

Deep manual flexors.—This series is separable into three layers, according as individual components migrate to different levels— contrahentes, deep short flexors, and intermetacarpals. The first of these characteristically arise from the connective tissue at the center of the palm and the units diverge to the digits for adduction. Characteristically, there are probably five in amphibians and reptiles (the naming of these muscle slips is probably not altogether accurate in Howell, 1936b). In mammals there is frequently progressive reduction in the number of these units, the middle ones first; and in man the slip to the pollex, m. adductor pollicis, is the only one remaining. The deep short flexors characteristically occur as five pairs of slips, arising from the metacarpals or slightly more proximal. The first two of these slips are known as m. opponens pollicis and the deep head of m. flexor pollicis; the next seven as mm. interossei; and the tenth as m. opponens digiti quinti. The interossei in mammals typically are arranged with axis through the third digit: four are dorsal interossei, and three in a more volar or palmar series. The status of the intermetacarpals is uncertain; but they are of no interest in the present connection, for in higher tetrapods they are unrepresented. The functions of these short flexors are for manipulating the digits in various ways. They are particularly well differentiated in reptiles, and that class in addition has interphalangeal flexor slips, absent in mammals. They are much less effective as manipulators of the individual digits than in mammals, however, because of their nervous control. The latter acts upon them in series, while in the generalized mammalian hand individual movement of the digits is essentially selective and more refined.

SPECIALIZATION OF THE FORELIMB MUSCLES FOR SPEED

Discussion of forelimb specialization requires scrutiny of conditions chiefly in such forms as the dog, cat, and ungulates. Windle and Parsons (1901–3) and Lechner (1933) have dissected a great variety of the last; and their reports, as well as those of others, have been freely utilized in arriving at my conclusions. There are so many kinds of ungulates that it will be many years before their anatomy is completely known, and some statements made now will probably require modification later.

Specialization of the forelimb musculature for speedy quadrupedal progression involves, from the gross aspect, chiefly a lightening of the distal end of the muscles, through the elongation of the tendons of insertion, a suppression of rotational limb action, and a tendency toward the distal migration of the insertion of certain muscles. Mammals in general exhibit a tendency for the distal migration of the origins of the muscles of the more peripheral segments (Straus, 1942). Translation into parasagittal movement of transverse action at the shoulder (Campbell, 1936) and the more distal joints is due not so much to muscles as to ligaments and the character of the joints, which oblige all muscles to work in the parasagittal plane.

Specialization in the muscles of the spinal accessory field involves chiefly those units regularly attached to the clavicle and is correlated with the reduction of the latter bone. When this occurs, there is fusion, in tandem, of the muscles from head to clavicle with those from clavicle to humerus. This serves to effect extremely powerful protraction of the upper arm. The muscle thus formed is usually termed the "brachiocephalicus" or cephalohumeral. It is formed by the fusion of the clavotrapezius and, usually, the cleidomastoid (and cleido-occipitalis if present) with the clavodeltoid; the line of junction, representing the position of the degenerate clavicle, often is a tendinous inscription. This condition is characteristic of all ungulates and carnivores. In the latter the cervical part of the trapezius is more concerned than in the former. In perissodactyls there is also fused with this mass a levator claviculae element.

Specialization of the suprazonal group of muscles shows no clear trend, and the parts effecting rotation of the scapula are not especially strong. The rhomboid is usually rather weak, and a capitis is present among ungulates only in hippos, pigs, and hyraces; among carnivores in cats, dogs, and also raccoons. A single sheet representing serratus anterior and levator scapulae is the rule, but the latter has origin as far forward as the atlas only in pigs and hippos. A levator claviculae is fairly constant and is correlated (in perissodactyls) with the absence of a well-defined acromion, and fuses with the acromiodeltoid to form a unit. The latter is either a separate transversohumeralis (tapir) or is fused with the trapezius to constitute a part of the brachiocephalicus. In either case it is of help in running.

Specialization of the axillary matrix seems to involve the more distal insertion of a latissimus with fibers frequently continuing onto m. pectoralis or into m. dorsoepitrochlearis (in artiodactyls). In carnivores some of the fibers may insert into m. panniculus carnosus. As already described, the clavodeltoid in carnivores and ungulates fuses in tandem with the more cranial part of the accessory field to form a brachiocephalicus. The acromiodeltoid may join the latter, or in perissodactyls it fuses with the levator claviculae. The deltoid often inserts unusually low in cursorial mammals, even into the forearm fascia, which is of great help in running. That it does so also in viverrid carnivores may reflect a specialization for climbing or some similar activity. Insertion of the brachiocephalicus is said to be usually upon the humerus in Canidae and into the forearm fascia in Felidae (Windle and Parsons, 1897), the latter condition being the more effective. Teres major and minor exhibit no cursorial trend, and the capsularis, reported in horses and pigs, probably has nothing to do with speed.

Specialization of the ventral shoulder musculature in runners at first glance appears to involve an unusual amount of splitting of the pectoral mass, but this is a character often encountered in the slowest carnivores and ungulates and probably has nothing to do with speed. One would expect to find very powerful abdominal pectoral and panniculus muscles for running, but no such trend is noticeable. The subclavius (or sternoscapularis) is often reported as absent in ungulates, but in many of them it appears to have become secondarily associated with the deep pectoral. The pectoralis major, as a rule, inserts low upon the humerus, often with some continuation into the fascia of the forearm. The latter should be a cursorial adaptation, but it is found in some of the most generalized kinds and may merely be characteristic of the ungulate stocks. The supraspinatus in cursorial adaptation tends to abandon its usual function of outward rotation in favor of aiding in protraction of the humerus; and its insertion then broadens to straddle the bicipital groove and include the lesser tuberosity (artiodactyls, including hippos and pigs; perissodactyls, including tapir; hyrax but not elephant; dog but not cat). The character is but rarely (sea lion) encountered in other orders. The infraspinatus and subscapularis apparently do not experience any cursorial adaptation, except that the latter is prone to undergo division.

Cursorial specialization of the triceps brachii complex appears to comprise subdivision and lengthening of the long head. The dorsoepitrochlearis is variable in development and sometimes, in both artiodactyls and perissodactyls, shifts its origin from the latissimus to the scapular border. The long triceps splits into two or more divisions in ungulates, in only the thylacine among marsupials, not in cat or dog, but in many of the terrestrial edentates. In ungulates the origin of the long triceps often occupies the entire glenoid margin of the scapula. This is frequently the case in viverrid carnivores, but neither in cat nor in dog. Both characters are to be considered advantageous in cursorial specialization.

Specialization of the ventral brachial musculature appears to include reduction of the medial head of the brachialis, accompanying diminution of rotation. Its insertion, upon radius or ulna or both, seems to have nothing to do with the habits of the animal. The tendency in carnivores and ungulates is toward the reduction of the biceps to a single head, arising from the glenoid border and inserting usually upon the radius in perissodactyls and carnivores and upon both the radius and ulna in artiodactyls. Single insertion into either radius or ulna has been reported in different species, or even the same species, and the actual insertion of this muscle is so easy to mistake that one distrusts the published statements.

Specialization of the forearm extensors is in the direction of simplification. The brachioradialis is absent in most dogs; only in the cheetah among cats; in hares; in all ungulates except hippos, tapirs, rhinos; and in elephants (Windle and Parsons, 1901). A single extensor carpi radialis is the rule in ungulates, although occasionally it is double, with an origin that has migrated above the condyle so that the muscle becomes a flexor in action. The humeroulnar element remains single, as is invariably the case in mammals. The humerocentral element shows some tendency for the origin to migrate distally, at least in the more cursorial artiodactyls and perissodactyls, with concomitant increase in the number of tendon branches. The number of digits involved differs and is at times individually variable (pig). It appears that, as a rule, insertion is upon all four digits in Suidae, Tragulina, hippos, tapirs; three in rhinos; and two in other ungulates (but three in muskox) except Equidae. Origin occasionally subdivides to some degree. In addition, however, there is always in ungulates an "extensor digitorum lateralis," comparable to the lateral proprii slips to the digits in generalized mammals. This goes to the more lateral functional digit in even-toed forms (digits 4 and 5 in pig), and to the single digit in the horse.

The deep antebrachial extensors are represented in carnivores and hares by the usual complement, although the supinator has disappeared in Dolichotis (Windle, 1897); but in ungulates all have disappeared (including the supinator, except in some pigs as well as in hyraces [Windle and Parsons, 1901]), except the abductor pollicis longus, which is usually decadent.

Of the forearm flexors the palmaris longus is often absent in carnivores, including the dog (present in the cat) and in all but the most generalized of ungulates and their relatives (such as the elephant). As an accompaniment of the disappearance of forearm rotation the pronator teres is decadent in most cursorial mammals (though large in dogs); but frequently it can be detected, even in some horses, in which case it undoubtedly acts in fixing the joint. The marginal flexors are rather weak and in some ungulates there is no ulnar origin of the flexor carpi ulnaris, or occasionally the humeral and ulnar origins are separate.

Many of the descriptions in the literature of the digital flexors are in disagreement as to what constitutes the sublimis and profundus elements; and the precise allocation of fibers is not always possible, for humeral slips sometimes join the profundus tendon or antebrachial fibers the sublimis. In some ungulates there is a tendency toward the splitting into several muscle units of the flexores digitorum, but then again they frequently are simple. The sublimis is said to be absent in the elephant, and I have found the profundus almost suppressed in some deer (Rusa), a small radial slip joining the sublimis tendon.

At times the two tendons are to all intents fused, but perhaps most frequently in ungulates the sublimis forms a tubular sheath for the profundus tendon. When separable, both tendons go to all functional digits and to the lateral ones also in the less specialized forms (as pig, hippo). It is the rule in ungulates for the digital flexor tendons to split into a number of branches, a tendency just the reverse of what one might expect in cursorial adaptation. In most sorts there is an interflexorial connection, largely tendinous but frequently partly fleshy, between the sublimis and profundus tendons (when they are separate).

A pronator quadratus is present in carnivores, for some obscure reason being particularly extensive in the dog; but with the reduction of forearm rotation it has disappeared in Dolichotis and in ungulates, except sometimes in the tapir (Windle and Parsons, 1901).

The short flexors of the manus are so reduced in all except the least specialized of the ungulates that the correct interpretation of conditions is well-nigh impossible. In the dog there is an abductor and a flexor of both pollex and minimus; but among ungulates thenar muscles are apparent only in pig, hyrax, and elephant, while hypothenar units are found in a few more—elephant, hyrax, hippo, pig, mouse deer, tapir, and rhino (Windle and Parsons, 1901). A superficial flexor digitorum brevis element is found in some subungulates (hyrax, elephant) and in the tapir.

There are reported to be present 4 lumbricales in the elephant, 3 in the tapir, 2 in the horse and hyraces, 1 in mouse deer, hippo, and pig (but none in peccary [Campbell]), and none in Cervidae, Bovidae, and the rhino (Windle and Parsons, 1901). Contrahentes occur in carnivores (1, 2, and 5 in the dog) and in most generalized ungulates (2 and 5 in hippo and pig; 2, 4, and 5 in tapir, according to Campbell, [1936]) but have disappeared in the more cursorial forms. Interossei in the more generalized ungulates, as also in the dog, occur, a pair to each functional digit, but are more reduced in the pig. In most of the specialized artiodactyls, however, the remaining interosseous elements form a chiefly tendinous, but partly fleshy, band deep to the long flexor tendons. In perissodactyls the individual units remain distinct. There are three such bands in the horse.

MUSCLES OF THE PELVIC LIMB

In the case of the pectoral limb there was no mention made of the muscles of birds, because of the lack of importance for cursorial adaptation of this member. The pelvic limb of birds, however, is highly specialized for running, and its musculature will be considered. Usually its details are very similar in plan to those of reptiles (Howell, 1938a).

Although the shoulder girdle was at first firmly anchored to the axial skeleton, it later became freely movable. Hence the muscles passing from it to the trunk insert upon the girdle and are considered to be extrinsic muscles of the appendage. The pelvic girdle, although originally free, has become firmly anchored to the axial skeleton, and the muscles passing from it to the trunk arise from the girdle and are considered in general to be axial muscles rather than muscles of the appendage. Thus in the latter category belong the abdominal muscles, rectus abdominis, and the abductors of the tail. The origin of one muscle element (caudofemoralis), however, basically from the tail to the appendage, has migrated onto the pelvis and become intrinsic. The final stage in mammals is that because of its mobility the shoulder girdle has numerous extrinsic but rather few intrinsic muscles, while the solidly anchored pelvic girdle is usually considered to have but one entirely extrinsic and numerous intrinsic muscles of the hip.

As in the anterior limb, the muscles of the pelvic extremity are basically divisible into a dorsal extensor mass for elevation and a ventral flexor mass for depression; these divided to a greater or less extent into sheets or individual slips. As the limb girdle developed, the ilium extended dorsally, making connection with the vertebral column and thus splitting the nerves supplying the limb muscles into an anterior, lumbar, or prozonal series and a posterior, sacral, or metazonal series, each with its dorsal and ventral elements. At first the lumbar and sacral dorsal muscle components were fairly continuous one with the other, as were the ventral components; but they later established a large degree of independence, so that in this limb it is convenient to recognize four main groups of muscles, two dorsal and two ventral. The muscles supplied by the prozonal nerves, however, do not extend distal to the knee in tetrapods, so in leg and foot there are but two groups of muscles, both metazonal.

It is a fact that in mammals the dorsal muscles of the hip region are associated with the ilium, the prozonal ventral matrix with the pubis, and the metazonal ventral matrix with the ischium. The encroachment of individual units of one matrix into the territory of an adjoining matrix, although occasionally taking place to some degree, is practically negligible. There is reason for believing that these arrangements are basic for tetrapods, but this statement does not apply so strictly for living lacertilians. In them there is exhibited a tendency for the origins of some of the hip muscles (puboischiofemoral and pubotibial extensors and intermediate adductor sheet) to migrate in a cranioventral ("inward-rotation") direction, evidently because of particular stresses incident to limb posture. This comprises additional evidence that the posture of the hind limb that was primitive for reptiles was quite different, with different influences, from that found in living reptiles. The condition of the hip muscles in urodele amphibians is also very specialized, but in a retrogressive direction.

It is convenient to consider the phylogeny of the muscles of the pelvic appendage as dorsal and ventral components of hip and thigh and of leg and foot.

MUSCLES OF THE HIP AND THIGH

Dorsal division.—These comprise basically a matrix with both femoral and peroneal innervation that tended to separate into a superficial two-joint sheet from pelvis to crus, a similar deep sheet from pelvis to femur, and, between the two, units of a femorocrural or triceps matrix that extended proximal to the pelvis. The main part of the superficial sheet in Sauropsida (reptiles and birds) consists of a prozonal and a metazonal iliotibialis, and caudal (iguana) or caudomedial (fowl) to this a metazonal iliofibular unit. In mammals the former has become the sartorius and the superficial gluteal (maximus and longus and short head of biceps), and the latter probably the tenuissimus, either decadent or absent.

The intermediate units of the femorocrural matrix appear to consist basically of two heads. In lacertilians and birds there is a medial vastus head and with it a long unit from the pubis, both of which arise caudal to the insertion of the iliopsoas. Neither is differentiated in mammals, and the long unit is the ambiens of birds. In mammals there is also a unit, the rectus femoris, that seems to be a proximal migrant of the part of the vastus, lateral or cranial to the insertion of the iliopsoas. This unit appears to be unrepresented in reptiles and birds.

The deep dorsal sheet of dorsal muscle bridging the hip tends to divide into a prozonal puboischiofemoral element, the homologue of iliacus and psoas major in birds and mammals, and a metazonal mass representing the deep gluteal musculature of mammals (glutei medius and minimus, tensor fasciae latae, piriformis).

Additional dorsal muscles of the thigh comprise the vasti, often termed the quadriceps or triceps complex of the thigh. This is a knee matrix that has migrated proximally, divided in different ways in different tetrapods but in all inserting by a common patellar ligament on the tibia.

Ventral division.—The ventral ischiopubic muscle mass bridging the hip joint appears to have followed a scheme most logically considered as basically comprising a superficial two-joint prozonal and metazonal sheet; a deeper one-joint sheet of similar character but which secondarily divides into two strata; and, from the posterior border of the entire mass, a variable series of metazonal crural flexor slips. In addition there has joined the latter complex the caudofemoralis element that fundamentally should probably be considered an axial muscle.

The superficial two-joint sheet is a flexor puboischiotibialis in the iguana, innervated by both obturator and tibial nerves. In a vertical limb it appears to be of decreased importance, for it is unrepresented in the fowl and is reduced in mammals, its representative in the latter class being m. gracilis.

The one-joint ventral element tends to divide into an intermediate and a deep sheet. The former occurs in the iguana and fowl as an adductor mass with both obturator and tibial innervation. In mammals only the obturator nerve is involved, and the muscles representing it comprise pectineus (with nerve following the femoral trunk) and adductor longus. The deeper one-joint mass comprises several flexor puboischiofemoral units with both obturator and tibial innervation, and a tibial ischiotrochantericus in the iguana. In the fowl there is a deep adductor complex with obturator, and an ischiofemoralis with tibial, innervation. In mammals also there has been complete separation of the two nerve fields. The prozonal (obturator) units comprise adductores brevis et longus and obturator externus, while the metazonal (tibial) slips consist of gemelli, obturator internus, and quadratus femoris.

The crural flexors, numbering as many as six units in reptiles (alligator), evidently should be regarded as having split off the more caudal portion of the ventral muscle mass. It is likely that the individual slips cannot be perfectly matched in different classes. The group has been joined by the axial caudofemoralis, inserting in reptiles and birds on the proximal part of the femur. Evidently in mammals it has migrated to the distal femur to become m. presemimembranosus. The other crural flexors in mammals are mm. semitendinosus, semimembranosus, and biceps femoris. Fused with the distal part of the latter may possibly be a femorocrural flexor element, as suggested by the digastric biceps of birds.

MUSCLES OF THE LEG AND FOOT

As in the case of the forearm, the muscles of the lower leg or crus, both dorsally (peroneal nerve group) and ventrally (tibial group), may most conveniently be regarded as basically occurring in two layers—a superficial one bridging the knee and showing a tendency to separate into two marginal and a central unit and a deeper division, originally concerned with the ankle, but with origins that have migrated proximally to a greater or less degree. In addition, there are short flexors of the pes, fundamentally divisible into superficial and deep components.

Superficial crural extensors.—In amphibians all three elements—tibial, central, and fibular—arise from the femur; but in reptiles the tibial has shifted completely, and the fibular component either partially or entirely, to the crus. In birds the central and fibular muscles arise from the crus, while the tibial comes from both femur and tibia. Both the central and the tibial elements retain the primitive femoral origin in a number of mammals, but in many others all three have shifted to the crus. The tibial marginal element becomes m. tibialis anterior; the femorocentral, m. extensor digitorum longus; and the fibular component, the peroneal muscles.

Theoretically, at least, the marginal extensors of the crus should have inserted, in most primitive condition, on the distal part of the respective crural bones, and the central unit to the fascia of the tarsus. But the former settled upon the tarsus and the latter into the metatarsus. The tibial marginal extensor (tibialis anterior) in mammals retains its tarsal insertion, while the fibular element has altered somewhat. It usually splits up into a peroneus brevis to metatarsal 5, not infrequently slips constituting a peroneus digiti quinti and even a quarti to the dorsum of the indicated digits, and regularly also a peroneus longus. The last has extended deeply by tendon across the sole of the foot from the lateral side to all plantar muscles and tendons and now inserts upon the first cuneiform and first metatarsal. In reptiles (iguana) this element has simulated the condition in mammals, but in crossing the plantar surface of the tarsus it has seized upon a different layer of fascia and now passes between the superficial and deep flexors. The history of the femorocentral extensor is simple. In amphibians it inserts upon the fascia of the tarsus, and in reptiles it has settled upon the metatarsus, in iguana inserting into the three middle bones, while in birds and mammals it has extended to the digits, evidently by seizing onto and following a sheet of fascia.

Deep crural and tarsal extensors.—These two together consist basically of a pair of elements, the short extensors of the ankle and the dorsometatarsals. The former comprises fibers extending from the fibula to the tibial side of the tarsus and base of metatarsus 1—really a supinator pedis—whose origin has migrated proximally beneath the superficial extensors to become m. extensor hallucis longus; and it includes, in addition, fibers from the fibulare or vicinity to all the digits, these becoming m. extensor digitorum brevis. The dorsometatarsals are present in reptiles, as they doubtless were in stem amphibians; but they have disappeared in modern urodeles—all of which are decadent—in birds, and in mammals.

Superficial crural flexors.—Allegedly because of the asymmetrical way in which the reptilian pes is used and therefore the effect of this ancestral condition upon mammals, the homology of the units of the superficial flexors of the crus is not easily established. Apparently gastrocnemius and soleus represent the marginal elements, and the plantaris a degenerate central one. The one responsible for the derivation of the popliteus is obscure, for it is not clearly present in any class but mammals (the muscle usually called popliteus in birds is a deep pronator or peroneotibialis; not infrequently present also in mammals).

In Necturus the femorotibial and femorocentral elements arise from the femur, while the femorofibular seems to be undifferentiated. In turtles the tibial element is from the femur or tibia or both. In Iguana the fibular and central units are from the femur, and what appears to be the tibial from the tibia. In birds a third, internal head of the gastrocnemius, a "soleus" (Gadow's plantaris), and a part of the perforating and perforated flexor slips (= femorofibularis?) have settled upon the crus. In mammals, gastrocnemius and plantaris are from the femur and soleus from the crus.

It appears that the primitive insertion of the femorotibial element was upon the tibiale or its vicinity, and that of the femorofibular upon the fibulare. In neither living reptiles nor mammals is the tibiale (or talus) involved; hence, either this muscle element is lacking or, more likely, its insertion has shifted to the calcaneus. The insertion of the femorocentralis has extended, by tendon, to the digits in the iguana; but in mammals this element, the plantaris, is decadent and usually ends in the plantar fascia with partial anchorage to the calcaneus. The insertion of some of the marginal fibers appears in mammals to have migrated proximally to form m. popliteus.

Deep crural flexors.—These appear undoubtedly to have been derived from muscle elements bridging the ankle, whose origins for the most part migrated proximally. They are quite as specialized, if not more so, in lizard-like reptiles as in mammals, and the homology of the individual units is not entirely clear. In mammals there is a long unit from crus to tarsus (tibialis posterior); two long units from crus to digits (flexor fibularis or flexor hallucis longus and flexor tibialis or flexor digitorum longus); a short tarsal unit (quadratus plantae) that has remained below the ankle; and not infrequently a

deep crural unit (peroneotibialis) that acts as a "pronator quadratus."

The dorsal muscles of the pes have been discussed. The ventral
short muscles of this segment appear to have had essentially the
same basic plan as in the manus, with a superficial and a deep series.

The superficial pedal flexors comprise two marginal abductors
(abductor hallucis and abductor digiti quinti); a more central group
of short flexors (flexor digitorum brevis) that provides perforated
tendons to the digits, pierced by the deep flexor tendons and in this
respect comparable to the tendons of the flexor digitorum sublimis
in the manus; and a paratendinous group of lumbricales associated
with the tendons of the long deep flexor.

The deep pedal flexors comprise a more superficial series of contrahentes, which experience reduction in mammals in the same order
as in the hand (sometimes, as in man, leaving m. adductor hallucis as
the sole representative), and idealistically a series of five pairs of true
short, deep flexors, a pair to each digit. The first two units comprise
the double flexor hallucis brevis, and the tenth, m. flexor digiti quinti.
Between are the seven interossei. The fundamental arrangement of
these in mammals is much as in the manus, except that the axis is
through digit 2 rather than digit 3. Four of the slips constitute the
dorsal interossei, and three the plantar interossei.

In birds there are short, chiefly tendinous, muscles present in both
the dorsal and the ventral series; but they are so specialized that any
present attempt at precise homology appears to be unwise.

SPECIALIZATION OF THE HIND-LIMB MUSCLES FOR SPEED

Adaptation for speedy progression involves the hind limb more
frequently than the forelimb. Not only does the former member
play a greater part in swift quadrupedal locomotion, but it is the
sole member concerned in saltatorial mammals. Specialization of
hind-limb musculature among the swifter reptiles could be discussed with profit if we knew more about the broad differences char-
acterizing the relatively generalized groups.

Other difficulties are encountered among birds. The legs of all
birds are constructed on a highly cursorial ground plan; and, in addition to bony and muscular proportions very favorable for speed,
there is a particularly advantageous angle of leverage in the origins of
both the extensor and the flexor muscles of the thigh, great development of the caudofemoral element, and presence of a powerful extensor iliofibularis (= tenuissimus), besides a number of less pro-

nounced adaptations. In fact, 90 per cent or more of land birds have pelvic limbs of higher cursorial specialization, anatomically, than all but the most highly adapted mammals. Accordingly, the most cursorial of birds have muscles that differ from those of slower forms in but very slight degree.

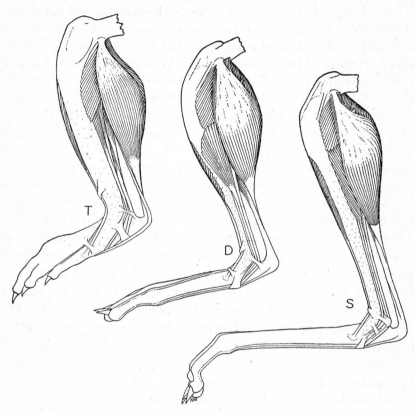

FIG. 9.—The medial surface of the right crus and foot of a pocket gopher (Thomomys), kangaroo rat (Dipodomys), and jerboa (Scirtopoda), on the same scale, to illustrate the lengthening of the crural tendons with cursorial development.

In the case of mammals a host of individual species involving a great many genera and numerous families have legs adapted for quite fast running or leaping. In addition, the more generalized mammals have hind legs better fitted for running than are the forelegs, and hence cursorial adaptation in the latter involves less extreme change than in the case of the former. Without carrying the present report to an excessive length it is practicable to consider here only a few of the more interesting, or extreme, or well-known varieties.

In considering the specialization of the hind-limb musculature one should bear in mind that separate movement of the pelvis on the trunk is impossible, as is also rotation of the lower leg on the thigh.

It has frequently been stated that cursorial habits increase the development of the iliopsoas muscle, probably because this muscle complex is large in the rabbit. Flexure of the vertebral column in the sagittal plane is very helpful to some mammals, such as the weasel, cats, and swift dogs during running; but the propulsive force concerned is furnished by the back muscles in straightening the column, while contraction of the iliopsoas in bending the back and advancing the thigh is merely the recovery action. As a matter of fact, I am unaware that the iliopsoas can be said to be proportionately of unusual size in any cursorial or saltatorial mammal except hares and the Patagonian cavy and perhaps kangaroos, in which there is also a tendency for the forward migration of its origin.

The gluteus muscles show a variability that is almost impossible to connect with cursorial habits. The gluteus maximus in artiodactyls ends in fascia, but it inserts upon the prominent third trochanter in perissodactyls and hence may be considered as more effective in the latter forms. Although the long gluteus occurs in both orders of ungulates, it is present only in certain carnivores (some of them slow); it is found in cats but not in dogs. It inserts upon the patella in cats and kangaroos, thus helping the quadriceps to straighten the knee and aiding in leaping. The deep gluteals appear to be better developed in the horse than in the ox and deer. Among saltatorial mammals a noteworthy specialization involves the abrupt termination of gluteus longus (but not maximus) and medius in long, thin tendons, which join and insert upon the patella.

Perhaps the only safe statement to make regarding the specialization of the ventral hip musculature for speed is that the units act increasingly to promote action in the sagittal plane at the expense of movement in the transverse plane; but in what precise respects it is often difficult to state. All the prozonal (adductor) units tend to form a single, closely knit complex in cursorial forms. The origin of a part (obturator tertius) of the obturator externus has migrated through the obturator foramen to add to the contractive potential in artiodactyls and hyraces, but not in perissodactyls (Parsons, 1903). Of the metazonal ventral hip units, the quadratus femoris is unusually long in some of the ungulates, and the obturator internus is double in some saltators (Pedetes, Dipodomys) but decadent in other, still more gifted, leapers (kangaroos, jerboas).

Of the prozonal units of the dorsal muscles of the thigh, the capsularis, too small to be of much significance, appears to have been reported only in Perissodactyla and Canidae. Of the other elements the sartorius is the most variable. In many carnivores and marsupials, as well as rodents, it ends in fascia proximal to the knee (Parsons, 1903). It is single and usually quite heavy in cats (and bears), but double in dogs (and hyenas) (Windle and Parsons, 1898). In ungulates it often arises from the iliac fascia or inguinal ligament but has an additional origin from the pubis in some artiodactyls (Windle and Parsons, 1903). The metazonal long gluteal unit has been discussed under the hip musculature.

In this connection it may be mentioned that the vasti and other femoral nerve units (including the ambiens) in birds appear, on the average, to be better developed for running than in mammals.

As already stated, the adductor muscles in cursorial mammals are usually a closely knit complex and particularly powerful, but I have detected no such particular tendency in this group among saltators. In ungulates the gracilis tends to have a fascial extension to the ankle, which adds to its power. Of the metazonal flexors, a caudal, in addition to an ischial, head should add to the effectiveness of the muscles, but both conditions are found in slow as well as in speedy mammals. In most mammals the presemimembranosus is a distinct unit, but sometimes (as in artiodactyls) it is considered as fused with the semimembranosus for most of its length. Added effectiveness of the hamstring muscles is usually afforded, in ungulates, saltators, dogs, and cats, by the extension of the insertion of these metazonal flexors to the sheath of the tendo calcaneus, but this occurs in slow rodents and carnivores as well. In kangaroos the semimembranosus, like the longer glutei, ends abruptly in a long, thin tendon.

Because of the fact that the homologue of the presemimembranosus—the caudofemoralis element—is very much better developed in reptiles and birds and passes from tail base to femur in a way that gives it very great power, these classes can retract the thigh with greater force than is probably possible in any mammal with comparable proportions. The shift that characterizes mammals in the origin of this muscle has weakened the limb for running in a manner that the class Mammalia has been unable to overcome by other devices.

In the case of the dorsal muscles of the crus and foot, a persisting femoral origin of the tibialis anterior is retained in a number of mammals (some edentates and rodents), including a few ungulates (horse, pig); but this can hardly be called a cursorial character. The muscle is unusually large in some leapers (kangaroo, kangaroo rat).

It happens that a femoral origin of the extensor digitorum longus persists in artiodactyls, perissodactyls, carnivores, and most rodents; but it is a primitive character that doubtless has been retained in spite of, rather than because of, the fact that it is a detail that should be of advantage in speedy progression. It is quite likely to be divisible into several heads in artiodactyls. In the kangaroo this muscle is relatively light; but there is still a distinct, though minute, extensor hallucis longus with a wisp of a tendon to digit 2. The latter attachment is characteristic of many mammals in which the hallux has become lost; but the precise fate of the long hallucal extensor in the more highly specialized ungulates is difficult to determine. In them it may occur as the muscle usually considered the most medial head of the extensor digitorum longus. Some trace of short extensors is usually retained by the ungulates, but they are most often lost by the most accomplished saltators.

The peronei are well developed in the least specialized of the ungulates (and in carnivores), as pigs and hippos, there being four divisions; but they are progressively reduced as the digits degenerate and disappear. In the most specialized of the ungulates the precise identity of the surviving peroneal unit may be in doubt. Thus it is usually considered that the surviving slip of this group, ending on the long extensor tendon of the horse, is the brevis, while Windle and Parsons (1901) have claimed that a brevis is never present in ungulates, the shorter unit in this group being the peroneus digiti quarti. In Dolichotis the brevis is absent. A somewhat similar situation obtains in saltators, in which the peronei are reduced or consolidated. In the kangaroo the larger element does not cross the foot, and there are two filamentous tendons to the lateral toes. In saltating rodents the longus is also reduced, accompanying diminution in eversion of the foot, and the brevis has disappeared in the most specialized forms. But the precise comparison of peroneal slips in highly specialized mammals is not regarded as always feasible.

The triceps surae in speedy mammals tends to be robust, the lateral gastrocnemius at times with an extra head or extension (kangaroo, some carnivores), this continuing so as to arise from the patella in some leapers (Macropus, Pedetes). The soleus tends to be reduced (ungulates) or indistinguishably fused in speedy mammals and is absent in kangaroos (but not in jerboas) and in dogs. This tendency may be more apparent than real, however, as the muscle is absent in pig and hippo. The plantaris shows no diminution.

The long deep flexors exhibit some tendency in speedy mammals toward fusion, with insertion by a common tendon to all digits; but the flexor fibularis is usually the larger.

The presence or absence of particular ventral muscle vestiges of the foot in mammals of high cursorial ability is often a matter that is very difficult to settle. Perhaps all that is important in the present connection is that there is drastic reduction of all short muscles, with the disappearance of their muscle fibers and often of their tendinous parts, accompanying the diminution of the grasping ability and of the independent mobility of the individual toes. The flexor brevis element is retained, eventually as a heavy tendon to provide a perforated unit and a plantar covering of the long deep tendon. An abductor and usually a short flexor of the fifth (the first has been lost) toe is retained if this toe be still functional. Lumbricales are supposed to be present in perissodactyls, as in leapers and in carnivores, but absent in artiodactyls except hippos. I believe that contrahentes in some form are present, if not in more apparent form, then at least as the deep part of the long tendon sheath. Some vestiges of the interossei occur, or at any rate in all but the most extreme instances. The quadratus plantae has disappeared in the most gifted runners and leapers except in carnivores.

Before leaving the subject of muscles attention may be called to the particular way that muscles and their tendons are allowed to function in cursorial specialization by the conformation of ligaments. Thus the remarkable structural features of the pes of a horse are rendered possible only by the pattern of the ligamentous support and the elasticity of the calcaneal tendon. Unfortunately, there is little that can be done toward an intelligent study and comparison of such ligaments.

CHAPTER VI

The Axial Skeleton

THE fact that vertebrates have a chain of articulated vertebrae is due to the basic segmental arrangement of the body. That it has persisted in this form, rather than becoming a solid rod with two or three joints, is doubtless attributable to the fact that effective swimming required a fusiform body with just the proper degree of limberness. The length of body, in relation to its bulk, was held, in the more generalized forms, within limits dictated by laws governing the propulsion by oscillations of a body through the water.

If a cylindrical body, such as that of a caterpillar, be bent while in the water, no progress will be made, for the movements at either end will equalize each other. In order that progress may take place, the center of gravity must be elsewhere than the middle, which results in a body essentially fusiform or cigar-shaped, not so long that a double S-curve is adopted while swimming and, in practice, with some sort of tail-fin structure at the more slender end of the body. This is the typical fish-shape termed by Breder (1926) "carangiform," and it reaches its most effective form in the mackerels and tunas. The action then involves the principle of a lever of the third order. The fulcrum, shifting in position to some extent with the action, is located immediately posterior to the head, the weight is the water to be moved sideways by the tail, and the power arm is the caudal part of the body and the tail. The action depends upon, first, a lateral curvature of the body, followed by a swing in the opposite direction, which forces the water obliquely away from the bent tail, resulting in forward propulsion of the whole body. Repetition of this action constitutes the act of swimming by a fish of this shape.

In fish the vertebral column constituted a flexible rod for separating the head and tail and for providing a multitude of anchorages for the body muscles. The success of the fish form in becoming a terrestrial tetrapod lay very largely in the fact that the piscine bony architecture was, for entirely aquatic reasons, excellently constructed for becoming a land girder with two-point suspension, to so efficient a degree that the basic principle of axial architecture has not been altered throughout tetrapod history, although it has been refined.

The skeleton of tetrapods has long been compared to a cantilever bridge. This idea was developed by D'Arcy Thompson (1917) in an interesting manner and has recently been discussed by Gregory (1937). The bridge idea, however, although appealing more to the imagination, is a less apt comparison than a girder supported by two pillars (Fig. 8). It will readily be appreciated that any such comparison of a highly dynamic body, having constantly varying stresses, with a static girder is highly unsatisfactory in many respects; but the idea of a girder enlivened by numerous joints and pulleys, with a crane on either end, will prove to be of considerable aid to an understanding of mammalian dynamics. First, however, the static condition should be explained.

In a beam supported at both ends (A, Fig. 10) the strain is greatest in the middle, and there are two sets or systems of strain present— compression of the substance along the upper part of the beam and tension along the lower part, the lines of each forming parabolas. There is also a shearing stress to be considered, and this is present in all positions except along the lines of maximum compression and tension, being greatest in neutral zones lying at an angle of 45° to lines of compression and tension (Thompson). The danger of shearing can, of course, be overcome by planning for sufficient strength to meet all stresses to be encountered.

If, however, the beam be attached to a support at only one end, in bracket fashion, the stresses will be reversed (B), and the factor of tension will occur above and that of compression below. The two (A and B) may be combined (C) for illustration. If, however, one conceive of the beam not as comprising a combination of A and B but as two beams, each balanced on one of the piers and loosely articulated in the middle of the span (as in D), the factor of tension will everywhere be above and that of compression below.

It is clear that this type of beam cannot have much strength if the vertical dimension is small. It can be made stronger, but much heavier, by increasing the thickness of the entire beam or only of those parts subjected to the greatest stress. It may be done by increasing the strength of chiefly the compression factor (*E*) or of the tension

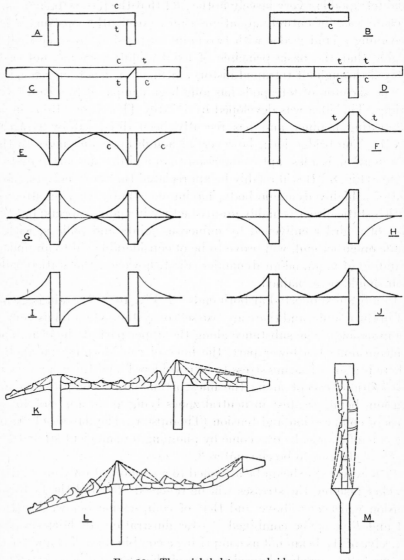

FIG. 10.—The axial skeleton as a bridge

factor (*F*) or of both together (*G*); or a combination of the two (*H* or *I*) may be employed. All these plans involve a double cantilever, and the above arguments are based on solid structural units.

The lines of compression and tension occupy particular situations in a solid-beam type of girder. Hence one may economize in weight by cutting away those parts through which the lines of stress do not pass. Synthetically, such a structure may be assembled on the lines of a skeleton iron girder, with cross-members, such as may be seen in most large iron bridges. Or one may have an upper compression member connected to a lower tension member by solid metal, resulting in an I-beam of familiar pattern. In mechanical practice the factor of compression may not be needed, in which case a rope or cable, hanging free between terminal supports, will furnish all lines of tension, the patterns of which will vary in accordance with the situation along the rope of an applied weight.

In a steel girder or bridge of conventional openwork pattern the strengthening members may conform to some sort of X-shaped design, or they may comprise well anchored vertical struts and oblique ties. If both be of inflexible steel, it matters but little whether they be employed in connection with the compression or the tension system. If, however, the ties be flexible (as in the case of a rope or a ligament), they can be used only in connection with the tension system. Hence with this type of strengthening the E-style of bridge could not be used, but the F-style (in Fig. 10) could be.

While comparing the vertebrate skeleton to a girder or bridge, one should call attention to the fact that the two piers often have to support very unequal loads, in which case the scheme may be compared to J.

Further comparison between bridge and skeleton is difficult, for in the former the force of gravity is the only primary influence, with minor forces of side sway and vibration under variable load; but in the skeleton the structure must be prepared to encounter stresses that are as strong in an upward or lateral as in a downward direction. In addition, the skeleton, instead of being solid, is articulated and yielding at a great number of points and in various directions. For purposes of illustration, at least, it may be compared to a number of articulated segments, the whole usually considerably heavier at one end (anteriorly) than at the other, with a heavier, stronger cantilever in the former situation, ending in a relatively heavy control room (head). It rests solidly only upon one (pair) of its two-pier supports, being supported by an elastic (muscular) sling from the other pair (anterior limbs). This idea is portrayed in K, Figure 10.

It should be noted in this somewhat idealized diagram that the plan of the double cantilever, with articulation between, is still borne out. The struts (spinous processes) of each of the segments concerned with one of the piers slope away from that pier. The ties (ligaments and muscles) of the struts of the left-hand cantilever are anchored to the superior end of the pier (innominate bone and sacrum); but this is not the case at the other end. Here the ties are anchored to other segments (vertebrae) and to the control box (head), for the reason that the load is not articulated solidly to the pier (shoulder) but is slung upon it by an elastic support (muscles). This plan of spinous processes sloping away from the pectoral and pelvic girdle, respectively, is characteristic of mammals; but frequently these processes in the lumbar and basal caudal regions are broadened, and thus strengthened, in the sagittal direction so that the slope is not pronounced, although the stresses doubtless remain the same.

It will be noted (K, Fig. 10) that high struts upon the right give great leverage to the ties controlling the free cantilever at that end of the structure. Thus, as might be expected, high spinous processes over the anterior thorax are characteristic of those mammals with extremely large heads or large antlers (Elephas, Brontotherium, Toxodon, Bison). Because of the angle of leverage, this feature is more pronounced in those forms in which the head is habitually held very low (as Bison). Correlated with it are heavy forequarters and light hindquarters. Accordingly, the former part of the body is required to do a disproportionate amount of work, to which the hindquarters contribute in minor amount. One would not expect extreme speed in an animal having this feature in very pronounced degree, but it can whirl about with surprising celerity.

On the other hand, there are some few animals in which the highest spines occur in the sacral or posterior lumbar regions, the spines anterior and posterior thereto shortening in gradual sequence. This character indicates disproportionate strength of the back musculature in this situation and consequent ability of the animal to seesaw the body with the sacrum as a pivot. It occurs pronouncedly only in heavy reptiles with heavy tail, not in the kinds that were exclusively bipedal but in such as Stegosaurus and in some of the larger sauropods. These were reptiles of a stock essentially bipedal but were genera that had again assumed a largely quadrupedal gait. It is indicated, however, that they had habits that may be compared to a "walking beam" or oscillating cantilever, frequently standing erect upon the hind limbs, probably for the purpose of feeding in the tree-tops. Very few large mammals have had such habits, and in the large ground sloths—a group in which this ability was marked—the length of the lumbar spines is not noteworthy. In the kangaroos, the only Recent bipedal mammals of some weight having a heavy tail, this character is definitely present, although not nearly to the extent as is to be found in reptiles.

In strictly bipedal animals there are two types of body suspension. In those having a heavy or long tail for a counterbalance the principle is a cantilever type of support with one pier. Animals in this category include all the strictly bipedal reptiles (now extinct), kangaroos, and the bipedal rodents. In the absence of a heavy tail (man, gibbon) the principle involved is not the one of a supported beam or bridge but that encountered in a structural iron tower or mast, balanced on one end and strengthened with guy wires. The former plan cannot be followed by a mammal without a tail, because the lack of structural equilibrium involves too great a strain on the muscles.

Unfortunately, it is entirely impossible to determine the stresses involved and the strength necessary to meet them. The stresses encountered during unusual movements are unpredictable, and strength is supplied not only by muscles but by ligaments. High spinous processes certainly denote strength, but low ones do not mean that strength is deficient.

The vertebral column is composed, of course, of a series of bony vertebrae connected in linear sequence by means of intervertebral cartilages, the latter permitting a degree of elasticity of the column as a whole that is highly variable in different types of animals. The degree of possible movement may be vastly increased with practice, particularly when young, so it is reasonable to state that, although there are very definite limitations imposed by heritage (the body of a hippopotamus could never become so limber as that of a weasel) and by the mechanical laws governing bodies of different weight, the degree of elasticity encountered in the vertebral column of a particular animal is the optimum for that individual, best fitting it for the sum of actions that comprise its most critical, or at least habitual, activities.

Movement of the axial skeleton as a whole during rapid quadrupedal locomotion consists chiefly of lateral bending in varying degree as a feature of the symmetrical gaits (as walking, trotting) and bending in the vertical plane in the various forms of the asymmetrical gallop. Bipedal running falls into the former category, and saltation, although symmetrical, into the latter. Lateral bending of the spinal column during locomotion is executed so as to lengthen the stride to a degree greater than would be feasible were the axial skeleton rigid. Thus when one walks rapidly the pelvis is oscillated, while the shoulders execute the same maneuver, but in reverse sequence. The same statement applies to the trot, but not to the pace, in which shoulders and hips are "in step." In such actions the optimum degree of lateral curvature of the vertebral column depends upon a very complicated factor, involving speed, mass, length of leg, width and length of body, and muscular strength; but in simple terms it is limited to the slight degree that will actually add to length of stride without putting an undue strain upon the body.

Bending of the vertebral column in the vertical plane during locomotion is also done for the purpose of lengthening the stride; but the degree to which it is accomplished is extremely variable and in a manner that is difficult to evaluate. It can readily be seen that the extreme manner in which the body is bent and then straightened during locomotion enables the weasel to travel much faster than its short legs would permit were the body less flexible. The whippet can clearly run faster by bending its back into a bow and extending the hind limbs considerably in advance of the forelimbs. But the horse indulges in this maneuver only to a limited degree. There is doubtless no one reason for these facts, but there are various possibilities. A ponderous body is not conducive to vertebral motility (horse); extreme length of limb accomplishes the same end (antelope); but perhaps the most significant fact is that all mammals that bow the back to a great degree while running have either a light head or short neck or both (rabbit, weasel, whippet). During a hard gallop a heavy anterior end of the vertebral column must be swung up and down, in time with the stride, and this pendulum action would doubtless make trouble if combined with a marked degree of back-bending.

The head has a very great number of functions to perform, many of them of vital importance. It is probably true that the head is less affected by the requirements for great speed than any other part of an animal. Hence an animal having a cumbersome head must either make the best of this handicap, as by increased vigilance, or else succumb. But conformation of the head and neck together has a great influence upon the speed, and often upon the gait.

An extremely heavy head is probably not the burden to an animal that one might suppose; for, at least in many kinds of mammals having this attribute, the ligamentum nuchae, along the mid-dorsum of the neck, is so arranged that its pull practically equalizes the weight of head and neck. This may be demonstrated on a dead ungulate. Grazing mammals in the wild must, for safety's sake, raise the head very frequently to gaze around for enemies. Some of the more nervous sorts do this every few seconds; and one would suppose that during the course of a day an immense amount of energy would be expended in raising and even in supporting a large head with heavy horns or antlers. As a matter of fact, there is evidence to indicate that in tetrapods the head and neck are a unit in physiological balance, by means of the nuchal ligament, when it is held in the position in which it is carried while the animal is at rest. From this position a very slight amount of energy is required to lower it to the ground or raise it to full height. There seems little or no doubt, however, that a heavy equipment of antlers, horns, or tusks constitutes a considerable and very definite handicap to locomotion, slowing up the animal at least during a long run. That it has not proved to be a critical handicap to the majority of species is doubtless due to the fact that the polygamous habits of the males, in which sex the heaviest horns occur, render a large mortality among them a matter of slight biologic importance.

The position in which a heavy head is habitually carried has a marked influence not only on the conformation of the skull but on the gait of the animal. In at least most kinds of mammals a line passing through both canthi of the eye will be parallel to the ground when the head is held in its habitual, or probably optimum, posture. The posture of the head in respect to the neck also is indicated by the slope of the occiput. In a mammal that holds the neck high (horse, giraffe) the occipital plane has a marked backward tilt, while in one with low-hung head, in which the cranial axis is more nearly parallel with the cervical axis, the occiput tends more toward the vertical, or even has a forward tilt (whales). But the influences determining this factor are probably too complex for analysis.

In any discussion of anatomical features associated with speedy locomotion one is obliged to include the ear. The evidence clearly points to the advantages of an acute acoustic apparatus in speedy types of plains mammals; and asses and most other ungulates, hares, Cape jumping hares, Australian jerboa mice, some jerboas, the speedier bandicoots, the marsupial Antechinomys, and many others have external ears of large, or sometimes of phenomenal, size.

The external ear, of course, is not a part of the skeleton, but might as well be discussed with the acoustic apparatus. Size of the external ear in itself doubtless is independent of speed but is probably influenced by the same sort of environmental factors, for it is true that the speediest desert mammals frequently have the largest ears. Even though the degree of interdependence is problematical, the subject is worth attention here.

It is generally accepted, I think, that Allen's Law holds good. This is to the effect that protruding parts of the body, as ears and tails, are relatively shorter in colder than in warmer climates. Certainly, the ears of polar bears are less prominent than are those of the Florida black bear, of the arctic fox than of the southern gray fox. Some degree of this difference is illusory because of the relatively heavier pelage of the northern animals, and, besides, the real difference is not so great as is generally supposed. For purposes of illustration there are usually selected for comparison not northern and southern species, but northern and *desert* species, which is something very different. Thus the Florida cottontail and the brush rabbit of central California have ears that, relative to body length, are no longer than in the Greenland hare. But desert jack rabbits do have very much longer ears, and those species of other genera having the largest ears are almost invariably desert dwellers.

It is broadly assumed that large ears increase acuity of hearing, and this is a logical supposition. Diurnal desert mammals rely for protection chiefly on keenness of sight, which is very pronounced in most animals of an open habitat. Those that are active at night are in equal need of equally acute sound reception, and there is much evidence that they have it. There is no evidence, however, that keen hearing may not be more easily acquired, and the result be far more effective, by middle- and inner-ear changes than by enlargement of the pinna. In fact, it seems not at all unlikely that the latter has been brought about by stimuli that have nothing to do with hearing proper, although it appears that large ears do help to some extent in hearing and probably have some slight selective value in those desert mammals having them.

The more likely function of a large external ear, aside from any help in hearing, is obviously that of increasing the total body surface, and hence of increasing the radiation of bodily heat. This is a function more complicated than might appear at first glance. Obviously, large ears could not efficiently cool the animal by providing a greater area for evaporation of surface moisture, for the latter must be conserved to the utmost by desert mammals. Large, thin, and almost naked ears could very definitely cool the blood stream by radiation of heat when the atmosphere was below blood heat but would have the opposite effect when the temperature was above that figure, as it so often is on the desert. The latter point would be of less concern to nocturnal jerboas than to partly diurnal hares.

It is hardly likely that the slightly larger ears of mammals as large as asses could give them an appreciable advantage in cooling area over horses, but it is a physiological likelihood in the case of small rodents. It is regarded as a likely theory that, in the latter, large ears were first developed to add to the body surface and that these proved of advantage as an aid to hearing. As in the case of so many bodily details, why all species of the same general environment are not highly developed in this regard is one of the great puzzles of evolutional morphology.

It is difficult to discover the acuity of hearing in a variety of wild animals and impossible to determine, without elaborate and lengthy experiments, which details of the acoustic apparatus are responsible for differences in the quality of perception. I do believe, however, that many desert mammals have an additional receptive appliance that is quite dissimilar in quality from ours and that develops independently of external ear size. It involves a disproportionate enlargement of the auditory and mastoid bullae and has no connection with size of pinna. The manner of functioning is unknown, but it seems likely that it is a resonance apparatus for the reception of vibrations of the sort incident to footfalls and similar activities. When foraging at night a kangaroo rat pays but scant attention to airborne sounds, but a tap upon the ground will send it scurrying.

This bullae development is found in marked form in the New World Heteromyidae and Old World Dipodidae. It may be studied to best advantage in the former, in which different degrees are well illustrated through the pocket mice to the kangaroo rats and mice. In these it is seen that the inflation involves chiefly the mastoid and to a lesser degree the tympanic part of the bullae. The mastoids enlarge first dorsally and then rostrally and medially. In final form (Microdipodops) the bullae of the two sides practically meet dorsally and quite meet in the pterygoid region. They have expanded ante-

riorly until the whole skull becomes very broad and flat, particularly
posteriorly, and triangular in shape, while the brain is crowded and
altered in form. In all the Heteromyidae the external ear is small, but
the existing variation in its size is independent of bullae size.

In Dipodomys the dorsal and caudal parts of the bullae are composed of mastoid elements, these being separated from the tympanic
part of the bullae by a bony septum. The mastoid sinus is also divided by a septum into dorsal and posterior cavities. The former is
the larger, and each communicates with the middle ear by a separate
fenestration. In this animal the tympanic membrane may be as large
as three-fifths of its size in man (see Howell, 1932).

In the Dipodoidea studied, the relative enlargement of the respective elements is slightly different, but the maximum attained—in
Salpingotus—is even more extreme than in the American family.
This genus has a small external ear, but another genus (Euchoreutes)
with a comparatively small bulla has an external ear relatively larger
than in any other terrestrial mammal.

A very remarkable development in Dipus, Scirtopoda, and doubtless in other members of the family is that there is an accessory auditory membrane covering an opening between the large mastoid
sinus and the external ear.

Very intimately concerned with speed in highly cursorial animals
is length of neck. The stem amphibians had practically no neck, and
the cervical series of vertebrae consisted only of the atlas. The same
may be said of the earliest reptiles, which had but one or two cervicals. Modern chameleons have 5 cervicals; lizards and turtles 8;
Crocodilia, Therapoda, and Ceratopsia 9; and Saurapoda as many as
15, while the extreme was encountered in plesiosaurs with as many
as 76 cervicals. It is likely, however, that cursorial reptiles were subjected to the same influences for neck length as those encountered by
birds and mammals. The details of birds have been so strongly modified by the strictly delimited requirements dictated by flight that it
is almost impossible to say what may now constitute cursorial adaptations. Rather is it better to affirm that all birds are basically cursorial and that in some this attribute has been retained but in others
it is much reduced. Each step of a bipedal vertebrate that is not a
saltator changes the center of gravity, and this must be adjusted
either by rhythmic swinging of the forelimbs (man) or by forward
and back movements of the head and neck, as in birds. Accordingly,
cursorial habits may be presumed to have a definite influence upon

the neck of birds. Its length is also correlated to a considerable extent with length of leg, so that the bird may comfortably feed from the ground, but not to the same extent as in mammals, for the bird may have a long bill and it may also tilt the entire body, which in a quadruped is less feasible. The bird's neck has a minimum of 8 vertebrae, according to Kingsley (1925), or 13, according to Zittel (1932), and a maximum of 25 in the swan, with an average of 14 or 15.

All mammals, from the tallest giraffe to the smallest shrew, have 7 cervical vertebrae, excepting the manatees (6) and the sloths (Choloepus hoffmani, 6; Bradypus, usually 9 but sometimes 8 or 10), the variation in neck length depending upon the length of the individual vertebrae. It would be helpful, though, if one could determine what the "average" neck length is; but it is never possible to judge the relative length of neck because of the lack of any standard or yardstick. One cannot be sure that an apparently shorter neck does not merely indicate a longer body. But the "average" mammalian neck length may be judged to be an attribute of rather small, fairly generalized mammals, particularly those not actively moving about while eating. A small mammal, even when moving about, may squat without fatigue and so bring the head to the ground to graze, in spite of a neck shorter than the legs (like the hares); or a large mammal (carnivore) may squat to eat if it does not have to move about while so engaged, and so may have a neck shorter than the limbs; or a mammal may have a relatively short neck if it is a browser and hence does not need to bring its head to the ground for eating. Among grazers, however, it is the rule that the neck must be as long as the forelegs, so that short grass may be cropped without undue inconvenience. The browsing giraffe and gerenuk also have long necks, but in the former case, at least, the length of neck seems not so remarkable as the length of leg. To be entirely accurate in this regard, however, it must be stated that the difficulty experienced by this animal in reaching the ground with its muzzle, while at the same time straddling with forelimbs wide apart, may be attributable less to a difference in the limb-neck ratio than to the fact that the dorsal part of the vertebral column slopes to an unusual degree, which should interfere with any very abrupt downward bending of the neck.

Thus it is probable that, on the whole, feeding habits have the greatest influence on length of neck, at least in mammals of considerable size. The next most important factor appears to be an adaptation to suitable locomotion, and this influence varies with the sort of locomotion employed. In the case of small mammals, high specialization for saltation involves a short, chunky body, to be catapulted as a unit, with a long, tufted tail acting as an aerial rudder. Movement of the head plays no part in guidance, and the tendency is for extreme shortening and fusion of the cervical vertebrae. This character is not strongly dynamic, for some highly saltatorial rodents (Allactaga) lack it, while one of the Dipodoidea least specialized for leaping (Cardiocranius) has the greatest number of fused vertebrae. That the character is definitely correlated with leaping is attested by the fact that fused vertebrae occur in three diverse groups—Dipodoidea, Pedetidae, and the Heteromyidae—but in no nonsaltatorial rodent with which I am acquainted. A degree of fusion may, however, occur in the burrowing Notoryctes (Reynolds, 1913), in armadillos, and in whales.

The atlas is invariably free, and there is some individual variation in the number of others that may be fused. Vinogradov (1937) has given 2–5 as fused in Dipus and Scirtopoda, 2–6 in Dipus and Jaculus, and 2–7 in Salpingotus and Cardiocranius. Hatt (1932) found all cervical vertebrae free in one specimen of Pedetes and 2–3 fused in another, while the same author reported all free or 2–3 fused in Microdipodops and Dipodomys varying from 2–3 to 2–5 fused, a range embracing the variation within my own experience. It is thus seen that with rare exceptions fusion progresses in a caudal direction from the axis. It is also likely that the mobility of the unfused cervicals is reduced in these saltatorial rodents.

A rather heavy head supported by a neck of considerable length— say in the case of an ungulate—is subject during locomotion to two influences of interest in the present connection—that concerned with the head and neck as a pendulum and that concerned with the inertia of the head. The period of oscillation of a pendulum depends upon the length (of neck) and not upon the weight (of head), while the weight of the head determines the inertia. The two together are influenced by the power of the controlling musculature.

In symmetrical gaits (walk, trot, pace) it may be said that the head and neck are held immobile, but this is so only in the broader sense. Actually, alternate use of the forelimbs involves accompanying slight elevations and lateral movements of the head as an aid to the contractions of those muscles passing from the neck to the anterior extremity. But, accepting the statement in the broader sense, it is seen that even the heaviest head will not interfere with symmetrical gaits (because its oscillation is unnecessary), providing the neck is not long (bull moose, elephant). If the neck be long, it still may have no effect upon symmetrical gaits, but this is difficult to determine. The longest-necked ungulates are giraffe, camel, and llama (and its relatives). At speed the last two prefer a symmetrical gait, while the giraffe apparently never hurries by any other gait than the gallop. This difference may possibly be because a neck of intermediate length may be more difficult to manage in a gallop than one either short or very long, because of laws of flexure similar to those determining the fact that a short eel-like fish is not so well equipped for locomotion as either a long eel or fish of carangiform (fusiform) shape.

The fact that the period of oscillation is slowed in the case of a heavy head (inertia) or a long neck (longer pendulum) has a very definite effect on asymmetrical gaits (gallop) when these are employed. Both bull moose and caribou appear to dislike the gallop and to favor the trot. Motion pictures of caribou that I have studied indicate that occasionally, as when startled, they will break into a gallop of slow rhythm, at which time the head will be carried as high and as far back as can well be managed and with much less oscillation than is characteristic of most ungulates employing this gait. In other words, it seems that the head is too heavy for a rhythm in synchronism with that of the legs. This is not the case with the giraffe. It probably does not favor the trot because its legs are so long that undue interference would result. During the gallop habitually employed the period of oscillation of its long neck has a rhythm in harmony with that of its long legs, resulting in an easy and truly graceful action with a speed much greater than one would imagine.

Most of the statements already made regarding the vertebral column as a whole, center in the vertebrae of the trunk proper—thoracic plus lumbar series. In amphibians and reptiles the cervical are to be differentiated from the thoracic vertebrae only by the position of the scapula. The number of presacrals within the class Reptilia varies excessively, from 16 to 105. The more speedy kinds are not characterized by extreme body length. In birds the "thoracolumbar" vertebrae are reduced in number, to the excessive degree where some vultures have only 4, while the maximum is said (Owen) to be 9, in the apteryx.

In mammals the number of thoracolumbar vertebrae varies from 14 in some armadillos to 30 in the hyrax (Flower, 1876), but no trend can be accurately gauged. The reason for the latter statement is that there is no unvarying yardstick with which to compare trunk length. The length of the body may vary with the number of vertebrae or their individual length, and there is no definite trend to be noted in cursorial species. Probably there are at work other influences more potent than locomotion. The evidence of one's eyes indicates that in the small saltators there has been reduction in trunk length, but this does not hold good for the large kangaroos. Hares have an unusually long lumbar region, possibly for the accommodation of their particularly well-developed lumbar musculature and hind limbs. In cursorial mammals having very long, light legs, in which the body tends to act as an anchorage for the appendages, a short, compact trunk is doubtless an advantage, while in others, in which locomotion is aided by much bending of the trunk (weasels, cats), a rather long body should prove helpful. Correlated with these details is the fact that a long, limber neck or tail may in large part subserve the functions, during running, of a limber body.

The spinous processes are of much interest in indicating in general the stresses to which the vertebral column is subjected, but not, strictly speaking, of the strength of the back musculature. As a rule, the more anterior thoracic spines tend to slope caudally, particularly in those forms with heavy heads and accordingly with long spinous processes of the anterior thorax. These decrease in height in caudal sequence to a point in the extreme posterior thorax, at which point there is a change in slope and in character, since the processes are here much broader in sagittal dimension. Spines sloping in one direction connote a stress from the opposite direction, although a straight spine need not indicate a lack of stress or a different one but merely that it has been met in a different manner. The reversal in direction of slope shows that most of the thorax is mainly supported from a point over the anterior-limb center, and the posterior thorax and lumber region from the sacrum and the ilia.

The degree of spinal inclination varies greatly, and the position of the interclinal point to some extent. No hard-and-fast statements are possible, but on the whole the spinous processes of the earlier, more generalized mammals are neither greatly developed nor show a very pronounced slope. This assertion applies particularly to the kinds of primitive mammals with a conformation suggesting poor agility. Nimble carnivores, even of primitive organization, had thoracic spines sloping toward the posterior thoracic region from both directions, suggesting powerful dynamic control of the vertebral column from the centers of suspension. On the whole, it may be said that the anticlinal type of spinous-process arrangement is characteristic of rodents, carnivores, primates, and the more agile, as well as some of the heavier, ungulates but is usually absent in the more lethargic and the heavier, clumsier mammals, such as elephants and titanotheres. The character is not marked in any reptile that I have seen. The position at which the slope changes is usually the eleventh or twelfth thoracic vertebra (it is sometimes difficult to decide the precise spine involved). However, it is T14 in the hyena; T13 or T14 in the American bison, but T11 in muskox and yak; T15 in giraffe, but T13 in okapi. Thus it appears that the anticlinal position depends not so much on the degree or quality of agility as upon the position of the center of gravity of the body and that in those mammals with disproportionately heavy forequarters (and more anterior center of gravity) there is a tendency for the anticlinal center to move backward.

As already stated, ungulates with heavy heads are prone to have very high thoracic spines. This character is most pronounced in grazers that habitually hold the head very low and least so in browsers that hold the head high. The reason for this fact is clearly apparent, for the ligaments and muscles attached to high spines have a particularly favorable leverage when acting upon a low-hung head. Many of the earlier ungulates with heavy heads (amblypods, etc.) did not have high thoracic spines, and accordingly it seems likely that requisite strength was obtained by means of ligaments rather than muscles. Long spinous processes are more characteristic of artiodactyls than of perissodactyls, and this correlates with the fact that the ligamentum nuchae appears to be better developed in the former group. The length of the anterior thoracic spines is not pronounced in horse and rhinoceros or in deer, which hold the head high; but these spines are well developed in sheep, some antelopes, muskox, cattle, and particularly the bison, in which an extreme length of 18 inches may be attained. They may be 10 inches long in the camel, in which the base of the neck is much depressed, but are poorly developed in the giraffe. In most forms the first or second is the longest; but with unusual stress, requiring long spines, the center often moves a bit to the rear. Thus in the giraffe, T4 is the longest, although T1 is longest in the okapi.

In the small saltators the anterior thoracic spines are either undefined or poorly so, because the forelimbs do not function strongly for support and the mobility of the head is reduced. The height of the spines increases in caudal sequence, however, and they are relatively long in the lumbar region, as a result of the one-pier cantilever influence of their posture. The same statements apply, but in less pronounced degree, to kangaroos. In all saltators the lumbar (and anterior caudal) vertebrae are robust, with strongly developed lateral processes. The diapophyses are particularly strong and in the hare are practically as long as the spinous processes. Hatt (1932) has called attention to the fact that in saltatorial mammals the spinous processes of the lumbar vertebrae are slender, rather than broad, anteroposteriorly, as in most mammals, particularly ungulates.

It seems to be unsafe to offer any particular comments about the lateral processes of cursorial forms, for their details have group differences that cannot be correlated exactly with habits and because the back musculature is too complex for us to be able to analyze the strength of any particular component. It is merely possible to say that as a rule the more agile or swifter mammals have well-defined transverse processes.

The sacrum is here considered to constitute the fused vertebral complex to which articulate the ilia. As the bony pelvis basically was without attachment to the axial skeleton, the lowest number of vertebrae attached to the ilia was one, in primitive amphibians and in reptiles (cotylosaurs). Apodial and marine reptiles may have none, of course; but in limbed terrestrial kinds the number of sacrals varies from 1 or 2 to as many as 7 in therapsids and 9 in trachodonts (Williston, 1925). Certainly there is a tendency in reptiles for an increase in the strength of that part of the vertebral column (sacrum) standing the greatest locomotor strain in those forms tending toward bipedalism in greatest degree. Perhaps it is unwise to venture more than this generality, for many of the reptile groups progressed and regressed toward and away from bipedalism a number of times and their locomotor trends are almost impossible to follow.

The position of habitual vertebral curvature during rest is a question that cannot be considered in detail at present, for it could be properly covered only by x-rays of fresh specimens, a feat of obvious difficulty in the case of ungulates. There tends, however, to be a depression in the vertebral outline of quadrupeds in the posterior cervical region, most pronounced in camels and least so in giraffes, and usually at least a slight elevation in the thoracic region. The latter is likely to be most accentuated, and most posteriorly situated, in those mammals in which there is a marked lumbar and sacral slope or declivity. This last is a complex character. It is a feature of the heaviest of the graviportals, evidently in relation to efficient support, and of a number of rather light forms of moderate to good cursorial ability, such as hares, the Patagonian cavy, agoutis, and the smaller (and less speedy) ungulates, including mouse deer, and musk deer. In the graviportals the character is an accompaniment of the columnar posture of the hind limbs, while in the lighter cursorial types it is found in such forms as hold the leg acutely flexed and hence in readiness for abrupt extension and instant escape.

The center of gravity must be determined by placing the forefeet of an animal on one set of scales and its hind feet on another; hence it is not feasible to secure these data for many animals. It is probable that in a reptile of lizard-like conformation the weight over the hind limb exceeds that over the forelimb, because of the robust tail base. In quadrupedal mammals, however, the reverse is the case. Several figures that I have for the horse fall between Thompson's (1917) extremes of 54.8–57.6 per cent of the weight carried by the front feet and 42.4–45.2 per cent by the hind. Thompson also gave data for the Indian elephant of 58.2 and 41.8 per cent, respectively; for the bactrian camel, 67.3 and 32.7; and for the llama, 66.7 and 33.3 per cent. Members of the camel tribe are particularly lightly built in the rear. This character is marked in the bison, hyena, particularly in the giraffe, to some extent in heavy-antlered bulls of Artiodactyla, and in some mammals that for various reasons are particularly powerful in the forequarters, such as swine and burrowing mammals. It is a character that is certainly not cursorial, but some (Bison) that have it are surprisingly swift for their bulk and can whirl about with great celerity. Perhaps one should say that bulky forequarters should be a hindrance to high speed, but the handicap can be largely overcome in other ways.

In birds the number of vertebral elements entering into the formation of the sacrum has increased at the expense of the thoracic elements. Eleven is supposed to be the usual number in perching birds, increasing to 17 or more in the ostrich and as many as 20 in the moa Dinornis (Zittel, 1932), in which the legs were very massive. So a large sacrum may be said to be a cursorial attribute in birds.

In quadrupedal mammals the sacrum varies from a single element occasionally (as in Perameles) to as many as 13 in some armadillos

(Priodontes, Tolypeutes). The most usual number in this class is 3 or 4. It is difficult, if not impossible, to detect any sacral trend correlated with cursorial ability or with variation in weight. It is true that some ungulates have more sacrals than any rodent, carnivore, or primate, but some individual hippopotamuses have more (8) than any other ungulate, while elephants have no more than 5 (Flower, 1876).

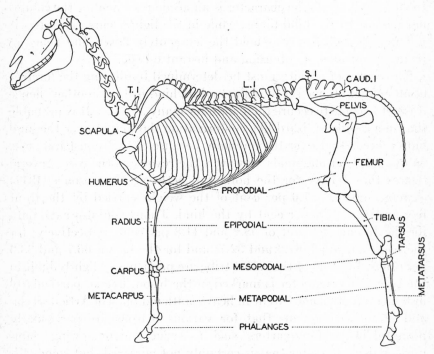

Fig. 11.—Skeleton of a horse. Redrawn from Sisson

The significant point here, of course, is not the number of vertebrae contributing to the sacral complex but the aggregate strength or weakness of the structure, and this depends more upon the ligaments than upon size of sacrum. Ligamental strength is a factor impossible to treat in a comparative manner.

By all odds the chief function of the tail in the generalized piscine ancestor of tetrapods was for swimming. It was merely the rather long, hinder end of the body, integral with the latter, irrespective of the position of the hind limbs. Thus it became a heritage, in turn, of the amphibian and of the reptilian line of ascent. In the reptile a tail of considerable length and mass is useful both for helping to curve the body from side to side in labored walking (and therefore it tends to be of a mass to conform to the rhythm best suited to the stride) but also as a balance. In mammals, with a mechanically better limb equipment for walking, it tends to be of less help in curving the body and of more aid in balancing, particularly in effecting adjustments in rapid alterations of the center of gravity. This statement, however, applies only to mammals of generalized habits or conformation. Actually, specializations have introduced factors that result in an enormous amount of variation in the length and size of the tail.

Long tails are characteristic of the swifter kinds of tetrapod reptiles and in those terrestrial forms with long necks. Heavy tails (long or massive) are usual in bipedal kinds. The largest, and therefore presumably rather clumsy, reptiles had very long tails; but, on the whole, it may be said that the shorter tails are found on the slower representatives of the order. Very exceptionally, as in the stump-tailed lizard (Tachysaurus), the tail may be almost lacking. It was very short in cotylosaurs and chelonians and rather short to medium in most synapsids, although some of the more lightly built theromorphs had very long tails. The member was also fairly short in some therapsids. Some of the largest dinosaurs with phenomenally long necks also had tails of extraordinary length, and there was probably some correlation in regard to these details.

Because some of the limb muscles arise directly from the tail in reptiles, this detail plays a more important part in locomotion than in the case of mammals. In swift, small lizards it acts as a rudder and in others largely as a counterbalance, particularly in those that are bipedal.

In birds the tail is of the utmost importance as a balancer, but this statement applies chiefly to the tail feathers. The shortened caudal series of vertebrae, usually composed of 9 elements, is of little interest to us here, except as its reduction in all forms appears to offer valuable evidence that the running birds (Palaeognathae) have been derived from an ancestor in common with flying birds. The truly cursorial (flightless) birds make no use of the tail while running but use the neck and, in extreme effort, the outstretched wings as equilibrators.

There appears to be but little doubt that the basic mammalian stock inherited from its reptilian ancestors a tail of considerable length and size, in proportion fully as long as, and even more robust than, in the opossum. Later, caudal variation was in all directions from this standard. Doubtless, some of the developments were haphazard, as there was a trend in some stocks for a longer, and in others for a shorter, tail. But on the whole, the factor determining the eventual length and weight of the tail was the use—preponderantly the locomotor use—to which it was put. Accordingly, caudal details may be predicted by habits. A small, light body is much more affected by a long tail waving in the air than is a large body. The mammal with a tail longer than the head and body almost always weighs but a few ounces or is arboreal (with a few exceptions, as the Manidae, which, however, can climb). If the small mammal has particular need of an equilibrator, as in climbing or in saltation, the tail will be particularly long and, if it is an inhabitant of open steppes, often with a conspicuous black and white terminal tuft of hair. If, however, the habits have become fossorial and most of the time is spent below ground, the tail will become very short. But the extreme reduction of tail, as in cavies, conies, and apes, is probably an inherent trend and not obviously correlated with function. A tail of moderate length could be no handicap to any mammal. If the mammal becomes bipedal, it should need a long balancer at one end. One possible trend is exhibited by birds, in which the tail was already short and a long neck is employed as an equilibrator in running. The opposite trend is shown by the kangaroo, in large specimens of which the tail is more powerful than in any living terrestrial mammal. But man probably lost his tail before becoming bipedal, and the hare's was drastically reduced to a useless stage before it became such an accomplished runner. Man balances upright and uses his arms as equilibrators, and the hare manages by making its gait as symmetrical as possible. It is likely that the early ancestors of the ungulates had a rather short neck and a rather robust and long tail. But the balancing apparatus needed by modern ungulates of cursorial habits is supplied by a long neck, or heavy head, or both. Other uses than in running, as in switching flies, may preclude the further reduction of the ungulate tail, but it is of practically no assistance in locomotion.

The number of caudal vertebrae varies from 1, in occasional gibbons and orang-utans, to 49 in exceptional scaly anteaters (Flower, 1876) and the length from 0 to almost 250 per cent of the head-body length in the saltator Salpingotus. It is difficult, however, to interpret the exact length. As Hatt (1932) has already pointed out for saltating rodents, an effective tail may be a long, slender, hairless member; a slightly shorter one uniformly well haired; a shorter one with a heavy terminal tuft; or a still shorter but more robust append-age. The effectiveness of the tail of a large mammal, even of the size of a large kangaroo, is unaffected by hairiness; and whether this member in an ungulate is patterned after that of a cow or that of a horse has nothing to do with locomotion. In saltators, effectiveness of the tail (length or hairiness or both) increases with the relative hind-foot length. In other words, the more highly specialized for leaping, as indicated by the foot, the longer the tail.

It is rather remarkable that the more highly adapted members of three diverse, saltatorial rodents in different parts of the world (Asia, North America, Africa) should exhibit a pattern of terminal tail tuft that is practically confined to them. These comprise some of the jerboas, the kangaroo rats, and the jumping "hare" (Pedetes). All tend to be buff-colored desert dwellers, with a black tail tuft tipped with pure white hairs.

The controlling musculature of the tail involves extensors dorsally, flexors ventrally, and abductors laterally. At the base of the tail these muscles are strong and fleshy and are to a large extent merely a caudal continuation of the trunk musculature. More distally, how-ever, the extensors and flexors are chiefly tendinous. The basal mus-culature is for controlling the tail as a whole, with violent swings in recovering balance or maintaining it in abrupt movements; the distal tendons are for those nice adjustments between individual vertebrae and contiguous groups of vertebrae involved in finer degrees of bal-ance. Accordingly, it is the rule, in mammals with long or medium-sized tail, for a variable number of the basal caudal vertebrae to be well formed, with prominent processes that decrease in caudal se-quence. In mammals with generalized habits these processes are frequently little, if any, shorter than those of the lumbar series; but in those kinds with a strong lumbar region, robust lumbar vertebrae, and heavy lumbar muscles the basal caudal vertebrae are relatively very much shorter. The number of these basal caudals is quite vari-able, and they are fairly abruptly superseded by the more typical caudals. There is a rapid diminution of processes and of the caliber of the spinal canal, and the vertebrae first become longer and more cylindrical, the canal disappears entirely, and the vertebrae then become more slender and shorter toward the tail tip. Throughout the length of the flexors of the tail, even at a level anterior to the anus, there is a ventral series of V-shaped bones. These, termed "chevron bones," straddle the ventral caudal vessels, and each articulates with the vertebrae at an intervertebral space. They are best developed in mammals with powerful caudal flexors, like kangaroos. Where the tail is weak, chevron bones are often indistinguishable, doubtless being unossified.

Ribs should not be regarded as process outgrowths from the vertebrae but rather as development *in situ* directly involving the intermuscular septa for the purpose of stiffening the parts of the body wall in which they occur. Their occurrence is variable in the lower vertebrates, but in these they are never confined to the "thoracic" region. In birds and mammals, particularly, the purpose of ribs is very clearly for providing a properly stiffened bellows box for respiration. In birds this bellows appears to function with great effectiveness, in a manner somewhat different from the plan in mammals. In the latter class the number of ribs varies from 9 pairs, in some toothed whales, to 22 in the hyrax and 24 in two-toed sloths (Choloepus). Neither ribs nor sternum, so far as known, reflect cursorial specialization.

Any variation in the form of the clavicle is of little or no interest here, but its presence or absence is a matter that should be noted. Clavicles are frequently said to be lacking in those mammals that use the forelimbs for support only, but the question is not so easily disposed of. The clavicle has two functions; it acts as a strut, to hold the shoulder away from the median plane, and it provides an anchorage for the parts of the deltoid, cleidomastoid, and trapezius muscles that occur in this situation. Hence it may be dispensed with in those mammals employing the forelimbs for support only, providing the muscles involved move elsewhere or fuse. Accordingly, it is rudimentary in carnivores and absent in ungulates. The clavicle is present in Monotremata, Marsupialia except one or two bandicoots (Perameles and possibly Choeropus), in Insectivora except Potomogale, in Dermoptera, Chiroptera, Primates, and Tubulidentata. It is present or absent in Edentata and Rodentia, incomplete in Lagomorpha, and vestigial in fissiped Carnivora. The clavicle is absent in pinniped Carnivora, Cetacea, Proboscidea, Hyracoidea, Sirenia, Perissodactyla, and Artiodactyla. Its absence perhaps permits a greater latitude of fore-and-aft movement of the shoulder joint, and hence this condition is a cursorial advantage.

CHAPTER VII

The Arm

IN THIS chapter will be discussed the skeleton of the pectoral appendage or anterior limb. Comparisons with the pelvic appendage will mostly be reserved for the chapter on that pair of appendages, while discussion of limb action and comparison of limb proportions will also be included in other chapters.

The pectoral and pelvic limbs can in nowise be considered as homologous, for they never were the same thing; but they are analogous. After all, they have similar structure and are used largely in the same way. In the earlier stages of evolution they both have tripartite girdles, the two halves anchored to each other in the ventral midline, one of the bony elements being dorsal and two ventral. Each has the same number of segments, with the same basic arrangement of bones in the corresponding segments, and both are fundamentally pentadactyl. The basic action is also the same, but one tends to develop as a mirror image of the other.

In adaptation to high speed the following developments are common to both pairs of limbs: a tendency toward restriction of limb movement to a single plane, with corresponding evolution of the controlling muscles and their attachments; lengthening and lightening, particularly distally, of the limbs; relative reduction in the length of the propodial (proximal segment of free limb), with relative increase of epipodial and metapodial length; reduction in the number of digits with the increase of speed; and change from a plantigrade to a digitigrade and then to an unguligrade (in some families) manner of progression.

The forelimb differs from the hind limb in the following essential features: The cartilaginous limb girdle develops at the base of an axial membranous girdle. This girdle is influenced by its position at the caudal end of the gill series and is affected by movements of the head and by the neighboring thorax. At first, it is anchored to the axial skeleton, but later it relinquishes this anchorage. The pectoral limb is, at first, the chief tractive apparatus, but later it is chiefly the supporting member. The limb becomes rotated, so that the manus turns forward like the pes, although the elbow is directed backward.

In discussing and interpreting the evolution of the limbs one must constantly bear in mind that they are not details that have developed, from their earliest inception to the present day, with the sole purpose of running over the plains with the greatest possible speed. Instead, they developed in tangential fashion, with specialization first in one direction and then in another, to conform with the environmental influences at the time experienced. The important point, apparently, is that changes in environment and in precise mode of limb utilization happened to be experienced by the ancestral stocks at just the proper stages of evolution, when the limbs had not as yet developed too far in any one direction to be plastic and readily molded by subsequent environmental factors. The present-day result, as seen in a horse or antelope, is not an ideal running machine but a mechanism that evolution has molded for speedy locomotion in as effective a fashion as the material permitted. The process, for purposes of illustration, might be compared to an aeronautical engineer directed to construct an airplane, not with the material he would desire, but only with what he might salvage and adapt from an oxcart, a bicycle, a buggy, and an automobile, each of them crude and imperfect at that.

For purposes of convenience the evolution of the limbs may, rather arbitrarily, be divided into seven stages, as illustrated by conditions in (1) Ordovician or Silurian ostracoderms; (2) Devonian crossopterygians or lobe-finned fishes; (3) Carboniferous stegocephalian amphibians, particularly of rhachitomous relationship; (4) Permian stem reptiles; (5) Triassic mammal-like therapsid reptiles; (6) early (Jurassic and Cretaceous) mammals of primitive organization; and (7) Recent cursorial and saltatorial mammals. These stages are selected merely in illustration of certain interesting phases through which the anterior limbs are believed to have passed, and there is abundant evidence in the fossil record that selected representatives of these stages are very close to the line of ascent.

There is a certain amount of doubt in connection with the ostracoderm phase. These bone-skinned "fishes" were the earliest known chordates. Some of them appear to have been without limbs, but others had anterior appendages that may or may not have been homologous with those of higher vertebrates. These were bottom-living creatures, as is indicated by the heterocercal form of the tail (see Howell, 1930), and the limbs were doubtless used not for free swimming but in helping the animal to wriggle over and between the inequalities of the bottom. In some of the fossils can be detected longitudinal rows of dermal scutes, evidently along the branchio-cloacal line.

Of interest in this connection are the acanthodians, a group of primitive placoderms. They may not have been on the direct line of ascent, but their fossil remains are better known than those of ostracoderms, and it is clearly indicated that in them there were five longitudinal zones critical for dermal development, each marked by lines of scutes or scales hypertrophied in varying degree. These comprise a single middorsal line, in reality continuous around the tail and along the mid-ventral line as far forward as the cloaca, and a pair of lines stretching from gills to cloaca. The same lines of hypertrophied scales can be seen in the living sturgeon. Some of the scales in these lines became still more developed in spikelike form, each, probably, with a connected membrane, forming a fin. In the midline these formed unpaired fins—the caudal, dorsal, and ventral fins. Along the branchiocloacal lines they formed the paired fins. The zone along the lateral-line organs appears not to have developed fins.

The development of the tail fin was determined by the logical function of this member as the primary locomotor organ, while the dorsal and ventral fins were developed to function as rudders, for keeping the body on an even keel when turning to right and left. It seems likely, however, that the stimulus for the appearance of the paired fins was more directly attributable to external stress and that the pectoral appendages appeared where there was greatest wear and tear while the animal wriggled over a rough bottom. They must have been first used for this purpose and only later as crutches or props when resting on the bottom, or still later as accessory equilibrators while swimming. It should be noted that the paired fins never act, oarlike, as primary locomotor organs in generalized fish or for speedy progression, but as equilibrators.

There is but little doubt that the initiation of the paired limbs at first involved tissue that to all intents was exclusively ectodermal. Thus surface scales changed form to become raylike, and this is the case with that part of the fins of living bony fishes or teleosts that is situated outside the body contour. Such structures, however, required controlling muscle slips, which passed to them from the trunk muscles, as is now found in the living sturgeon. As degree of movement increased, at first cartilage and then bone developed at the fin base.

As already indicated, living elasmobranchs or cartilaginous fish (sharks and their kin) and bony fish are so far off the line of ascent that no reliance can be placed on a study of their details.

The basic condition of the shoulder girdle seems to be illustrated in the Devonian crossopterygians, the arrangement in the genus Eusthenopteron being the best known. The general situation in these involves the membranous circle of bone continuous from the head around, behind, and beneath the gill series and the covering opercular apparatus. This comprised four elements: posttemporal articulating with the skull, supracleithrum, cleithrum, and clavicle. These, accordingly, are a part of the axial skeleton, and the series of the two sides were anchored to each other ventrally by means of the unpaired interclavicle. The pectoral fin was situated adjacent to this membranous girdle, and the basal-fin skeleton, as it gradually increased in size, was closely associated with, and soon became attached to, the membranous girdle. This basal-fin skeleton comprised a scapulocoracoid element of cartilaginous derivation. As air-breathing gained the ascendancy and the importance of the branchial apparatus for breathing decreased, coincident with the gradual adoption of terrestrial habits in the late piscine and early amphibian stages, the membranous girdle decreased. First, there was relinquishment of the attachment to the skull and disappearance of the posttemporal and later of the supracleithrum. As the membranous girdle decreased in size, there was relative enlargement of the cartilaginous girdle.

The free part of the pectoral appendage in lobe-fins is not composed solely of exoskeletal elements, as in living teleost fishes, but involves a fleshy pedicle containing bones and muscles. Little can be told of the basic plan from living fish, but there are two genera of

crossopts from the Upper Devonian—Eusthenopteron and Sauripterus—known by their skulls to have been close to the line giving
rise to the Amphibia, with a fin plan that could easily have evolved
into that characteristic of the tetrapod limb. The former genus illustrates the plan believed by Gregory (1935) to have been basic, while
that of Sauripterus seems to me (Howell 1935a) to hold more
promise.

Characteristic of both crossopterygian fin plans is that all the
basal bones are fairly small and the plan is asymmetrical. The humerus, although wide, is no longer than some of the carpal elements.
All bones were short, and all apparently had equal potentiality for
elongation.

One of the "forearm" bones was considerably longer than the
other. Romer and Byrne (1931) believed that the shorter was the
radius, and formerly I was of the same opinion; but Gregory and
Raven (1941) have carefully reviewed the exact posture of the known
fossils and are convinced that the longer bone was the radius. Their
arguments fit in well with logical theory. At any rate, it seems certain that the primitive limb plan was essentially asymmetrical and
that the alterations that took place were in the direction of symmetry and with transverse joints.

As previously remarked, the stegocephalians and, more particularly, the Rhachitomi comprise the group of amphibians believed to
have given rise to the reptiles. They had a shoulder girdle different
from other Amphibia and very suggestive of the earlier reptiles,
while the other groups of amphibians, including living urodeles
(salamanders) and anurans (frogs and toads), are not suggestive of
the same arrangement.

In the amphibian stage the shoulder girdle lost its connection with
the skull, and the posttemporal and then the supracleithrum disappeared. The cleithrum and the clavicle changed from the form of a
large plate, covering much of the scapulocoracoid, in the embolomerous stegocephalian Eogyrinus to a condition in which these
bones constituted but a narrow border along the cranial margin of
the scapulocoracoid in Eryops. All trace of the membranous girdle
has been lost in living urodeles, but the disappearance of the clavicle,
at least, is probably a result largely of degeneracy.

Of much significance is the character of the shoulder joint in these
rhachitomous amphibians, most of which were of considerable
weight. The glenoid cavity of the girdle was directed laterally, in-

dicating a humerus that was held out to the side and parallel with the ground. The articular surface curved in a manner described under Reptilia, whose later remains are better known.

In the typical rhachitomous amphibians the propodial and epipodial bones were very massive, as they had to be in sprawled position to raise the body off the ground. The humerus was tetrahedral and relatively short in comparison to its mass. The forearm bones were also robust, the distal radius very broad and the proximal part

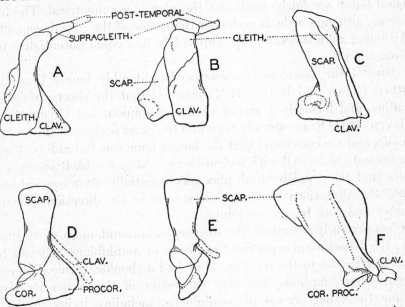

FIG. 12.—Phylogenesis of the pectoral girdle. *A*, Sauripterus (a Devonian crossopt lung fish); *B*, Eogyrinus (a Carboniferous embolomerous amphibian); *C*, Eryops (a Permian rhachitomous amphibian); *D*, Moschops (a Permian dinocephalian reptile); *E*, Cynognathus (a Triassic theriodont reptile); *F*, Macaca (an Old World Recent monkey).

heavy. The carpus, too, was heavy and the digits short. Throughout the history of the class there has been a reduction in the number of carpal bones, in the number of the manual digits, and in the phalanges.

It is difficult to feel sure regarding the precise basic plans of the carpal bones. Certainly, the primitive carpus was asymmetrical, and not of the symmetrical order of the turtles as postulated by Gegenbaur and others. Fusion or fission occurred very easily, as attested by the fossil record. There is reason to assume, however, that the general arrangement believed primitive for mammals also held, in the main, for both amphibians and reptiles.

It is generally believed that the basic amphibian condition involved five digits in the manus, although the point cannot be determined with accuracy from the imperfect state of the earlier fossils. However, all amphibians above the Embolomeri (Carboniferous and Lower Permian) have had no more than four functional digits in the manus, although what has been interpreted as a vestige of a fifth is frequently present. There has been much controversy over the question of whether the digits represented may not include an element lateral (a postminimus) or medial (a prepollex) to the regular series. But the arguments in favor of the thesis that any tetrapod has ever had more than five functional digits are not convincing, although a supernumerary horny or even fleshy spur upon the manus is known in all three classes of tetrapods. This frequently comprises a radial sesamoid bone.

The statement is often made that the primitive phalangeal formula is 2-3-4-5-4 (or 3). This may be so in regard to the manus of reptiles, but it appears to me that the evidence for the statement is inconclusive for amphibians.

In primitive posture the podial was lateral to the body, with the preaxial border receiving most of the stress incident to contact with the ground. This has resulted in reptiles in an increase in the length and the number of phalanges of the postaxial digits. But in this primitive position the manus is not held so much to the side as is the pes, and accordingly the stimulus for the lengthening of the postaxial digits may not have been so great. Be that as it may, there appears as yet to be no satisfactory evidence to indicate that the early amphibians had a phalangeal formula in the manus that was very much different from the 2-2-3-3 characteristic of most living urodeles.

In Amphibia the pectoral girdle is situated directly behind the head, so that the cervical vertebrae comprise but one, or possibly two, units. The mechanics of the more efficient locomotion of reptiles, however, appears to have demanded forward support not quite so near the anterior end of the body; and in this class the limbs, and consequently the pectoral girdle, have migrated posteriorly. Because of the presence of cervical ribs in Reptilia and the lack of a sternum in the more primitive types, it is not always easy to determine the actual number of cervical vertebrae in fossils or just where the pectoral girdle belonged. It is known, however, that within the class the girdle had migrated to a variable extent, with an extreme far transcending anything occurring in mammals, for some plesiosaurs had as many as seventy-six cervical vertebrae. In living reptiles, however, the position of the girdle in relation to the number of vertebral elements is about the same as in mammals, possibly with an average a bit further to the rear, for the axis of the brachial plexus varies from the fifth (as in Chamaeleo) to the ninth (as in some Crocodilia) cervical nerve, with the seventh or eighth as the average.

In Reptilia the cleithrum was lost during Triassic times, having been present only in some cotylosaurs and theromorphs. As is the case in mammals, the clavicle has been present in some kinds and absent in others (chiefly flying and swimming and, of course, limbless types). But it is lacking in crocodilians, also, and absent or vestigial in dinosaurs (Williston, 1925). Primitively, the clavicle lay against the cranial border of the cartilaginous girdle, and it was only later that its medial end diverged from the girdle in response to the same changes in forelimb posture that initiated the acromion, spine of the scapula, and suprascapular musculature.

In the earlier embolomerous amphibians the scapular girdle was simple and smaller than the membranous or clavicular girdle, but in the later rhachitomous kinds the former had increased at the expense of the latter. The broad blade had areas for the attachment of dorsal and ventral muscles, but characteristically the two areas were not clearly separated by suture.

It is usual to consider the reptilian shoulder girdle as consisting of three elements—scapula, procoracoid, and coracoid or metacoracoid. A more logical approach is to regard the primitive scapula as comprising a paraglenoid ossification for the attachment of associated muscles. This is the only "element" concerned. The muscles operate in natural groups, the stresses upon the bone varying with the strength and direction of pull. Accordingly, the latter varies widely with limb posture. Processes develop, and these may be marked off by sutures. In truly primitive reptiles the shoulder blade was broad, and there was usually one suture between the dorsal (scapula) and ventral (coracoid) parts. Frequently, another suture divided the latter into an anterior procoracoid and a posterior coracoid. These were not bony elements, however, but merely indications of two diverse stresses. If the latter were not of the proper sort, no sutures appeared, or if present they were often obliterated by advancing age.

It is unquestionable that there should also be recognized a fourth and very distinct area of the shoulder blade, sometimes termed the "suprascapula." This constitutes the more dorsal part of the scapular expansion and provides attachment for the serratus complex of musculature. It is usually cartilagenous, so that its extent is not indicated in fossils. In living anurans and urodeles and in lacertilians it is large and important, but it is smaller in crocodilians and not well developed in turtles.

The ventral area is without suture in crocodilians, chelonians, and at least most dinosaurs, but the first two, and undoubtedly the last, have both procoracoid and coracoid muscle units attached. In the primitive reptiles of the Permian this area was relatively broad; but the tendency in later kinds was for a reduction in its width, except that it is still broad in modern lizards, with their sprawling posture. The stimulus for the recession of the coracoids, so pronounced in mammal-like reptiles, was undoubtedly the change in posture, which was accompanied by a shift elsewhere (to interclavicle or sternum or scapula) of fibers of the procoracoid musculature and reduction in size of the coracoid-muscle origins.

The alteration in limb posture was reflected in the glenoid. In primitive amphibians it was directed laterally, and its articular surface was screw-shaped, denoting a labored arm movement. As the functioning became less clumsy and the arm was brought beneath the body, this shape was lost, and the glenoid tended to face more posteriorly as well as inferiorly. This alteration is well illustrated in the girdles of selected parieasaurs (Fig. 13).

Most reptiles, including fossils, and monotreme mammals have no scapular spine. In these the muscles now concerned with the spine (chiefly trapezius and a part of the deltoid) were attached along the cranial border of the scapular blade. The spine of mammals has been formed by the building-out, cranial to this point, of a shelf of bone to accommodate m. supraspinatus. The stimulus for this was a particular limb posture, and its initiation is indicated in fossils of a number of the Cotylosauria, especially in parieasaurs. Otherwise, it is clearly shown, in reptiles, only in dicynodonts and theriodonts (Therapsida), with their more mammal-like postures.

Monotremata have an essentially reptilian type of pectoral girdle, as their posture is more reptilian than mammalian. In other mammals, however, the girdle is little more than a scapula. The trend exhibited in the therapsids has been carried to completion: There is a high spine; all of the procoracoid musculature has shifted elsewhere, and there is no procoracoid discernible, unless the supraglenoid tubercle be a remnant; and the coracoid is reduced to the coracoid process, because both the group of muscles associated with it has shrunk and the origins of the remaining fibers have become cartilagenous and narrow, rather than diffuse and broad. All these changes have undoubtedly occurred in relation to the change of posture. The suprascapula "element" is present in all mammals, providing attachment for the serratus complex of muscles. It is usually entirely cartilagenous, but sometimes bony in part.

At first thought the shape of the mammalian scapula might seem to depend on the requirements of the suprascapular and infrascapular fossae and therefore on the size and strength of the two muscles concerned. Instead, the relative sizes of these two fossae appear to be

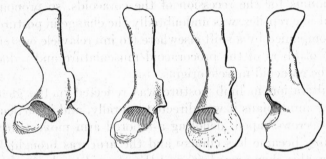

Fig. 13.—Parieasaur scapulocoracoids selected to show rotation of the glenoid cavity. Left to right; Embrithosaurus, Bradysaurus, Pariasaurus, and Pariasuchus. Redrawn from Watson.

determined chiefly by needed position of the spine of the scapula, while the shape and size of the entire blade reflect principally the requirements of the suprascapular musculature. The most important unit of these is the serratus anterior, the chief muscle supporting the anterior half of the body when a quadruped is standing. A heavy body needs a strong one; and the vertebral border of the scapula is very broad in graviportal mammals, while it is narrow in the lighter, more agile ungulates. A projecting, falciform glenovertebral angle, for strongly rotating the shoulder, also broadens the vertebral border.

Absence of the clavicle or reduction in strength of the muscles inserting upon the acromion reduces the definition of this process, and fusion of the local muscles to form a cephalohumeral allows shrinkage of the adjacent part of the scapular spine. The tendency is for the poor definition of both in the ungulates (less so in carnivores), culminating in the camels; and the character may be called a cursorial one.

An infraspinatus muscle sometimes does not nearly fill its fossa, or a supraspinatus may bulge over its proper bony confines. Hence the relative size of the fossa is no indication of the muscular power involved. At any rate, the supraspinous is smaller than the infraspinous fossa (as much as one-fifteenth the size in Tragulus) in almost all ungulates and dogs, the two are about equal in rhinos and cats, while the supraspinous is the larger in tapirs. In the present study I made an extended effort to correlate various scapular proportions with cursorial specialization, but without success. The influences evidently are too complex.

The rhachitomous amphibians and the cotylosaurs had ponderous humeri, hour-glass shaped but with flattened extremities in different planes. The distal part was more massive than the proximal, to increase the leverage of powerful forearm muscles. The proximal articular surface was long, narrow, and curved, indicating action in very circumscribed direction and extent. As the extinct reptiles, during their evolution, brought the elbow beneath the body and straightened the limb, the humerus became much lighter.

In reptiles the humeral head is on the end of the shaft, while there are two expansions at the proximal end opposite each other. In Iguana these constitute an anterior process, homologous with the mammalian greater tuberosity but with pectoral and deltoid influences, and a posterior process, equivalent to the lesser tuberosity of mammals. In the latter class this lesser tuberosity has migrated mediocranially.

Of some interest to us is the humeral torsion angle, which is the angle made by the two planes passing through the long axes of the two terminal articular surfaces of the bone. If it were properly interpretable, this index would be of great importance; but it may be very misleading from a functional viewpoint. In an ungulate, as, indeed, in most mammals, the action of both elbow and shoulder is in the sagittal plane. The torsional angle should therefore be 90°. Close scrutiny of the humeral head in a horse, for instance, demonstrates that this is so; but the articular surface extends sideways at one point so that the long axis of this surface is thereby distorted 22 per cent, and the torsion angle appears to be 112°. This is so, but to a lesser degree, in a number of other mammals examined. With the exception of some kinds with waddling gait, however, examination of articulated extremities of purely quadrupedal kinds has shown that the planes of action of the two joints just about coincide. Man and to a lesser extent the larger anthropoid apes are interesting in this respect. In man to a particular degree the throwing-back of the shoulders has spread the glenoids and caused the scapulae to point considerably to the side. Hence a line passing through the long axis of the head of the humerus in living man is not directed straight forward but somewhat laterally. Neither is a line through the distal axis directly transverse, but the joint faces inward to a large degree. Thus the two articular surfaces have gradually rotated in opposite directions, to the extent that the torsion angle in man varies from 134° in Australians to 164° in French and Swiss (Martin, 1928). This has been accomplished more by a gradual migration of the surfaces than by a twisting of the shaft. Most of what appears to be the latter is an illusion caused by the spiral course of n. radialis and to a lesser degree of the fibers of mm. brachialis and triceps brachii.

In the case of the generalized mammal, the head of the humerus is not in a line with the shaft but is somewhat offset. In the more ponderous graviportal mammals, such as the elephant, the head of the humerus tends to shift back to the end of the shaft, in correlation with the columnar plan of weight support. In mammals in which the arm is freely movable in all directions (characteristic of primates) the humeral head is essentially spherical; but as action tends to become restricted in a single plane, in cursorial modification, the head assumes more the form of a section of a cylinder, with axis transverse. In the graviportal type of body conformation, as exhibited by elephants and titanotheres, the tuberosities are raised and expanded above the head of the humerus, and the deltoid crest is in the middle of the shaft. In cursorial types the tendency is for lower tuberosities (although they are still high in heavy cursorial types, such as the horse) and for a more proximal deltoid crest. Primitive ungulates inherited a large entocondyle and a smaller ectocondyle (Gregory, in Osborn, 1929), while in modern cursorial types the two are practically equal but of slightly different conformation. In cursorial mammals there is a change in the distal articular surface of the humerus; it is flatter (less rounded) and of a somewhat different conformation, owing to the absence (in the more specialized kinds) of a coronoid process of the ulna and the change in the elbow articulation. The generalized condition involves a capitulum (for radial) and a trochlea (for ulnar) articular surface side by side. As action becomes restricted to one plane, these surfaces change, and the radial articulation expands across the whole distal humerus while the ulnar articulation retreats to the rear. In species with fused epipodials the radial articulation is still broader.

In the generalized condition the epipodials are unfused, the proximal part of the shaft of the radius is smaller than of the ulna, and the distal part of the shaft of the ulna is more slender than that of the radius. An olecranon is present as a distinct process, except in bats. It must be realized, however, that it is a long step from the generalized condition to one in which the epipodials are fused. The latter situation obtains only after—and long after—all rotation of the forearm has ceased. First, there must be a long period during which there is progressive reduction of rotation and progressive tightening of the ligaments to prevent rotation. Hence, increasing restriction of elbow movement to one plane is a cursorial adaptation; but actual fusion of the epipodials, even in minor degree, is characteristic either of a stock whose members have become very highly adapted in a cursorial direction or of one in which fusion has developed with unusual ease. In the latter category may be placed the agouti Dasyprocta, in which there is some fusion of the epipodials, although the animal is only slightly modified in a cursorial direction.

The radius and ulna are mostly unmodified in saltatorial mammals. In the elephant shrews, quite highly modified for speed, the bones are said to be fused distally in the five-fingered macroscelids but unfused in the four-fingered rhynchocyonids—the reverse of what one would expect. The latter group has the shorter limbs and is probably incapable of so high a speed. In the elephant shrews studied by me (Elephantulus and Cercoctenus) the bones are fused and the distal third of the ulna absent. The two bones are free in all carnivores but are quite slender in the more cursorial species. The radius is more slender than the ulna in some cats (European wild cat, cheetah) but not in others (leopard, lion). The two remain unfused as a rule in rodents, except the agoutis, although they are lengthened in the swifter kinds and the ulna is reduced to a mere thread in the Patagonian cavy. The relationship of radius and ulna is extremely close in the hare; and, although they should probably be considered as unfused, they appear to be immovably bound together. The fusion of the epipodials in the flying lemurs (Dermoptera) is, of course, not pertinent to the present discussion.

As in so many other details, it is the ungulates that furnish the most interesting information on the epipodials. Among the subungulates (hyraces, elephants), hyodonts (swine, peccaries, hippos), and less modified perissodactyls (rhinos, tapirs), it is the rule for the radius and ulna to remain unfused, at least until old age. In old hyraces and old tapirs and in peccaries there is fusion, and in the rhino the distal ends of the two bones interlock. The two are tightly bound together in all of these, however, and probably no rotation is permitted.

In ungulates other than those mentioned above there are various degrees of fusion of radius and ulna. The typical condition may be said to involve a large olecranon and a very slender but complete ulnar shaft, these occurring in musk deer, most antelopes, some

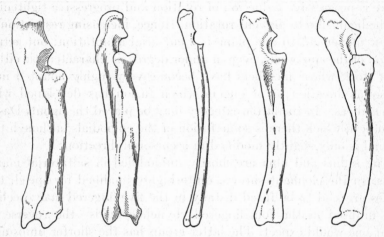

Fig. 14.—Degrees of reduction and suppression of the distal ulna in cursorial adaptation. Left to right, pig (Sus), mountain beaver (Aplodontia), Patagonian cavy (Dolichotis), goat (Capra), and horse (Equus).

deer, and some cattle. In musk deer and some true deer the distal part fuses with the radius; in caribou the shaft also fuses; and in some cattle, including the ox (Flower, 1876), fusion is complete. In the okapi the distal inch of the ulnar shaft has disappeared, in the giraffe the distal half, in the horse the distal quarter or more, and in the camel still more. Occasionally in horses and in asses, however, the ulna extends to the external facet of the radius. In all of them the olecranon remains large, as it must be to provide anchorage for the triceps brachii muscles.

As already mentioned, the cursorial tendency at the elbow is for the coronoid process of the ulna to disappear; for the articular surface of the ulna to move entirely to the rear of the radius, so that the articulations of the two with the humerus are fore and aft rather than side by side; and for the radial articulation to broaden transversely.

In the generalized mammal the articulation at the wrist is such as to throw very little strain upon the ulna, and the radius bears most of the weight. In rather rare and specialized instances, as in armadillos and elephants, this condition is reversed. As there is progressive decrease in the size of the distal ulna in cursorial adaptation, the radius broadens (or the wrist narrows) so as to occupy the entire width of the wrist. Accompanying this change is an alteration in the character of the radiocarpal articulation from an ellipsoidal or condyloid (modified ball-and-socket) character, allowing movement in several directions, to a ginglymus (hinge) joint, permitting movement in one plane only.

I repeat that it is difficult at present to be certain of the precise arrangement of the carpal (or tarsal) bones that was primitive for tetrapods. This is because the general plan was asymmetrical to a considerable degree and because there is a great amount of variation in the plans presented by the more primitive fossils, whose remains are often poorly preserved or fragmentary. At least, however, one can be sure of an idealized plan acceptable as a base from which mammalian carpal details may be studied. This is fairly symmetrical and involves a proximal row of elements comprising a radiale (scaphoid) and ulnare (cuneiform) upon the radial and ulnar sides, respectively, with an intermedium (lunar) between. A basic element appears to have been a centrale between the distal ends of radiale and intermedium. There are two or more of these in many reptiles. The second or distal row of carpal elements is composed of carpales 1 (trapezium), 2 (trapezoid), 3 (magnum), and 4 and 5. The two last are fused in mammals to form the unciform, or in some cases the fifth may be lacking. Radiale and intermedium also often fuse to form the scapholunar. In addition there are two sesamoids, one on the radial and the other on the ulnar side (pisiform), developed in the tendons of the flexor carpi radialis and flexor carpi ulnaris muscles respectively. The carpal differences between therapsid reptiles and mammals comprise (1) an intermedium that is situated between the radius and the ulna in the former and articulates with the radius in the latter and (2) the disappearance of more than one centrale and of the fifth carpale as separate elements in mammals. The trends of individual elements can hardly be detected. Scaphoid and lunar are fused in all Carnivora and separate in all ungulates, and both conditions are met in generalized mammals and those fitted for habits other than cursorial. (The carpal names that are placed in parentheses are the ones commonly employed in mammalian comparative anatomy, and their accompanying equivalents are for reptiles and amphibians.)

Much argument has resulted over the significance of the two carpal arrangements, the one having the bones largely in line longitudinally (the serial type) and the other alternating (the displaced type). In the former the magnum articulates mainly with the lunar (and centrale when present) or even with the cuneiform, but not with the scaphoid. In the alternating type the distal carpal row is displaced medially, and articulation of the magnum is mainly with the scaphoid. All surviving ungulates belong in the latter category, and it has been argued that this arrangement better resists any force tending to split the carpus. This contention seems very weak. Form of carpus may have much phylogenetic significance of a taxonomic nature, and undoubtedly functional significance as well, but probably to a definitely lesser extent than has often been claimed. However, it is certain that cursorial adaptation results in a more slender and more compact manus.

Mesopodial elements survive longer than their corresponding digits. Thus the only carpal unit lost by either perissodactyls or artiodactyls (the centrale is absent in all) is the trapezium, and that is present in the least-modified forms (tapir, rhino, hippo) and even occasionally as a vestige in the horse, some deer, and some antelopes. Among artiodactyls the trapezoid and magnum are fused in Tragulina and Pecora and separate in Suidae, Hippopotamidae, and Tylopoda; but it is doubted whether this point has much functional significance.

Fossil reptiles had various kinds of feet. In the heavier types the toes were often short and stubby and suggestive of those of graviportal mammals. In the primitive condition, as well as in living lacertilians, the sprawling posture was accompanied by toes of unequal length. As the number of phalanges increased from digit 1 to digit 4, so did toe length, and this inequality is particularly pronounced in lizards. Such a foot is fitted for projection sideways. If its axis be directed sagittally, it will be found not only that the toes are too long but that the joints do not match with one another.

The method by which these joints in reptiles were aligned and the digits shortened to conform to the mammalian plan is suggested in a number of the mammal-like theriodonts, in which there was excessive shortening, evidently on the way to elimination, of some of the phalanges (Fig. 15). Curiously enough, some of the armadillos, as illustrated, appear to be going through the same process in order that their digital skeleton may be adapted to their great development of claw and still allow them a length suitable for easy walking.

It is regarded as certain that the ancestral mammal was pentadactylate, and it seems highly probable that it was partly arboreal, to the extent that the first digit on manus and pes was to some extent opposable for grasping. This opposability has been retained for a

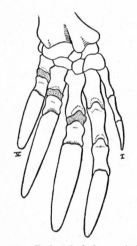 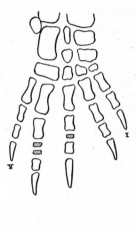

Fig. 15.—Reduced phalanges (*stippled*) in the right manus of (*right*) a Permian theriodont (Lycaenops) after Romer, and of (*left*) an armadillo (Dasypus). In both cases this reduction is for the purpose of providing a manus, held in the sagittal axis, with digits of a length suitable for locomotion.

very long time, to a variable degree, in mammals that still use the hand in grasping; and this function is more readily usable, as a tool in feeding and for other purposes, in the manus than in the pes. Hence it is more frequently lost by the pes than by the manus. Opposability of the first digit is also lost by those animals using the extremities purely for nonarboreal progression, and even of arboreal forms (such as sloths) when the thumbs are not used for grasping. As the pes plays a greater part in terrestrial progression than the manus, this is another reason why opposability is less frequently encountered in the hind limb than in the forelimb.

Whether because the pollex has fewer joints and tends to be shorter than the other digits or for some other reason (its medial position, different muscular equipment, or what not), it is the first to suffer in progressive digital reduction. Reduction in the number of digits appears to result from a definite stimulus, of which cursorial specialization is the most frequent; but it also occurs in arboreal, aquatic, and fossorial mammals.

The forelimb tends to be more conservative than the pelvic extremity, except for such specialized habits as involve only the former (like digging). It is usually used for grasping longer than is the hind limb, and it plays a less important part in locomotion. So it is slower to change and frequently, in cursorial mammals, has one more digit than the pes.

In cursorial adaptation there is change from a plantigrade to a digitigrade and finally to an unguligrade posture, with accompanying lengthening of the foot, usually the metacarpus. So the shortest digit is the first to be raised above the ground and therefore to lose its function as a digit. An exception to this rule—that in mammals with four digits in the manus it is the first that is absent—is found in the armadillos, in which digit 5 is at times so reduced as to be practically absent. The following is a summary of those mammals in which the pollex has been lost or reduced to the state where it may be regarded as vestigial.

Didelphia: Peramelidae (bandicoots) only.

Insectivora: The rhynchocyonid group of elephant shrews and Chrysochloris (the golden mole).

Primates: Colobus, Ateles (both highly arboreal).

Edentata: Sloths and, in varying degree, anteaters and armadillos.

Rodentia: Reduced chiefly in octodonts and cavies, but to varying degree also in many others.

Carnivora: Only in hyenas and the Cape hunting dog.

Cetacea: Absent in rorquals but reduced in some others.

Tubulidentata: Absent.

Hyracoidea: Vestigial.

Perissodactyla: Absent in all.

Artiodactyla: Absent in all.

Of these, additional digits have been suppressed, in complete or partial degree, in the following:

Didelphia: In bandicoots also digit 5, and even 4 (Choeropus).

Edentata: In sloths digit 5, and sometimes 4 also absent, and in the anteater Cyclothurus, the same three digits are represented by little more than metacarpals.

Perissodactyla: Digit 5 is also absent in rhinos, and all but digit 3 in living horses.

Artiodactyla: Digits 2 and 5 also vestigial or absent in all except Hyodonta (swine, hippos).

Of the above, only those will be discussed in which digital reduction accompanies cursorial habits.

Among the Didelphia, the Peramelidae have the manus functionally tridactyl (Thalacomys, Isoodon), with digit 2 slightly smaller than 3, 4 smaller than 2, and 1 and 5 reduced to useless nubbins. Cursorial adaptation has then reduced digit 4 still further (as in Perameles myosura), and finally (Choeropus) to the merest vestige,

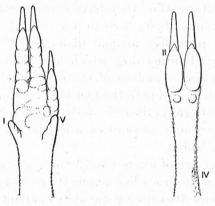

Fig. 16.—Specialization for cursorial habits in the bandicoot manus, after Wood Jones; Perameles to the left, and Choeropus to the right.

with digits 1 and 2 entirely suppressed. This last genus is thus artiodactylate in the manus, but with digits 2 and 3 involved, instead of digits 3 and 4 as in Artiodactyla. Other marsupials that one might expect to exhibit cursorial modification in reduction of the manual digits are Antechinomys and the thylacine or marsupial wolf, but neither of them does.

Among Insectivora the rhynchocyonid elephant shrews have the first digit represented by a vestige of the metacarpal. They are definitely cursorial or semisaltatorial, and yet their hind limbs are not so long, relatively, as those of the closely related macroscelid group, with five manual digits.

In Rodentia the first digit is reduced in many genera with diverse habits. Absence of the pollex, however, is characteristic only of some of the Hystricomorpha (Coendu, Lagostomus, Kerodon, Lagidium,

Dolichotis, Galea, Hydrochoerus, Ctenodactylus, Dinomys, and several others). Most of these are rather indifferent runners, with limbs lengthened to a very moderate degree, if at all. Some have the same number of digits on each limb, and not a few (Proechimys, Octodon, Capromys, Atherura, Hystrix) have four digits forward and five in the rear. The latter circumstance makes one suspect that digital reduction in this group may be the result of stimuli other than cursorial. Cavies, with four manual and three pedal digits, are cursorial, particularly Dolichotis. The less speedy kinds of these probably (because of digital specialization) are descended from swifter ancestors. In no rodent are the manual digits reduced to three.

It should be mentioned that, although hares are highly cursorial in habits and in conformation, they have experienced no reduction in the number of manual digits (four in pes).

All Carnivora have five manual digits except the hyenas and Lycaon, the Cape hunting dog, which have four. Hyenas are far from the most speedy members of the order, and this exceptional manual pattern may be due to the fact that they are relatively very heavy forward and light in the rear, so that the forelimbs are required to do a disproportionate amount of work, both in support and in propulsion of the body.

The Hyracoidea are of interest in the present connection, not because of their speed, for they live among the rocks and are indifferent runners, but because they are subungulate in affinities and have four manual and three pedal digits. Paleontology does not indicate that they had ancestors very much more gifted in running, so it is not unlikely that they, and other ungulate types as well, were particularly plastic to influences for digital reduction.

The Litopterna is the only extinct order of mammals that will be considered here. They were exclusively South American and in many respects paralleled perissodactyls, without having any basic relationship. They were essentially tridactyl, but in prototheres the lateral digits were reduced, in some cases probably to the extent of dew claws. One (Thoatherium), the size of a small dog, was more completely monodactyl than any other known mammal. The basic limb difference between it and the horse is that in the latter the reduction of the digits was accompanied by an adaptive readjustment of the carpal (and tarsal) articulations so that the mesopodials bore more completely on the dominant metapodial, while the litoptern was inadaptive in this respect and the lateral metapodials maintained their original mesopodial relationships. The significant consideration in this respect is that every single ungulate surviving to the present day is in the adaptive category. Also, in horses the metapodials are relatively considerably longer in relation to combined phalangeal length than in litopterns (Scott, 1937).

The name "ungulates" is employed for the orders Perissodactyla and Artiodactyla, the term meaning an animal with hooves and con-noting one that walks on its nails (unguligrade) rather than merely on its digits (digitigrade). The unguligrade condition is, of course, the highest type of cursorial adaptation; but among living ungulates the hippopotamus and the rhinoceros have not attained it, having a fibrous cushion at the back of the foot that bears the weight of the body, while the camels have secondarily retrogressed in this regard and no longer have hooves.

Perissodactyla today are greatly surpassed in numbers and in diversification by Artiodactyla, but during the Tertiary period the reverse was the case. The ordinal character that is of chief interest to us here is the manner in which the digits have experienced reduc-tion, in an odd-toed, mesaxonic, progressively tridactyl fashion, with digit 3 dominant, the toes bordering this symmetrical, not each in itself but in relation to each other and to the podial axis, and any digits in excess of three (the fourth toe, digit 5, in tapirs) asym-metrical.

Major groups of perissodactyls that have become extinct include the titanotheres or brontotheres, graviportal forms that achieved great size with four digits in the manus and three in the pes; chali-cotheres, amazing beasts, with forelimbs longer than the hind ones, with three digits bearing claws on each foot; and paleotheres, aber-rant equids with rather heavy legs bearing three digits each. Living families include tapirs, rhinos, and horses.

Tapirs are veritable living fossils, depending upon the protection of a forest habitat rather than upon speed. They have four toes in the manus and three in the pes and are the only perissodactyls since the Lower Oligocene to have four manual digits.

Living rhinos seem to be clumsy beasts, yet they have surprising agility and speed, and they appear to have descended from ancestral types with more of a cursorial build. Living forms have digits 2 and 4 lighter and slightly shorter than 3, and 5 represented by a vestige of the metacarpal. One extinct group, the hyracodonts, first with four and finally with three manual digits, were of light build and markedly cursorial.

From the wealth of fossils of horses almost every gradual stage in their development is illustrated, dating from the little Eohippus, with four manual digits and probably the vestige of another (the first). All Eocene horses are considered to have had four, and Oligocene three, manual digits, there having been progressive reduction, first, of digit 5 and increase in relative size of the central, with diminution in both length and thickness of the lateral digits. This was continued through the Miocene, the lateral toes then not reaching the ground, until in the Pliocene there occurred the first truly mono-

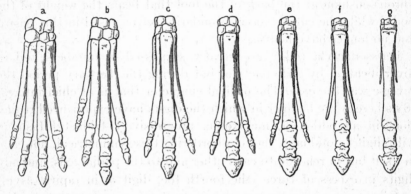

Fig. 17.—Evolution of the right manus of the horse, reduced to same size. *a*, Eohippus and, *b*, Orohippus, both Eocene; *c*, Mesohippus and, *d*, Miohippus, both Oligocene; *e*, Merychippus, Miocene; *f*, Pliohippus, Pliocene; and *g*, Equus. Redrawn from various sources.

dactyl horse (Pliohippus), but still with long, slender lateral metacarpals. It is singular, however, that a nodule representing the fifth metatarsal was retained until after the middle of Pliocene times. All these horses were lightly built, Plesippus of the Upper Pliocene being the first horse with truly equine, as opposed to antelopine, build, and its limbs were essentially like those of the modern animal. In the latter all signs of digit 5 have disappeared, as have the phalanges of digits 2 and 4, leaving merely splints of these metacarpals.

In Artiodactyla the digital reduction has progressed in a paraxonic, basically tetradactyl fashion with the axis of the podial between digits 3 and 4, these digits not being symmetrical each in itself but the pair being symmetrical in respect to the axial line. There have been many diverse sorts of artiodactyls, but the extinct forms exhibit no very important points of distinction in limb development, and we can here confine ourselves almost entirely to existing groups.

The most generalized condition of the digits in Artiodactyla occurred among the more primitive selenodonts and related oreodonts,
in which a well-developed, though short and nonfunctional, pollex occurred. In the early Tertiary period a functionally tetradactyl manus
was common, but among living forms this statement may be said to
be true only of the hippopotamus. In pigs, musk deer (Moschus), and
caribou (Rangifer), digits 2 and 5 are also better developed than in
any other living artiodactyl except the hippo but are not functional
except on soft ground. In other members of the order, digits 2 and 5
experience all degrees of reduction from the subfunctional condition
in swine to the total disappearance encountered in the pronghorn and

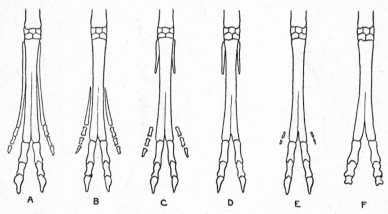

Fig. 18.—Semidiagrammatic plans of the manus occurring in Artiodactyla. *A*, Tragulus;
B, telemetacarpalis type; *C*, plesiometacarpalis type; *D*, Muntiacus and Elaphodus; *E*, sheep;
F, camel.

in camels. In the changes involved the functional metapodials in all
living members of the order broaden proximally so as to embrace the
carpal articulations originally concerned with the depauperate digits.
This modification Kowalevsky (1873) has called "adaptive," in contrast to the inadaptive method followed by some of the extinct
groups of artiodactyls, in which all metapodials retained their original carpal relationships.

The typical condition in the even-toed ungulates involves fusion of
the two dominant metapodials into a cannon bone, but with each element having a distinct distal trochlea, for articulation of the digits,
and a median bony septum between. This fusion does not occur in
the Hyodonta (swine, hippo) or in one genus (Dorcatherium) of Tragulina, but it does in the other (Tragulus), although in it a median
sulcus is marked. Also, where fusion occurs, the bony septum is par-

tially absorbed in a few kinds, just how many has not been determined, but the classic example usually cited is the yak (Bos grunniens).

In the antlered ruminants the lateral digits (2 and 5) are reduced below functional level (except partially in Moschus and Rangifer), but the precise degree is difficult to state for all, or even many, kinds because of the impossibility of personally examining them. Many years ago it was realized (Brooke, 1874) that it was possible to recognize groups of Cervidae according to the degree of development of the

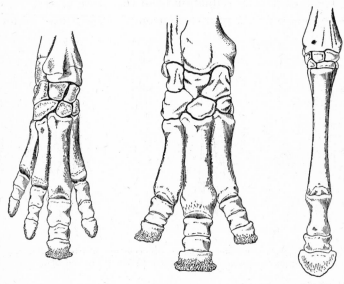

Fig. 19.—Bones of the right manus of Perissodactyla: tapir (Tapirus bairdi), rhinoceros (Rhinoceros), and horse (Equus). Redrawn from Flower.

lateral digits. In one group (1), which Brooke termed "Plesiometacarpalia," there are splintlike vestiges of the proximal (but not the distal) lateral metacarpals, and these are separated by a considerable space from their corresponding three phalanges, the proximal one of which is smaller than the other two. Into this group fall all the Old World deer that may be termed cervine (the genus Cervus in the broad sense) but including the American wapiti. In the second group (2), the Telemetacarpalia, there are splintlike vestiges of the distal (but not the proximal) lateral metacarpals, with their corresponding three phalanges, the proximal one of which is the largest. In this group fall the New World deer, as well as Alces, Rangifer, Hydropotes, and Capreolus. A third group (3), which Brooke included in

the Plesiometacarpalia, has the proximal ends of the lateral metacarpals, but neither the distal ends nor any vestige of the corresponding phalanges. In this group belong Muntiacus and the related Elaphodus.

It is difficult to see how these podial differences in the Cervidae
have any cursorial implication. Apparently, in the first two groups
the reduction of the lateral metacarpals was from either one end or
the other, without any connection with speed. The members of the

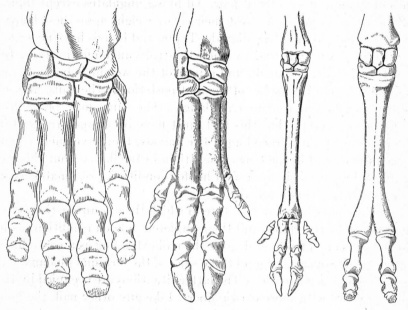

FIG. 20.—Bones of the right manus of Artiodactyla: hippo (Hippopotamus), pig (Sus), deer
(Cervus), and camel (Camelus). Redrawn from De Blainville and Flower.

third group are very small animals of the densest cover, but they may
be descended from a more highly cursorial ancestor.

In the Bovidae, including cattle, antelopes, sheep, and goats, cursorial adaptation has progressed further than in the deer. In the former, fusion of the central metapodials is complete, the distal ends of
the lateral metapodials are always absent, and there are never any
phalanges to these digits, although external remnants, in the nature
of dew claws, are present in all except a few antelopes (such as Aepyceros and, at times, Nanotragus, Tragelaphus, Cephalaphus). In addition, the proximal parts of the lateral metacarpals are usually absent or represented by a short piece of the fifth. The pronghorn, giraffes, and camels are still further advanced than the majority of

Bovidae, for they have lost all parts of the lateral digits. Lower Eocene camels still had four toes; in the Upper Eocene they had two toes and lateral splints. In the Oligocene the latter were reduced to nodules, which disappeared in the Miocene.

An ungulate is generally considered to be a mammal having a hoof or enlarged nail surrounding the distal phalanx of each functional toe. In perissodactyls the central hoof (digit 3) is symmetrical in itself, but in artiodactyls the two central hooves (3 and 4) are each asymmetrical but make a symmetrical pair. All living ungulates except tapirs, rhinos, hippos, and camels rest their entire weight upon these hooves and are thus said to be unguligrade. Tapirs and hippos have never become sufficiently cursorial to reach the truly unguligrade stage. Instead, their nails are small, and a part of the weight is borne by an elastic pad upon the "sole" of the foot posterior to the nails, inferior to the middle and proximal phalanges. The same may be said of rhinoceroses, except that this pad must have been much reduced in the more cursorial hyracodonts. The camels, too, have such a pad, more pronounced in the true camels than in the llamas; but this has developed retrogressively from a hoofed condition, presumably as an adaptation to a sandy terrain.

The difference between the state in which there is an elastic pad on the foot, as in the rhino, and the completely hoofed condition, as in the horse, is one merely of degree, the nail extending as an extremely dense, horny covering around three sides of the terminal phalanx, but not inferiorly or posteriorly. The latter situations are occupied by tissue less dense with more elastic fibers. Like any other nail, the hoof grows continuously from a proximal nail bed.

The size of the hoof and its angle with the ground vary much in ungulates. To a considerable extent the size of the area applied to the ground is indicative of cursorial adaptation—the smaller the foot, the greater the speed; but the matter is not so simple as this. For the purpose of adequately supporting weight, the area of the hoof probably varies as the cube of the mass; hence the area in a horse is disproportionately greater than in a small antelope. Size of hoof area is also dependent to a considerable extent on the character of the ground in the habitat most favored. A dweller of shifting sands tends to have a larger foot than an inhabitant of rocky terrain. Some of the swamp-dwelling antelopes have a hoof of almost ludicrous length, tending toward a "hoofed digitigrade" condition, while in some of the sheep, and notably the small antelopes of the African kopjes called "klipspringers" (Oreotragus), the digits are perfectly vertical, only the extreme distal end of the hoof is applied to the ground, and the animal appears as though standing on tiptoe. The latter condition is not to be considered as the extreme of cursorial adaptation, for such mammals are indifferent runners over a flat surface. Rather is it a specialization for rocky surroundings and for taking advantage of every slight irregularity along narrow ledges of cliffs—a situation in which anything but the smallest possible hoof would be at a disadvantage. So far as known, the forefoot of ungulates is always larger than the hind foot, in line with the former's function of chief support and the position of the center of gravity.

The degree to which it is possible for the digits to separate in artiodactyls reflects usual habits. In species living on hard ground each pair of toes is bound together by tough ligaments and joined by skin extending practically to the hooves. In inhabitants of softer ground the spreading of the toes, to supply the greatest possible supporting area, is an advantage; hence the ligaments are more lax, and the skin between the toes does not extend so far distally. This tendency culminates in the caribou (Rangifer) and musk deer (Moschus), in which animals the lateral digits are also unusually developed.

CHAPTER VIII

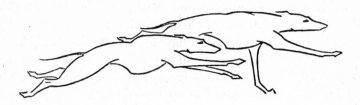

The Leg

I N MANY respects the pelvic limb resembles the pectoral extremity, and the arguments advanced for the latter apply to the former as well; but in many other ways they differ, for the two are only analogous rather than homologous.

In its evolution the hind limb differs from the forelimb in the following essential features: The girdle is initiated without connection with the axial skeleton but later becomes anchored to it; it is associated with the cloacal outlet and the base of the tail rather than with the gill series and the base of the neck; it is at first the chief supporting member but later becomes the chief propulsive apparatus; and the knee comes to be directed forward, rather than backward like the elbow.

The postural changes in the hind limb have been different from those of the pectoral appendage. As well as can be told from the fossil record, the habitual posture of the terrestrial amphibians and primitive reptiles was with knee directed laterally and foot also lateral, thus with the lower leg in the transverse plane. No living cold-blooded tetrapod assumes quite this position. In living urodeles and lizards the knee is directed laterally, but the lower leg points mostly to the rear.

It proved to be not very difficult for reptiles to bring the knee forward, so that the foot was beneath the body. All bipedal reptiles, including the ponderous dinosaurs that regressed to quadrupedalism, and undoubtedly the most advanced of the mammal-like reptiles accomplished this.

One cannot follow and compare the evolutional history of the hind limb step by step with that of the anterior member, for in the earlier stages the fossil record is incomplete. Thus the details of the initiation of the pelvic girdle are largely conjectural, although one may be fairly sure of the broader plan. The basic crossopterygian pelvis is not well known, and the early amphibian material is very unsatisfactory in this respect. The evidence, however, indicates that the pelvis began as a simple bar, sagittally disposed near the midline, with original dynamic association more particularly with muscles of the cloaca—excretional and reproductive—than with the free pelvic fin. This cloacal association may have been the cause, but at any rate the original plan appears to have involved a bone concerned with muscles exclusively ventral—an ischiopubic bar—rather than both dorsal and ventral (iliopubic) as was the case with the shoulder (scapulocoracoid). The femur appears to have articulated with the more dorsal border of this bar. At first there was no true ilium, the dorsal muscles of the limb arising from the fascia of the trunk, as they still do in some fish; but an iliac process soon developed, thrusting dorsally into the back musculature, so that it provided attachment for muscle slips of the back in one direction and of the tail in the other.

As in the shoulder, the critical point in the hip is the hip joint; hence the para-acetabular ossification is the important element in the hind-limb girdle (if not in supporting the cloaca), and the muscles anchoring the limb base and controlling movements of the upper segment have been so disposed as to favor the definition of bony processes in three directions. Two of these were either continuous (at first) or connected (later) along the midline, where there has occurred articulation with the antimeres of the opposite side. The third, the ilium, has a variable inclination. These bony "elements" are often separated from one another by sutures, marking points of changes in stresses. It is practically certain that the basic condition for reptiles involved association of the ischiopubic bar with the ventral muscle elements of the limb, while it is very likely that the only limb muscles at first attached to the ilium were those belonging to the dorsal (femoroperoneal) group. In the adaptive radiation that has occurred among reptiles, however, ilium, pubis, and ischium have assumed a great variety of forms; and from a study of recent species it is indicated that, because of differences in muscle functions, individual muscle slips have migrated from one element to another, so that in Recent reptiles the pelvic element from which a muscle arises is not invariably an indication of its group relationship (and innervation). In mammals, however, there has been a more orderly realignment, and with minor and slight exceptions the dorsal limb-muscles arise from the ilium, prozonal ventral muscles from pubis, and metazonal ventrals from ischium.

It seems likely that the inclination of the ilium was at first essentially vertical, but in response to the stimulus of the limb posture typical of reptiles, and doubtless influenced by attached back musculature, it developed a pronounced caudal process. When the knee and foot were brought more beneath the body in the mammal-like reptiles, a more anterior anchorage for the iliac muscles was required. The caudal process of this tended to decrease, while a cranial process developed (Fig. 21) at the expense of the former to attain the condition characteristic of mammals.

It is assumed that the ischiopubis was at first barlike and later developed a suture in a more or less vertical direction. Reptiles afford evidence that sometimes at least this suture was partly cleft by a ventral notch, which upon occasion migrated more dorsally, thus effecting a thyroid (shield-shaped) foramen in the plate of bone ventral to the acetabulum. At the same time it is likely that upon the anterior border of the pubis there was a notch, to accommodate the obturator nerve, comparable to the suprascapular notch in the shoulder girdle. Bone developed around this, transforming it into a pubic foramen of the sort seen in many early reptiles; and undoubtedly this and the thyroid foramen eventually merged to form the obturator foramen of mammals. Various stages in these suggested changes are exhibited by fossil reptiles.

The same influences that changed the inclination of the ilium into an anteriorly directed process caused a dorsocaudal migration of the ischium (and therefore the pubis) in order to provide a better retractive angle for the vertical femur.

But the foregoing is merely the hastiest of résumés of the probable trends from fish to mammals. In reptiles one should scrutinize conditions in the truly bipedal sorts.

Many bizarre pelves are found in some of the more varied reptilian types, but those of chief interest here seem to fall into three general categories: the platelike pelvis, of various shapes, basic for the most primitive of reptiles—the cotylosaurs—and found also in mammal-like reptiles; the diverging, triradiate pelvis of thecodonts, Crocodilia, saurischian dinosaurs, and, to some extent, living lacertilians; and the diverging tetraradiate pelvis of ornithischian dinosaurs and birds.

The archosaurs tended very strongly toward bipedalism, although some never attained it and others regressed to secondary quadrupedal habits. For this posture a strong pelvis was needed, and anchorage to more than the primitive two sacral vertebrae was the rule. Muscular strength was furnished by a flaring, triradiate type of pelvis rather than by a platelike type. This tendency is exhibited even in primitive thecodonts, which appear to have been ancestral to the dinosaurs. The ilium was also long and the acetabulum high.

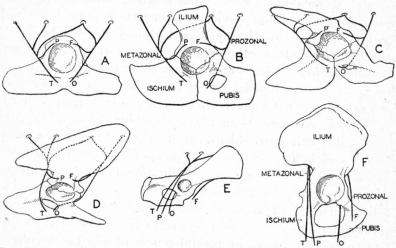

FIG. 21.—Morphological stages in the evolution of the pelvic girdle and of the four nerve groups of the lumbosacral plexus, right side. *A*, hypothetical basic stage; *B*, Galechirus (dromasaurian therapsid reptile); *C*, Iguana (Recent reptile); *D*, Cynognathus (theriodont reptile); *E*, dog; *F*, man. The nerve arrangement in the fossil forms is hypothetical. *A*, femoral, and *B*, obturator, elements of prozonal (lumbar) nerves; *C*, peroneal, and *D*, tibial, elements of metazonal (sacral) nerves.

A second group—the Crocodilia—is of interest because these are the only living archosaurs and because the pubis is excluded from the acetabulum. It has been argued (Williston, 1925) that this is merely a prepubic process similar to that of pterodactyls, while the true pubis is represented by the anterior process of the ischium. This contention, I feel sure, cannot lead to a logical conclusion, for it predisposes inflexible bony elements. Skeletal conditions can be properly interpreted only when one knows the identity of the attached muscles. The arrangement of the muscles of the hip in crocodilians is very different from that of lacertilians, and some of the muscle anchorages have shifted. Hence it is my opinion that, strictly speaking, neither ilium, pubis, nor ischium is quite the same in the two groups, and very likely they were still different in dinosaurs. But, although not strictly homologous, these three bony elements are entirely analogous, and for convenience—if for no other reason—the same names should be applied uniformly in the different groups.

Of the two chief kinds of dinosaurs—Saurischia and Ornithischia—the former have the triradiate pelvis of thecodont archosaurs. This group is secondarily divisible into theropods, which were carnivorous and highly bipedal with quite birdlike conformation, and sauropods, long-necked, ponderous, herbivorous reptiles, retrogressively quadrupedal from a condition previously more or less completely bipedal. Ornithischians are for the most part clumsy herbivorous reptiles (trachodonts and other orthopods, stegosaurs, ceratopsians) that had reverted to a four-footed posture, in whole or in part, from bipedalism. None were so bipedal, either in habits or in architecture, as theropods. They had a pelvis that is frequently termed "tetraradiate," its chief character being two long pubic processes, one diverging ventrally, as in saurischians, the other paralleling and in close relationship with the ischium. The postpubic process, however, at times is vestigial (ceratopsians), or the prepubic extension may be very poorly developed (ankylosaurs).

The significance of the pelvic differences between saurischian and ornithischian dinosaurs cannot be satisfactorily analyzed. Both are adaptive, and the reasons for the differences are chiefly muscular; but which muscles were involved can never be completely determined. Many attempts, presented in plausible form, have been made to reconstruct the musculature of fossil vertebrates. The most obvious, and usually the less important, muscles can be allocated; but it is totally impossible for even the most skilful myologist to reconstruct in satisfactory manner the musculature of a fossil, particularly reptilian, that differs importantly from a living representative available for study.

Birds show a tendency toward fusion of skeletal parts, and they need a strong pelvis. This detail is firmly anchored (except in the flightless penguins and great auk) to the part of the axial skeleton termed "synsacrum," composed usually of two or more of the posterior thoracic vertebrae, all the lumbars, the two true sacrals, and about one-half the caudals (Thomson, 1923). The pubis is directed largely posteriorly, paralleling the ischium, with which it may or may not fuse distally. Formerly it was thought that this character indicated that birds were directly descended from ornithischian dinosaurs, but at present this resemblance is ascribed to convergence. One of the reasons for this view is that in the embryonic development of birds the pubis changes from an anterior to a posterior inclination; but this in itself is no proof, for ornithischians may have done the same. This process never fuses with its fellow of the opposite side to form a symphysis in birds, except in the ostrich (and Archaeopteryx).

An anterior or "pectineal" process is usually lacking in birds, or else it is poorly defined, never reaching the development characteristic of ornithischian dinosaurs. Furthermore, it may not be precisely homologous throughout the class, for it is said to be a process of the ilium only in flying birds, of the pubis only in the ostrich, and of both elements in the kiwi (Thomson, 1923).

No fossils yet known serve adequately to bridge the pelvic conditions typical of therapsid reptiles and of mammals, although it seems perfectly apparent what these changes would involve, as already mentioned. The plan characteristic of mammals is an ilium directed cranially, instead of dorsally or caudally as is found in reptiles, an ischium that has migrated dorsally and is now directed caudally, and an inferior pubis, with the last two inclosing an obturator foramen and the pubes of the two sides meeting in the midline. As in reptiles, the three bony elements radiate from the acetabulum. Basically the ilioischial axis in mammals almost parallels the vertebral axis, but this varies with weight and habits.

The number and quality of stimuli operating upon the pelvis or innominate bone are so complicated that the proper interpretation of conditions is almost impossibly difficult. Hence, there are relatively few points about which a conservative investigator can feel much assurance. The pelvis, however, is obliged to be of such conformation as to permit the birth of the young, and this point has been of paramount importance in its evolution.

Slope of innominate axis in respect to average body axis (or ground surface in most quadrupeds) varies according to the vertebral curvature, or it may vary in regard to the sacral axis. In the former case the innominate axis is less horizontal in light-bodied animals, such as the musk deer, mouse deer (Tragulina), and agoutis, in which the lumbar curvature is extreme and the rump slope is pronounced. This appears to be in adaptational response to specialization of the back musculature for an unusual degree of extension from a rather flexed position, as an aid to sudden bounds. It is a posture that one would not expect to find in a heavy animal. An increase in a pelvis toward the vertical, in respect to the sacral axis, is probably a character not so strictly associated with graviportal conformation and locomotion, as stated by Osborn (1929), as with increasing weight. Graviportal mammals are heavy and so have this character. It is extreme in elephants and titanotheres, but it is almost as pronounced in the horse as the rhino, and more in the horse than the tapir.

Length of ilium depends not upon the power of the hip muscles but chiefly upon the requirements of the sacroiliac anchorage and the surrounding ligaments. A long ilium permits cushioning, by elastic ligaments and back musculature, of shocks and other stresses transmitted from the femur. Breadth of ilium is undoubtedly dependent partly upon ligamentous factors, which are hard to evaluate, and largely upon the part that this bone plays in anchoring the abdominal muscles. Influencing its shape is also the quality of control furnished by the iliacus and deep gluteal hip muscles—whether each muscle is narrow and confined to one direction (narrow ilium) or whether they are broad or need to pull from different directions (broad ilium).

Position and possible motility of the sacroiliac joint are undoubtedly of much importance, at least to certain animals; but their influences are almost impossible to analyze, chiefly because of the difficulty of interpreting the degree of limiting function of ligaments. Thus the diathroidal character of the sacroiliac joint is particularly marked in marsupials, allowing an unusual degree of movement, and the joint is pronouncedly far back in kangaroos and bandicoots (Elftman, 1929). On the other hand, this articulation occurs extremely far forward in some of the ungulates that are gifted leapers (such as goats). Undoubtedly its position is important and has much functional significance, but proper analysis is elusive.

In cross-section the primitive ilium has a triangular pattern. Medially there is the surface for sacral articulation, anterior to which is a part of the origin of the back musculature; dorsolaterally the gluteal fossa for the deeper gluteal muscles; and ventrolaterally the iliac fossa for the iliacus muscle. Broadening of the ilium usually is caused by the expansion and outward projection of the gluteoiliac line between these two fossae. A ventral iliac and a dorsolateral gluteal fossa are then both broad, adjacent surfaces of the iliac blade, while the sacral surface is narrow, as in man and those ungulates having a broad ilium. In such cases the angle between iliac and sacral surfaces is usually increased, so that the ilium loses much or all of its triangular conformation in cross-section.

Gregory (in Osborn, 1929) has declared that in graviportal mammals the ilium is short and spreading, its peduncle broad and short, the suprailiac border broad and continuously convex, and the tubera coxae and sacrale continuous; while in cursorial mammals the ilium is narrow and long, the peduncle narrow and long, and the tubera coxae and sacrale separated by a concave border. Length of ilium, as previously mentioned, is not a cursorial character, although a long ilium is frequently present in cursorial species. Titanotheres have longer ilia than horses. The forked form of ilium, with prominent tubera joined by a concave crest, is found in varying degree in most cursorial ungulates; but in itself it does not appear to be a good criterion of speed. True, the character does not occur in graviportals, but neither does it occur in camels, some of the extinct species of which had extreme length and slenderness of limb. Rather does it appear to me more closely linked with *manner* of locomotion. Thus it is not found in mammals that shuffle (graviportals) or in those that depend on the pace or trot; but it is more closely associated with habitual progression by a bounding type of gallop. Whether the stimulus is more particularly muscular or ligamentous is uncertain.

Prominence of the tuber sacrale depends upon the need of m. gluteus medius for a pull in one direction, and that direction high. The concave crest and narrow peduncle are a reflection of the comparative unimportance of the muscles—chiefly deep gluteal—that arise from parts of the ilium other than the tubers. Prominence of the tuber coxae is probably correlated chiefly with the requirements of local anchorage of the abdominal muscles, but also with the origins of mm. iliacus and tensor fasciae latae.

A long ischium means a favorable angle of leverage for the retractors of the thigh and crus, so it is a character to be expected in speedy mammals, both cursorial and saltatorial. Similarly, a prominent, high tuber ischii indicates powerful hamstring muscles. A projected ascending ramus of the ischium is indicative of unusual power in retraction of quadratus femoris and the deeper adductors (brevis and magnus) in varying degree, and at times of the presemimembranosus. This character is not strictly cursorial, but it is pronounced in some saltators.

The pubis, providing attachment for the adductor group of muscles, tends to be poorly developed (dorsoventrally) in those mammals in which adduction of the leg is of decreased importance—or, in other words, in forms in which the action of the limb tends to be confined in one plane. Thus a shallow pubis can be regarded as a cursorial attribute. It is probable that the extent of the symphysis pubis is without much interest here. The pubes do not meet in some mammals (such as bats, moles), or the symphysis is dissolved after the first pregnancy (cavies, pocket gophers); but all mammals of any weight need a good symphysis, and in ungulates it frequently is long.

Man is a biped with a unique pelvis, and, although neither cursorial nor saltatorial in a strict sense, his adaptations should receive some attention. His pelvis has been shortened (craniocaudally) and broadened. The ilium has expanded not only ventrally but dorsally (thereby accentuating the greater sciatic notch). The chief muscular stimuli concerned with the shortening of the ilium seem undoubtedly to be the proper anchorage in the erect posture of the abdominal muscles and the broadening and shortening of the gluteus medius complex; the iliacus is probably but little responsible. The position of the thigh in the upright posture has tended to reduce to zero the angle of leverage of the hamstring muscles—a quandary that the ischium has met by migrating dorsally, thus helping, but to a rather poor degree, the functioning of the hamstring muscles. As a result, the ilioischiatic angle (of the axes of these two elements) apparently is less than in any other mammal. The pubis tends to follow the ischium dorsally. These facts, coupled with the lumbar curvature, suggest that in man the pelvis is making some effort to revert to the quadrupedal position in respect to the thigh.

It is perhaps justifiable to say that in the generalized mammal the acetabulum faces directly laterally. In highly saltatorial (like kangaroos) and cursorial mammals the acetabulum tends to be directed downward, even exceeding 45°, apparently as an adaptation to the restriction of limb action to a single plane.

The general statements regarding the morphology of the crossopterygian stage of humerus and forearm bones are believed to apply to femur and lower leg, but less is known regarding the latter. An important point to consider is that in the pectoral fin of living fish the surface applied to the body is that controlled by the dorsal musculature, but by the ventral limb musculature in the case of the pelvic extremity; and it can only be assumed that the same situation occurred in crossopts. Hence, in order that the digits may point forward, there has been a rotation of the manus, through the antebrachium, that the pes has never experienced.

The primitive amphibian femur is not so well known as the humerus, but in main features the thigh bone in this class is not very different from that in primitive reptiles. In both groups it is somewhat longer and more slender than the corresponding humerus, lacking the pronouncedly tetrahedral character of the latter. The details of chief interest are the head, and the arrangement and identity of the processes or trochanters.

In a primitive tetrapod form the head of the humerus is at the proximal extremity of the shaft and is broader anteroposteriorly than it is deep, with an irregularly elliptical articular surface. In some reptiles, including many lacertilians, the articular surface is inclined slightly dorsal ("lateral") to the axis of the humeral shaft, as in monotremes, indicating a posture in which the knee is habitually held higher than the acetabulum. In this kind or in those with a terminal articular surface the thigh cannot be forced to a vertical position without disarticulation, and an elliptical head is an indication that thigh movement is pretty well confined to the horizontal plane. In mammal-like reptiles and in dinosaurs, however, there is a tendency for the femoral head to shift to the ventral (medial) side of the femoral axis, indicating a thigh held more vertically; but in no reptile is there a well-defined femoral neck.

I have been unable to draw any morphological conclusions from the straightness or degree of curvature of the femoral shaft. In mammals, at least, this character appears to be correlated not with posture (the claims anent man notwithstanding) but with other complicated dynamic influences.

In vertebrates the homology of the humeral tuberosities is readily determined. The question of the femoral trochanters has proved to be more of a problem, for three reasons: (1) because the muscles concerned have migrated from the positions that were primitive; (2) because many errors have been made in homologizing the muscles of reptiles with those of mammals; and (3) because an insertion will cause a process in one class and often no process in another in which the posture, and therefore the direction of pull of the muscles, is different. Thus tuberosities may be only partly homologous. The first two of these were considered, and some of the previous mistakes corrected, by Romer (1922, 1924), although he regarded the greater trochanter of mammals as a neomorph.

These trochanteric problems comprise the following (Howell, 1941): the identities of the external and internal trochanters of reptiles in respect to the greater and lesser trochanters of mammals; the identity of the "third trochanter"; and the identity of the "fourth trochanter." First, it seems advisable to stress the fact that the identity of such processes depends exclusively on which muscles have caused the process. At times muscle mass A will insert on a process and muscle mass B at its base, while in another kind of animal whose muscles have a different angle of leverage the opposite condition may occur. Still more frequently a compound muscle mass inserts on a process in a primitive form, and only one unit of that mass in a more specialized form. The question then is to what degree the two processes are homologous. There is much variation in conditions among different reptiles, and I make no attempt to analyze the trochanters of the various groups of fossil reptiles, feeling that the results could be nothing but unreliable.

In mammals the greater trochanter is located laterally, and it may be termed the "deep gluteal process," because the muscles of this group insert upon it, while the short muscles of the tibial group (gemelli, obturator internus, quadratus femoris) insert at its base. In some mammals the superficial gluteus inserts upon its distal part, but farther away in other kinds, causing a prolonged gluteal crest or even a pronounced process—the third trochanter. This occurs in a considerable number of Insectivora, terrestrial Edentata (not sloths), a great variety of Rodentia, in Lagomorpha, Tubulidentata, apparently Hyracoidea, and in Perissodactyla. In a number of forms not having this process the element itself is lacking, for in such case the muscle concerned does not insert upon the femur but passes to the lower leg, usually in fusion with m. biceps femoris. The lesser trochanter of mammals is situated medially and marks the insertion of iliacus and psoas major.

In the fowl there is a large lateral process upon the anterior part of which inserts the deep gluteal muscles and iliacus, and posteriorly the short tibial flexors and flexor iliofemoralis, which latter appears to be undeveloped in mammals. To the distal part of this process is attached the caudofemoralis; but in some birds (as in crocodilians and undoubtedly in dinosaurs) this muscle inserts still lower, and a distinct process is developed—the fourth trochanter. Birds have no true inner trochanter, although a part of the extensor puboischiofemoralis (probably the equivalent of the psoas major) inserts in this situation. So the large lateral trochanter of the fowl is essentially equivalent to mammalian greater trochanter plus a minor part (iliacus) of the mammalian lesser trochanter plus the element that in certain birds forms the fourth trochanter.

In the iguana, as representing reptiles, the large trochanter is situated internally. Upon it insert the short tibial-obturator sheet (flexor puboischiofemoralis = gemelli, obturator internus, quadratus femoris of mammals) and a part of the short prozonal extensors (seemingly psoas major), while associated with it, at the base of the process, is the short peroneal element (iliofemoralis = deep gluteals); hence, this process is largely comparable to the mammalian greater trochanter, but it also includes some of the stimulus that in that class forms the lesser trochanter. Only in some reptiles is there an external trochanter, but it is poorly defined at best. Upon it inserts the more lateral head of the extensor puboischiofemoralis. This appears to be the equivalent of the iliacus, separated from the rest of the short prozonal extensors by the origin of a vastus division. Hence, in spite of its situation, this process must be judged as the homologue of a part of the mammalian lesser trochanter.

The fourth trochanter is a process upon the caudoinferior (caudomedial in the avian position) aspect of the femoral shaft proximal to its middle that is present in some archosaurs, including Crocodilia, theropod and ornithischian dinosaurs, and some birds. Its definition varies from very poor to an extreme falciform process (Camptosaurus). In the alligator and birds (the only two living groups having it) it is clear that the reason for this process is chiefly the caudofemoralis (= coccygeofemoralis) muscle. Its definition appears to be an accompaniment of the bipedal posture, or at least of stocks that are partly bipedal. In the iguana there is no such process, the muscle inserting along the base of the internal trochanter. When the process occurs in mammals it is the so-called adductor tubercle, just proximal to the medial epicondyle of the femur, upon which inserts the presemimembranosus or, in man, the distal part of the adductor magnus.

The condition in monotremes merits mention in passing. Because of the posture, with knee held above the acetabulum, the femoral head is offset toward the gluteal, rather than the adductor, side, with trochanters anterior and posterior thereto.

A subspheroidal femoral head with constricted neck is characteristic of the majority of mammals. The articular surface is more spherical than in the case of the humerus, in spite of the fact that in the generalized condition the forelimb is probably more mobile than the hind limb. The latter assertion is pure supposition, and I know of no way in which it can be verified. If so, then the reason for the extent of the articular surface is probably that the acetabulum is immovable while the position of the glenoid may be altered. The spherical character of the head is reduced in some mammals in which the mobility of the limb is reduced, such as the ungulates and subungulates. Similarly, the head is not so greatly offset in graviportal as in most mammals and even in the heavier kinds of cursorial ungulates, like the horse. This character likewise is encountered in some other mammals with specialized habits, like the sloths. All mammals of interest to us here, except the elephant, have the depression in the femoral head for the ligamentum teres.

The greater trochanter is located just caudal of lateral to the femoral head. It has been stated that the former is higher than the head in mammals that can jump effectively and lower in others; but the situation is not so simple as this. True, it is high in ungulates and kangaroos; it is also lower in bears than in cats and dogs; but it is just as high in hyenas, is equal (with some variation) to the height of the head in the chimpanzee, higher in the gorilla, and lower in man. All that can be said is that a high greater trochanter denotes a powerful, efficient, deep gluteal group of muscles; and this is a characteristic of runners and leapers but is also found, for different purposes, in some other mammals.

The lesser trochanter is situated upon the laterocaudal aspect of the femoral shaft, at a level somewhat distal to the greater trochanter. It is well defined in most mammals; but in graviportals (elephant, titanotheres, rhinos) and some others of the heavier ungulates (tapir, horse, larger deer) the process tends to be poorly marked or even represented by a mere rugosity one-third of the way down the shaft.

The third trochanter, distal to the greater in a number of mammals, as already mentioned, has considerable phylogenetic, but little or no adaptive, significance, except possibly in the broader sense. Its extreme development, as in the rhino, is a reflection of very strong musculature in general rather than a disproportionately powerful superficial gluteal muscle.

The patellar groove and its marginal ridges appear to be unusually prominent and located particularly far from the condyles in mammals having need for markedly strong extensors of the crus—i.e., graviportal, cursorial, and saltatorial mammals. Also there is indication that in mammals of this sort having a patella (absent or rudimentary in marsupials), this bone is large and favorably placed, the whole extensor complex about the knee having high efficiency. But the differences are small in apparent degree, and a careful study, with roentgenograms, would be necessary for unqualified conclusions.

Osborn (1929) has remarked that the angulation of elbow and knee is greater in cursorial mammals than in graviportal types. Better is it to state that the free limbs tend to be straight in large mammals. As the metatarsals lengthen in cursorial forms, the knee retreats upward and is held at a relatively acute angle, as it is in smaller, more generalized species.

There are many different arrangements of the lower leg and ankle in reptiles, and reconstructions of fossils cannot always be accurate. The conditions of the epipodials in the higher amphibians and terrestrial reptiles of both primitive and higher (theromorph) organization seem to involve a tibia that was larger than the fibula, articulating proximally with both femoral condyles but chiefly with the preaxial one (particularly in bipedal reptiles) and distally with the astragalus only. The fibula articulated proximally only with the postaxial condyle and distally with both calcaneus and astragalus (Williston, 1925). In other words, the proximal tibia received most of the body weight, but this weight was transmitted to the ankle only through the distal fibula. The arrangement was inefficient and appears to have been a heritage from an amphibious life which it took some terrestrial reptiles an immense amount of time to alter. In reptilian bipedalism the tibia progressively took a greater part in weight-bearing at the ankle joint.

In birds the fibula is said to be incomplete distally, although its slender shaft extends for the full length of the lower leg in most water birds. In land birds the shaft is of varying length and fused with the tibia. Its proximal end has a definite articulation with the lateral condyle of the femur. The tibia is fused with the proximal row of tarsal bones and is regularly termed the "tibiotarsus." Typically, it has an anterior cnemial crest, for insertion of the quadriceps femoris, which largely takes the place of the patella of mammals. In diving birds this is projected into a long process above the knee, thus simulating at this joint the condition of the olecranon at the elbow.

In mammals the tibia bears all the weight applied by the thigh and alone transmits this weight to the ankle through the astragalus. The torsion angle of the tibia is of some interest. This is the angle formed by the long axes of the proximal and distal joint surfaces, but it can be determined only approximately. In the great majority of quadrupedal mammals, including primates other than man, this angle averages a minus quantity (although there is often much individual variation), for in them the knees "toe" out, while the foot toes forward or inward. This may be expressed as inward rotation of the distal tibia. In highly cursorial and saltatorial mammals there is a tendency for the torsion of the tibia to equal zero, for in them the goal is for all limb segments to function in a single plane. In man, however, the tendency is for the knee to toe forward and the foot outward, although there is an immense amount of individual variation. This is probably a rather recent development, concerned with the erect posture, for, as shown by Straus (1927) and others, the positiveness of the torsion angle increases greatly with growth, both fetal and postnatal.

The fibula is quite variable in development. It is excluded from articulation with the femur in all mammals but monotremes and some marsupials, and it applies no weight to the ankle in most mammals (artiodactyls and elephants being exceptions). The distal part is always present; the proximal part is frequently absent. The progressive tendency for the exclusion of the bone from the knee joint was regarded by Walmsley (1918) as associated with the reduction in rotation of the foot. This author considered that the condition of the fibula in mammals may be grouped into three categories, which may be termed the "usual," the "equid," and the "artiodactyl" conditions. In my opinion this is too restricted in implication, for there are all conditions of intermediacy.

In the generalized mammalian condition the fibula is entire and unfused with the tibia but is excluded from articulation with the femur by the spreading of the tibial head, while the distal end bears no weight, articulating only with the side of talus (not in marsupials) and forming the lateral malleolus (malleoli absent in monotremes). Progressive fibular changes then involve increasing slenderness of the bone and apposition of the distal part with the tibia, which progresses in degree (as in carnivores) to fusion or virtual fusion of the distal part in the more cursorial varieties (as dogs). But fusion and obliteration of the distal part of the shaft (with retention of the fused distal extremity) is frequent in many mammals, such as insectivores, many rodents, lagomorphs, as well as the tarsier. Some of these are now slow-going, and either these had more speedy ancestors, or the character was the result of different stimuli. In this type of arrangement the proximal fibular shaft is usually bowed out, to provide a large extent of interosseous membrane for the origin of muscles. Yet distal fusion does not occur in kangaroos, except reputedly in Hypsiprymnodon.

The equine type of fibula is characterized by Walmsley (1918) as having the proximal part styliform (giving rise to soleus and peroneal muscles), the distal part of the shaft usually absent and unrepresented by ligament, and the original distal extremity fused with the

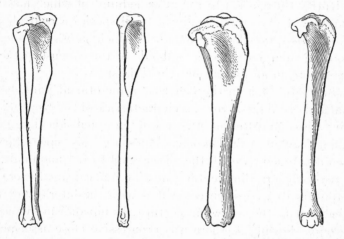

FIG. 22.—Lower leg bones, illustrating progressive reduction of fibula in specialization for speed. From left to right: racoon, with fibula free; elephant shrew Cercoctinus, with most of fibula fused with tibia; horse, fibula represented only by partly free proximal and fused distal extremity; goat, with fused proximal and free distal extremity.

tibia and not resting on the os calcis. These points vary with the degree of specialization and have developed gradually throughout the phylogenetic history of the horses and some other stocks in which they are present to a greater or less degree. In the type of fibula characteristic of most artiodactyls the proximal portion is a small spur of bone fused with the lateral condyle of the tibia, the shaft is absent but represented by a ligament, and the distal end is represented by an os malleolare, usually free but often in close contact with the tibia in highly cursorial forms. There are some kinds (like giraffes and mouse deer) variously intermediate between the equine and the artiodactyl types of fibular arrangement, and it is probably impossible to state which is the most efficient. They represent merely two manners in which different stocks have responded to cursorial stimuli. In short, reduction of the fibula is a character accompanying restriction of limb action to a single plane.

The tarsal bones consist of tibiale, intermedium, and fibulare proximally, five tarsalia distally, and a variable number (basically three or four) of centralia. As in the ground plan of the carpus, the arrangement appears to have been asymmetrical, with the ankle joint at first probably between the proximal and the distal tarsals, although Schaeffer (1941) thinks it was between tarsus and metatarsus.

In the reptile tarsus the proximal row consists of but two units, the exact identity (in relation to the intermedium) of which has caused much argument. There is usually in fossil species a centrale and a maximum of five tarsalia, the fourth of which shows a tendency in Synapsida to enlarge to form a "cuboid" at the expense of the fifth, which is absent in all forms since the Triassic.

Our chief interest is in the fact that a mesotarsal joint, between proximal and distal tarsal rows, is characteristic of the great majority of reptiles, fossil and Recent. It was only in Synapsida that a crurotarsal joint developed, first in pelycosaurs; and this type of tarsal action then continued through the Therapsida to the mammals.

In many early, crawling reptiles the talus and calcaneus were large, which appears to have been correlated with the lateral foot movements incident to the sprawling posture. As bipedalism increased in those groups showing it, there was progressive close association of talus with tibia and of calcaneus with fibula, but actual fusion was rare—in flying pterodactyls and stegosaurs—and therefore without definite cursorial interest. In most of the carnivorous theropods the talus had an ascending process applied to the anterior tibia, thus simulating the situation in birds. This process was lacking in sauropod and ornithischian dinosaurs.

Dinosaurs, as well as some other reptiles, show an unusual tendency for reduction of the tarsus. The centrale and tarsalia 1 and 5 are always absent, while tarsalia 2 and 3 are often fused. In ornithischians the tarsus (like the carpus) is much reduced, and in some forms, such as trachodonts, talus and calcaneus appear to be the only details remaining. In no reptile except the theriodont bauriamorphs is there a posterior calcaneal process forming a heel, such as is characteristic of mammals.

In birds, as in most reptiles, the ankle joint is between the proximal and the distal row of tarsals. But in birds the former is fused with the tibia, while the latter is fused with the metatarsals to form the tarsometatarsus. The elements present are somewhat problematical. During embryological development a separate fibulare element occurs distal to the fibula; but whether this is absorbed, together with the distal fibula, or whether it fuses with the other proximal tarsals has never been determined, so far as I know. It seems to be generally believed that intermedium, centrale, and tibiale fuse with the tibia, and tarsalia 2, 3, and 4 with the metatarsals.

In mammals the ankle joint is between the lower leg and the tarsus. The latter typically consists of seven bones. Proximally there is a medial astragalus or talus, this being the fused tibiale and intermedium, and a lateral calcaneus, representing the fibulare. The distal row comprises three cuneiforms representing the first three tarsalia, and the cuboid the fused fourth and fifth tarsalia, while between talus and cuneiforms is the navicular, the mammalian equivalent of the centrale. Why the fourth and fifth elements of the distal row should fuse in both manus and pes is a puzzle.

Particularly noteworthy are the changes typical of the Mammalia that have occurred in the two proximal bones because of the posture of the foot in this class. Instead of having the arrangement of the proximal row of carpals, the talus has largely overridden the calcaneus, so that the latter is more inferior (or posterior) to the talus than medial thereto. The talus has developed a roller articular surface that makes of the ankle a hinge joint in which tibia and talus are almost exclusively concerned. The calcaneus develops a posterior process, the tuber calcanei, for the insertion of the tendon of Achilles, which adds enormously to the effectiveness of the superficial flexors of the crus. It is a development that could occur only in a foot held at essentially a right angle to the crus and is therefore correlated with the mammalian posture. There are, of course, other changes in these bones brought about by the mammalian arrangement, but the above are the most important.

One of the most noteworthy tarsal specializations in the entire class consists of elongation of either the proximal or the distal row of bones, both being specializations for leaping. In the frog (Fig. 33), tibiale and fibulare are lengthened. Remarkably in Tarsius, to a lesser degree in Galago, and decreasingly in some of the lorises and some of the smaller lemurs, there has been elongation of both calcaneus and navicular (but not of talus), to a maximum of one-third the length of the femur. Why this tendency occurs uniquely in some of the primates is unknown, but clearly it is in response to a stimulus for elongation of the pes in a type of mammal that needs to use its digits, including metatarsus, for grasping small branches. The latter is an essential habit, the effectiveness of which would be destroyed by marked elongation of the metatarsus. This may be stated in another manner, thus: marked elongation of the pes may be expected to occur in the metatarsus only when the digits are not employed for grasping small limbs and probably not when the hallux is markedly opposable. If the latter be the case, the elongation might be expected to occur, if at all, in the tarsus.

Elongation of the distal row of tarsals, but to a very modest extent, occurs among living mammals in the Macroscelidae or elephant shrews. This is very probably correlated with elongation of the metatarsus. With this exception in Macroscelididae there are not many readily apparent tarsal changes in cursorial mammals. Naturally the relative proportions of the bones are affected through narrowing of the pes or suppression of the digits and consequent diminution of the corresponding tarsal details. Thus when the hallux is lost, cuneiform 1 may be vestigial or absent, the cuboid is reduced, and cuneiform 1 and 2 are fused in the horse. It is obvious that in cursorial and saltatorial mammals with elongated pes the motility of the individual tarsal bones must be lessened, in order to increase lateral stability. In kangaroos the cuboid is much developed, and the remaining distal tarsals are small. Osborn (1929) has pointed out also that the axis of the articular facet of the talus tends more toward the horizontal in graviportal, and more toward the vertical in cursorial, types. Thus in the former the body is pulled over a gentle, and in the latter over a steeper, rise.

In Perissodactyla the talus articulates more with the navicular than with the cuboid, and there is no articulation of the calcaneus with the fibula. In Artiodactyla the talus articulates equally with navicular and cuboid, and the calcaneus articulates with the fibula.

In Hyodonta all tarsal bones are unfused. All the remaining artiodactyls exhibit fusion of one or more of the tarsal elements, but it is difficult to make hard-and-fast statements in this regard. Sometimes there is progressive fusion with advancing age, varying individually; it is frequently difficult to decide whether units should be considered as fused or merely closely applied; and it has been impossible to investigate the actual condition in many genera. Accordingly, the following statements are tentative and subject to modification.

I have examined no artiodactyl having but two elements fused. Cuneiform 2 and 3 are fused, and cuboid is fused with the navicular (*B*, Fig. 23) typically in Tylopoda and in Pecora except Giraffidae and Muntiacus. Cuneiform 2 and 3, cuboid, and navicular are all fused in Tragulina and adult Muntiacus (and assertedly also in Pudua) (*C*); but the cuboid is free in some young individuals. Cuboid and navicular are fused, and all cuneiforms are fused in the two giraffes examined (*D*). And all distal elements are fused in the one okapi seen, so that in this animal the tarsus is composed of but three units. This condition is approached, if not sometimes actually attained, in Elaphodus. Also the unit composed of the fused cuneiforms 2 and 3 may at times join with the metatarsus in old age. So in even-toed ungulates there is a tendency toward consolidation and

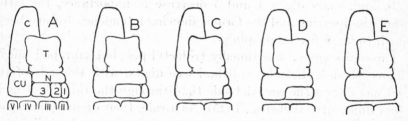

Fig. 23.—Scheme of the right tarsus in artiodactyls, illustrating the progressive fusion of elements. *A*, Hyodonta (Sus); *B*, typical Pecora, Tylopoda; *C*, Tragulina, Muntiacus; *D*, Giraffa; *E*, Okapi.

simplification of the distal tarsus, not actually related to cursorial specialization but probably in respect to the degree of restriction of ankle movement to a single plane and the amount of that movement.

The primitive pes, like the manus, undoubtedly was pentadactylate. In addition there seem to have been marginal carpal elements that have been interpreted as a prehallux and a postminimus; but there is no evidence that any tetrapod normally had more than five functional digits. It is probable that in length the digits had the following formula: $4 > 3 > 2 > 1 > 5$, as in most lacertilians. Thus there was progressive lengthening of the digits from the preaxial toward the postaxial margin of the pes, except for the fifth. Typically, the toes were long; but the fifth digit in many early forms, and in later ones with similar sprawling posture (including the lacertilians), was the shortest. It diverges more proximally and has a certain degree of opposability which makes it somewhat hallux-like. Something in the posture is probably responsible for this, but what it is I am unable to say.

There are so many differences in the pes of individual anamniotes that it is difficult to summarize, or interpret, all the interesting variations. The same statements apply to early reptiles. We may examine the conditions particularly in dinosaurs.

The types of terrestrial, reptilian pedal digits of interest in the present connection may be said to number three: (a) what may be called a generalized, plantigrade reptilian type, with the long unequal digits characteristic of the sprawling posture (as in lacertilians); (b) the type suggestive of the condition in graviportal ungulates, in which short, subequal digits support a lower leg held vertical to the ground, as in some of the heavier basic types, chelonians, and orthopods; and (c) the birdlike type, of the digitigrade, theropod sort, usually associated with an elongated tarsus.

In archosaurs digits 1 and 5 decrease in importance, the latter often disappearing and the former showing a tendency to turn backward, to be of use in grasping.

Dinosaurs have a functionally tridactyl pes; but sauropod saurischians (semiplantigrade) still had five digits, with the axis of the foot more upon the preaxial side than through the third digit as in other dinosaurs (Williston, 1925). As a rule, their digits were rather short, the more lateral ones less developed. In theropod saurischians, however, with their birdlike feet, digit 5 was reduced to a functionless vestige, and in many digit 1 was also shortened but offset at an angle, suggesting the condition characteristic of birds and of a consequent ability to grasp tree branches. Except in the lightest ornithischian dinosaurs the toes were short and held in a manner suggestive of graviportal mammals. They were functionally tetradactyl or tridactyl.

In summary, the first pedal digit to be lost in reptiles is the fifth; but four digits occur only in some dinosaurs and a few lizards and archosaurs; the first digit is lost only in a few dinosaurs.

In archosaurs the metatarsals at times were somewhat elongated, but not to a very definite extent in sauropods or in theropods, particularly the more quadrupedal kinds. In ornithischians, however, elongation of the metatarsals was very pronounced. The three functional units were closely adpressed, but rarely (as Ceratosaurus) actually fused. The central one of the three, however, was much reduced proximally, especially in the large carnivorous types (Romer, 1933).

The phalangeal formula for the pes that is believed to have been basic for reptiles is 2-3-4-5-4. In many of the sauropods the postaxial digits in both manus and pes were decadent and seem to have lacked claws, while the preaxial digits had large claws. In the other dinosaurs the digits were essentially symmetrical in length with respect to the third, although with the characteristic reptilian phalangeal formula. The latter condition was attained by the unequal longitudinal development of individual phalanges. This arrangement was also characteristic of the mammal-like reptiles, in which some of the phalanges were drastically shortened, although their number was reptilian. The ones affected were usually, if not always, the second phalanx of digit 3, and the second and third of digit 4. This fact is fundamental. Thus all digits could bend at the same places, which is essential to the proper functioning of a pes of a vertically held limb in

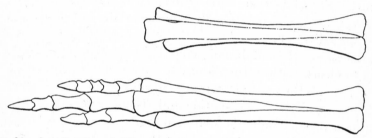

Fig. 24.—Anterior view of right metatarsals of chick (*above*), and metatarsals and foot of the extinct reptile Struthiomimus (*below*). Adapted from Heilmann.

which the toes are held close together, although it is not a requirement for the widely spread toes of the avian type.

In birds there are four metatarsals, at least in early ontogenetic stages. A fifth is always absent, and the first is reduced and unfused. The second, third, and fourth (third and fourth in ostrich) become fused into a slender complex before hatching, and this fuses with the distal row of tarsalia to form the tarsometatarsus unit. The disposition of the other digits is usually in a pattern with the first pointing to the rear and the other three arranged forward, the second and fourth symmetrical in respect to and shorter than the third, although the length is asymmetrical in many specialized kinds. The fourth toe, as well as the first, also points toward the rear in Cuculiformes (plantain eaters, cuckoos, anis), Piciformes (jacamars, barbets, honey guides, toucans, woodpeckers), and some Coraciiformes (motmots, hornbills), while all four toes point forward in swifts, goatsuckers, and colies. The reptilian phalangeal formula (2-3-4-5) obtains (except in swifts and goatsuckers, with four phalanges in the outermost digit). The first digit articulates at the level of the others in perching birds (for grasping), but higher in terrestrial and aquatic varieties. This toe is reduced to a functionless degree in not a few birds; but the only major group in which it is uniformly absent is in the ostrich-like birds (although it is present in kiwis). Rheas and cassowaries have only three toes, while the ostrich has but two—the third and fourth. In these massive running birds the foot is liberally padded with fibrous tissue, suggestive of the heel pad in graviportal mammals.

In mammals the digital condition, with a view to cursorial modification, is of interest in the following orders: Marsupialia, Insectivora, Primates, Rodentia, Lagomorpha, Carnivora, Hyracoidea, Litopterna (extinct), Perissodactyla, and Artiodactyla. Among the terrestrial Edentata the pes is exceptionally tetradactylate, but hardly for cursorial specialization.

Reduction of the number of pedal digits is probably chiefly influenced by disuse. Other stimuli may be involved in exceptional cases; but by all odds the most important factor is a tendency toward digitigrade (or unguligrade) locomotion and, usually, an elongation of the metatarsus. As a result, the marginal digits play a decreasingly important role and are elevated above the ground, followed in litopterns and horses by the suppression of the second and fourth digits, and in the more specialized artiodactyls of the second and fifth. Other disturbing factors may intrude, however, as illustrated by the case of the marsupials.

In marsupials the hallux when present is markedly opposable, indicating not only a basically arboreal ancestry for the group, as pointed out by Dollo, Bensley, and many others, but an arboreal ancestor sufficiently heavy to need to grasp small branches for support rather than of a size sufficiently light to run along the branches, like the placental tree shrews. The marsupial hallux, however, is reduced or absent in many forms. Among the didactylates the phascogaline pouched mice show a reduction and retreat of the hallux, as the foot increases in length, to a vestigial condition in many forms and final disappearance in Antechinomys. And in dasyurine forms there is disappearance (sometimes vestigial) of the hallux in Dasyurus, the Tasmanian devil Sacophilus, and Thylacinus (a node of metatarsal 1 remaining). The reduction of the hallux in these diprotodonts is entirely comparable to that usually obtaining in placentals. In syndactylate marsupials, however, reduction of the digits in bandicoots (Peramelidae) and kangaroos follows a unique plan.

Syndactyly in marsupials involves extension of the interdigital membrane between the second and third digit as far as the terminal phalanx. Some of the muscles and tendons of these two digits show a tendency to fuse and to act in unison, so that one cannot be used without the other. In effect the complex acts as a single digit with twin claws (Jones, 1923). These claws are used to comb the fur, and hence it has been claimed (*ibid.*) that syndactyly has been developed for this purpose. This appears to be extremely unlikely. The condition is frequent in gibbons and usual in one group (Symphalangus), involving the same two digits, but for a variable distance. In addition, it is not infrequently reported in man—the tendency being hereditable—with syndactyly of the second and third pedal digits sometimes alternating with syndactyly of the third and fourth manual digit in curious fashion (Straus, 1926). The latter author regarded syndactyly as probably an arrested embryonic development. Although adaptation cannot be ruled out as a factor, it is possible that it is a mutant character that has appeared in stocks of those mammals that exhibit it, without regard to any function to which it may subsequently have been put.

Occasionally (Phascolomys) each of the syndactylous digits is practically as large as the third, but it is more usual (as in Phascolarctos) in nonspeedy kinds for both together to be as large as the third. In those developed at all for speed, however, the syndactylous pair is much shorter than the third and about the length of the fifth, so that functionally the foot is tridactyl, the central toe being considerably longer than the marginal units. The lateral toes become progressively shorter as the foot lengthens in respect to its breadth, until finally, in bandicoots but not in kangaroos, it becomes functionally monodactyl (Choeropus). Reduction and disappearance of the first digit seem to take place in approximately comparable stages of pedal development in both groups. Mention should be made of the case of the tree kangaroos, in which the foot has increased much in width as an accompaniment of their having taken to an arboreal habitat.

In explanation of the fact that in speedy marsupials the fourth is the dominant digit, but the third in perissodactyls, Dollo (1899) called attention to the circumstance that the former is derived from

an arboreal type already specialized for grasping, while the latter had
an ancestor with a nonprehensile type of pes.

In kangaroos the pes is much compressed laterally, particularly
proximally, so that the bases of metatarsals 2 and 3 lie beneath metatarsal 4, as pointed out by Flower (1876), and the proximal part of
metatarsal 5 is very much broader in vertical than in horizontal section. The skeletons of digits 2 and 3, although perfect, are phenomenally slender throughout, to a much greater extent combined than is
the case of the fifth digit alone. In extreme specialization in bandicoots, however, the fifth digit is not markedly larger than either the
second or the third; but that animal is to all intents monodactyl, as
already mentioned.

Among placentals the earlier stages of digital reduction in the pes
follows a rather uniform pattern. There is a tendency to "toe" directly forward, so that, as the pes begins to lengthen in response to
cursorial stimuli, the central toe or pair of toes pushes forward to become dominant. The hallux, left behind, diminishes both functionally and in size until it disappears, a vestige of its metatarsal usually
being the last to go, although occasionally a dew claw (as in dogs)
may persist. If the phylum has a perissodactylate tendency, the
fifth is the next toe to recede, followed in extreme cases by the second and fourth together (as in the horse); but if it is artiodactylate in
propensity, then the second and fifth recede together. Only such
mammals as are exceptional to the above plan in some respect will
now be discussed in detail.

Among Insectivora the elephant shrews (Macroscelidae) exhibit
elongation of the pes, as an adaptation for speed; and most of them,
but not all, lack the hallux.

In Primates the adaptations for leaping shown by Tarsius comprise chiefly the elongation of the calcaneus and navicular, as discussed in chapter ix. The only other primate of interest in this connection is man. Although not truly specialized for either running or leaping, the elongation of his legs for bipedal activity simulates such
specialization to a considerable degree, and his foot has followed a
unique course of evolution, differing from that of the great apes.

As a result of his posture, man's knees are held closer together
than in other primates. This amounts to inward rotation of the leg,
and in compensation man's tibiotalus articulation is, in effect, rotated outward. In other words, if the transverse axis of the superior
tibial articular surface in man and in a monkey such as the macaque

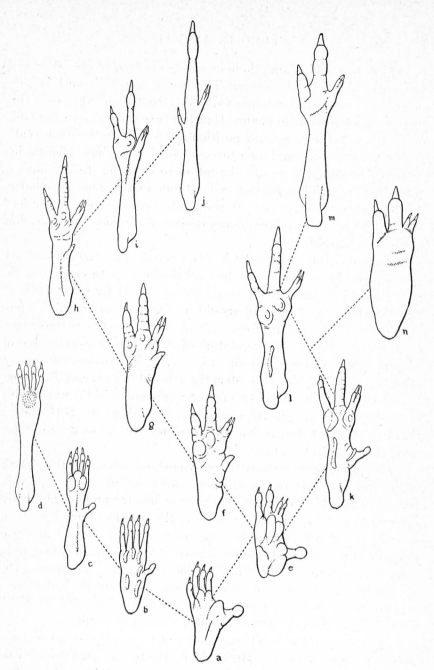

Fig. 25.—Phylogeny of the marsupial foot structure from a pentadactyl, arboreal, basic type *a:* *b–d*, saltatorial development in the didactylous stock; *e–j*, the syndactylous bandicoot group; *k–m*, the syndactylous kangaroo group, with a secondarily arboreal, tree-kangaroo branch *n*. Redrawn mostly from Bensley. *a*, Metachirus; *b*, Phascogale; *c*, Sminthopsis; *d*, Antechinomys; *e*, Pseudochirus; *f*, Perameles cockerelli; *g*, P. raffrayana; *h*, P. bougainvillei; *i*, Thylacomys; *j*, Choeropus; *k*, Hypsiprymnodon; *l*, Potorous; *m*, Macropus; *n*, Dendrolagus.

be held in the same plane, the foot will toe inward in the latter and usually outward in the former. The word "usually" must be employed because of the extreme variability that man exhibits in this feature. Another human change that has taken place, seen in man's ontogeny, is in the transverse position of his foot. In the fetal condition of both monkey and man the sole of the foot is held slightly inverted ("supinated"), as an adaptation to climbing. In the human adult this is much less pronounced, although one cannot say that it has been entirely overcome. At rest, as in bed, the soles of the feet are a bit inverted, and a far greater degree of inversion than eversion of the foot is possible.

From a locomotor viewpoint it seems certain that the norm of action for hip, knee, ankle, and toes all should pass through a single plane. In other words, the knee should swing strictly in the sagittal plane, and the knee and foot should toe exactly forward. But a few people direct the knee anterolaterally, probably because of imbalance of the outward and inward rotators of the hip; many people toe in with the foot; and the majority toe out. In locomotion the former condition is preferable. This alters the axis of the foot, and it appears to be influenced chiefly by two factors: differences in the ankle joint in the horizontal and in the coronal (or frontal) plane. If the latter tilts in the inverted direction, the tendency will be to toe in; if toward eversion, to toe out.

Although some mammals (as graviportals) have an arched foot supported by a pad of elastic tissue, man appears to be the only mammal with his particular character of plantar arches. These are three: a transverse arch, at the level of the tarsometatarsal joints; a lateral longitudinal arch, from calcaneus through cuboid and two lateral metatarsals; and a more important medial longitudinal arch, from calcaneus through the three medial metatarsals. The axes of the longitudinal arches vary individually and with posture, but at rest the foot tends to have a triangular base, with the heel and the distal metatarsal of the first and of the fifth as the three apices.

In progression, the functional length of the foot tends to be from heel to distal metatarsus. Mechanically the toes in man are of little consequence, except as they are necessary for anchorage of muscles. It is obvious that long toes would be a handicap to the human manner of walking, and man and Gorilla have relatively the shortest toes of any primate. And they are the only forms in which the hallux is almost (or quite) as long as the neighboring digits. Schultz (1926) has

given figures showing that in a comparison of the fetal with the adult
condition the howling monkey (Alouatta) exhibits relatively great
elongation of the four lateral digits and a practically arrested development of the great toe as compared with the rest of the foot, but
that in man (and presumably in Gorilla) there is arrested development of the four lateral toes and slight increase of the hallux. Thus in
man the hallux is relatively large and long, the other digits short, the
foot narrower, and the tarsus longer, as compared with the general
primate condition.

The question of the relative length of the first and second digits in
man (hallux usually longest in whites, second toe in Negros) is of no
functional significance, but relative length of the metatarsals is. In
plantigrade mammals that toe directly forward, the pattern of the
distal termination of the metatarsals is in the form of a curve, with
convexity forward. If the functional stresses of the foot are symmetrical, so will this metatarsal curve be, with the most anterior point of
the latter where the line of stress crosses it. Thus in dogs and cats the
curve is regular, with anterior point of the curve following the termination of the equal third and fourth metatarsals and curving back to
the shorter second and fifth metatarsals. The line of stress is in the
interspace between digits 3 and 4. In the tapir the stress passes
through the dominant metatarsal—the third—curving back to the
shorter second and fourth units. In the bears, however, the foot toes
in, the line of stress passes to the lateral side, the force is asymmetrical, and the more lateral metatarsals functionally dominant, with
the fifth tending to be longest. The fourth is longest in some other
plantigrade carnivores.

Man, however, usually toes out, or such appears to be the average
condition, although the character is not yet uniform and hence probably still unstable. The line of stress is displaced toward the medial
side of the foot, the fifth toe is regressive and in process of retreat,
and the result is a tendency toward functional tetradactyly. In the
latter situation metatarsals 2 and 3 should be longest and of equal
length, and 1 and 4 shorter and of equal length. But the fact that he
toes out and that the hallux is dominant, both in form and in function, throws the stress still farther medially. The average line of
stress thus tends to pass through the second toe, with metatarsal 2
longest, 1 and 3 shorter but of equal length, and 4 shorter still. The
variability in the postural angle of the foot and in the horizontal
angle of the tibiotalus articulation has caused much variability in

these details. Such evidence as is available indicates that there is little difference in this character between the lowest and the highest races of man.

It has been claimed by Morton (1935) that a first metatarsal shorter than the second and third is a structural defect predisposing to foot ailments. This is not in accordance with general orthopedic belief. True, an unusually short first metatarsal might be troublesome as a result of wearing particularly high heels; but at man's

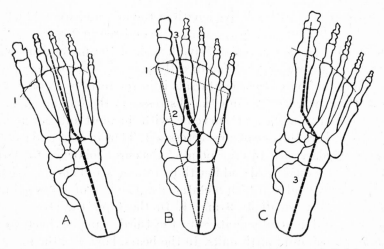

FIG. 26.—Plantar view of left human feet, with metatarsal lengths adapted from x-ray photographs. *B*, a fairly average foot, toeing forward, showing (1) metatarsal curve, (2) the triangular line of support at rest, and (3) the resultant of pressure and its plan of shift during a single step; *A*, a foot with short first and long third metatarsal, best fitted for in-toed progression, with its altered metatarsal curve (1) and approximate resultant of pressure; *C*, a foot with long first metatarsal, best fitted for out-toed progression, with its altered metatarsal curve and approximate resultant of pressure.

present stage of development his metatarsus embodies laws of foot pattern fully in accord with that of other mammals.

Elftman and Manter (1935) for the first time have devised a satisfactory method of investigating the forces exerted by the human foot in walking. They employed a rubber mat with minute cones upon the under surface, which rested upon a glass plate. Their data seem to be entirely accurate, but their interpretation of some of them appears to be subject to disagreement.

At the beginning of a step by a foot pointing straight forward, the line of stress must be from the heel to a point midway between the anterior terminations of the first and fifth metatarsals. But if the

foot toes in or out, this line is displaced laterally or medially, respectively. As the center of gravity shifts over the transverse plantar
arch, it is displaced toward the dominant (medial) side of the foot, to
a greater extent in one who toes out and to a less extent in one toeing
in. This shift becomes accentuated as the center of gravity crosses
the curve following the metatarsophalangeal joints. The point to be
accentuated is that this line of stress, or resultant of pressure, varies
enormously in different people, with the variability of their foot action. It must also be recalled that natural human foot action involves
a foot whose muscles and bones have not been distorted by shoes, for
the latter hold a naturally somewhat abducted hallux close to the
second toe.

The fact that occasionally the terrestrial edentates have a tetradactylate pes is probably without significance in the present connection.

Among the Rodentia more than in most orders pedal conditions do
not necessarily reflect present capacities for speed but rather a heritage from fairly remote ancestors. Most rats have five digits; but the
capybara, viscacha, chinchilla, and Dinomys have four or three, although none of them appears to be very speedy. The tridactyl Patagonian cavy, and to a lesser extent the agoutis, are definitely cursorial.

As compared to the usual ratlike rodent, the American kangaroo
rat, Dipodomys, has a narrower foot, with longer metatarsals more
closely grouped, a hallux either vestigial externally or reduced to a
metatarsal splint (the difference being specific in some groups and individual in others), and a fifth digit somewhat reduced. The jumping
mouse Zapus, has a foot at approximately the same stage of specialization, except that the hallux is better developed. From this, in the
Dipodoidea, there is a regular gradation of almost every degree,
through elongation and closer apposition of the unfused metatarsals
in Cardiocranius to proximal fusion in Salpingotus and total fusion,
except for the extreme distal portion, of the three metatarsalia to
form a birdlike "tarsal bone" in most dipodids (of the Allactaga,
Scarturus, Scirtopoda, Dipus, and Jaculus types). The reduction of
the lateral digits in this group is not uniform with other foot specializations, however. Cardiocranius lacks the lateral digits, but the
otherwise much more saltatorial foot of the Allacataginae has both
digits 1 and 5. Both of the latter are lacking in the Dipodinae, except
for the presence of a reduced hallux in the odd Scarturus.

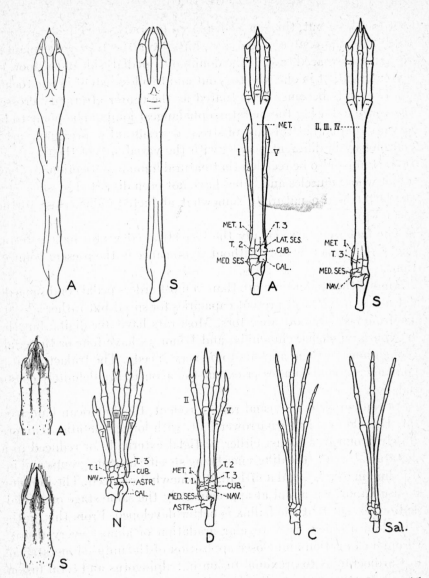

FIG. 27.—Saltatorial specialization in the right pes of rodents. *N*, the relatively unspecialized Neotoma; *D*, Dipodomys; *A*, Allactaga; *S*, Scirtopoda; *C*, Cardiocranius; *Sal.*, Salpingotus. The last two redrawn from Vinogradov.

It is difficult to evaluate the trend shown by saltatorial rodents. At first glance the pes appears to be functionally tridactyl; but the digits are held during use closely pressed together in curious fashion so that it is in effect monodactyl, while in some of the most advanced forms (as Jaculus) there is a tendency toward reduction in diameter of the central digit and increase in robustness of the second and fourth, suggesting a didactyl tendency (Fig. 27).

Digital reduction in the pes is frequent among hystricomorph rodents but appears to follow no uniform pattern. Some have a strictly pentadactyl foot; and in others with five toes the pes is functionally tridactyl, the marginal digits having retreated (Cuniculus)

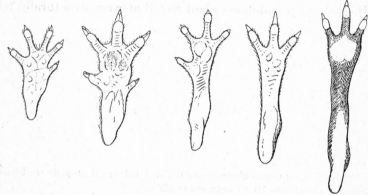

Fig. 28.—The development of cursorial specialization in hystricomorph rodents as illustrated by the right pes of (from left to right) Octodon, Coelogenys, Chinchilla, Dasyprocta, Dolichotis. Redrawn from Pocock.

in a manner suggestive of the jerboa Allactaga. In those in which the hallux is lost the same general arrangements are encountered: the four toes may be bunched (as Ctenodactylus) and all much of the same value; the fifth may retreat, leaving a functionally tridactyl pes (Thrynomus, Lagidium, Chinchilla, with Coendu more extreme); or the second and fifth may show a tendency to retreat, suggestive of an artiodactyl condition (Dinomys). Reduction to three pedal digits is not rare (Dasyprocta, Lagostomus, Kerodon, Dolichotis, Galea, Hydrochoerus), the middle toe then being dominant; but not all of these are cursorial. Not all the rodents mentioned above have been examined by me, and I have relied upon Pocock (1922) for some of the details.

The Lagomorpha lack the hallux, suggesting a more cursorial ancestor for the little pika, Ochotona. In hares and rabbits the foot is functionally tetradactyl, with digit 5 slightly the shortest, and at times with a tendency toward an increase in the robustness of digit 2.

In the Carnivora there are four pedal digits in Canidae, Hyaenidae, and Felidae (both with a vestigial metatarsal 1), in the aardwolf (Proteles), and exceptionally in the Viverridae (Suricata). In these, in which the metatarsus is usually somewhat elongated, the two middle units are longest and the two lateral units shorter and of equal length, so that the foot is symmetrically tetradactyl.

In Hyracoidea the pes is functionally tridactyl, but with a vestigial digit 5. The condition may reflect an ancestry more cursorial than are the living animals.

Among the extinct Litopterna of South America the family Proterotheridae or pseudohorses had feet that were structurally tridac-

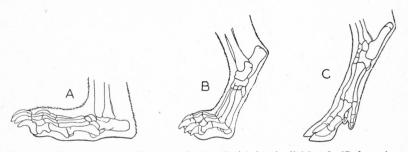

Fig. 29.—Foot postures to illustrate plantigrade (A, bear), digitigrade (B, hyena), and unguligrade (C, pig) types. After Pander and D'Alton.

tyl, but usually the lateral digits were carried well above the ground and were very decadent; and in one genus (Thoatherium), the size of a small dog, the lateral metatarsals (2 and 4) were reduced to small scales, thus making this animal more strictly monodactyl than any mammal yet known. In spite of this fact, the epipodials were unfused, although fused at their extremities in the far less cursorial litoptern family Macraucheniidae. Unlike horses, however, litopterns had a carpus and tarsus that were inadaptive, the distal bony elements not changing to conform to the metapodial alterations.

In general osteological study, discrimination between metacarpals and metatarsals is often not of paramount significance. In ungulates, however, these elements are of more importance, because of high specialization and their greater percentage of total leg length and because skeletons are usually disarticulated. A difficulty here arises, for I know no certain way of readily telling metacarpals from metatarsals. In the great majority of cases the latter are the longer, but in many artiodactyls they are of practically the same length. As a rule, the metacarpals are heavier and stouter in cattle, sheep, goats, and camels; but the opposite condition often obtains in other groups. The fused metatarsals are frequently more definitely grooved and with more of a posterior process on the proximal end. But, in order to make sure, one must study the articulated skeleton of a member of the subgroup in question.

There is no trace of a hallux in any but the most ancient of the Perissodactyla or odd-toed ungulates. Tapirs still possess the other four, but rhinos have only three, as had the titanotheres. In these

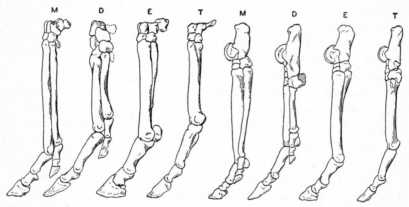

Fig. 30.—Four details to the left, the manus, and four to the right, the pes, of Mesohippus (*M*) and Equus (*E*), both horses; and of Diadiaphorus (*D*) and Thoatherium (*T*), both litopterns or pseudo-horses; to show comparable stages of podial development in unrelated stocks. Redrawn from Matthews.

three groups, all essentially graviportal or mediportal types, the feet, although unguligrade in pattern, had small nails and a thick, elastic heel pad, even in the cursorial rhinoceros Hyracodon, but to a lesser degree.

The pes in fossil horses was slightly more specialized than the manus, as is usual in tetrapods; but otherwise the evolution of forefeet and hind feet was very similar. Eohippus had three functional pedal digits, with the splints of the first and third in some species, although that of the first very quickly disappeared and that of the fifth somewhat later. Thereafter the middle digit became heavier and the marginal ones lighter until in Merychippus these no longer touched the ground. In the more advanced species of Pliohippus the marginal toes had disappeared externally, although their long metatarsals remained.

In Equus the lateral digits (2 and 4) are represented in the pes only by splints. The genus appeared in the Pliocene and is the only genus of horse to have survived to the present.

During the above changes the phalanges of the third digit kept pace with the corresponding metatarsal. There is a keel upon the distal end of the latter bone that interlocks with the first phalanx and adds to the rigidity of the pes, a feature lacking in the South American pseudohorses (Litopterna).

In the Artiodactyla, or even-toed ungulates, the development of the pes largely parallels that of the manus, except that the former is somewhat less conservative. The dominant digits are the third and fourth, arranged in paraxonic fashion, each symmetrical with respect to an axis passing between them. In hippopotamuses the lateral (2 and 5) toes are fully functional, and there is an elastic heel pad. In true swine, digits 2 and 5 are reduced and are not functional; but in the peccaries digit 5 is lacking, the lateral digits being represented by 2 alone. In all these the metatarsals remain unfused or at most are only partially fused in old age, although closely associated. In the Tragulina there are four complete toes, the lateral ones high, nonfunctional, and with very slender metatarsals. The central metatarsals (2 and 3) are partly fused, at least in well-matured individuals.

In the Pecora the central metatarsals are firmly fused into a cannon bone, the lateral metatarsals are never complete and are almost always lacking, and their toes are vestigial or sometimes absent. In the deer (Cervidae) the lateral digits and phalanges are almost always present and often the distal part of their metatarsals. In muntjacs, however, the lateral digits are represented only by hooves. In the Bovidae vestigial phalanges of the lateral digits are frequently present, and dew claws occur except in a few antelopes. In the prongbuck (Antilocapridae), giraffes, and okapis (Giraffidae) and in the camels and their allies (Tylopoda) no remnants of the lateral digits remain.

In spite of the fact that in some respects the camels are among the most highly organized of mammals for a cursorial existence, their feet are retrogressive, and, instead of having hooves (better developed in some of the light, swift, extinct forms) like the speedier ungulates, they have padded feet, more like the graviportals, undoubtedly as an adaptation to a life among aeolian sands. The same statements regarding size of hooves, as already made in discussing the manus, apply to the pes.

CHAPTER IX

Proportions

THROUGHOUT many hundreds of years various beliefs have become established in the minds of horsemen regarding points of conformation and bodily proportions considered to be desirable or undesirable in race horses. Some of these are certainly erroneous and hardly more than superstition or folklore, but others are based on fact and the experience of generations. Few of them can be either proved or disproved; but a number relating to locomotion, mentioned by Cousté, Lamb, Hayes, and others, are here included as of considerable interest.

Horses with stamina usually have heads of good size. A long neck, but flexible and well-muscled, is an indication of speed and jumping ability. An unduly heavy neck gives a horse too much weight forward, which is hard on the front legs. This assertion would seem to be proved by the fact that stallions, with heavier necks, do not stand hard work at fast gaits as well as geldings.

The trunk should be deep for its length. A short body can carry more weight, and the thorax should be deep, to accommodate large lungs and a long scapula. The barrel should be well rounded and the last rib within an inch or two of the pelvic bone, to allow for a capacious thorax. The abdomen should not be "tucked up." Withers that are high and well back are desirable, to accommodate a powerful nuchal ligament, strong dorsal neck muscles, and a long, sloping scapula. Horses broad between the forelegs seldom have stamina, because this detail indicates too much weight forward and requires too much lateral oscillation of the center of gravity during locomotion. The dorsal line should be nearly straight. Breadth across the croup indicates desirably powerful gluteal muscles; and the sacral line, to the root of the tail, should be convex.

A relatively vertical scapula and phalanges (pastern) promote speed in a sprint but are hard on the horse, for obliquity of these bones reduces the shock of landing, facilitates muscular control, and lightens the weight forward. A long scapula likewise improves muscular action. A horizontal humerus is said to favor speed but to reduce stamina; but it has also been claimed that a sloping humerus naturally accompanies a vertical scapula. The humerus should be relatively short and the radius long, with a good fore-and-aft thickness. It is desirable to have a short metacarpus (cannon bone) as compared to the radius. Relatively vertical pasterns or phalanges reduce the strength of the vertical thrust by the front legs, so it is desirable, from the practical viewpoint, to have them sloping. Horses from a dry country are likely to have the pasterns more sloping than horses bred on softer ground. The hoof should not be too small.

Some authorities claim that speed is indicated by a horizontal, and others by a sloping, croup, as well as a sloping femur. Goubaux and Barrier in 1884 (in Cousté) found that the best horses of their time (probably meaning those of good stamina as well as speed) had a croup with an inclination of 30° and a femur of 80°. Certainly, a short femur is desirable, and a long tibia, with the hock (heel) relatively straight rather than angular (cow hocks).

Before considering limb proportions it will be necessary to gain some understanding of the way the limbs function and the mechanical influences working upon them.

The limb in reality is a compound lever whose action is too complicated in practice for the mathematical determination of the results. Even in the case of a single limb joint, although it is easy to compute the effect that a particular muscle of given power will have, it is virtually impossible to determine the group action at high speed of the muscles. But it is feasible to get some understanding of the principles involved.

Considered as a single lever or unjointed crutch, the variable factors concerned, reduced to their simplest terms, comprise the actual strength of power as well as the point where it is applied, length of limb, and its weight, particularly of its distal part. If the power be applied more distally, the action of the lever will be slower but the strength greater. In other words, raising the insertion (the power arm) or actually shortening the muscle will increase speed but decrease strength. Lengthening the limb will increase the stride but reduce its power. Decreasing the weight of the foot will quicken the stride and reduce the energy output.

The strength of a muscle in diverse animals is extremely variable and very imperfectly understood. As a rule, however, a very strong muscular equipment means heavy weight not only of the muscles themselves but of the skeleton and other parts. A very strong animal is seldom a very speedy one. Obviously, for an animal of a given weight there should be some optimum muscular development for speed, of sufficient strength but not so heavy as to prove cumbersome.

The exact positions of muscle insertions upon the leg of a cursorial animal vary in accordance with other cursorial specializations. Relatively higher insertions reduce strength but raise the center of gravity, lighten the limb, and quicken the action.

Length of limb is of great moment. A short leg oscillating rapidly can cover as much ground as a long one swinging more slowly; and a wart hog can run as fast as many mammals with much longer legs. While it is true that the change in the rate of motion is proportional to the force applied, it is inversely proportional to the body mass; and such factors as fatigue enter here, so that short legs are not found in speedy animals with much stamina. Obviously, there must be a happy medium between legs that are too short or too long for a particular animal well equipped for running. The wart hog works his legs too fast; the legs of a giraffe are so long that their period is probably too slow for best efficiency. The length of stride increases with quickening of step but only to a certain point, after which the length decreases (Haycraft, 1900).

Mass of limb, particularly of its distal part, is one of the most important details of the extremities in relation to cursorial specialization. It may here be recalled that the weight of the bob does not affect the period of the pendulum. The leg, however, is not a pendulum but a lever; and the heavier the foot, the greater the force necessary for its recovery during a stride. The change of rate or of direction of motion is inversely proportional to the mass. But, although the heavy foot means more work, it lengthens the stride, so the trainer may increase the weight of his horse's shoes in the hope of better speed in the sprints. Again it is seen that for a particular cursorial animal there should be a weight of distal leg optimum for a beast of that conformation. Lengthening of the limb promotes speed, but it may become too long for the most effective locomotor cycle.

To be considered in this connection is the fact that the weight of an animal varies as the cube of its linear dimension, but the strength of the leg varies as its cross-section, which increases by squares. Hence, if an animal doubles its length, its weight increases eight times and its legs must be four times as strong. These facts impose structural limitations. An elephant could not possibly have the form of a light antelope, and the legs of a horse must be relatively heavier than those of a gazelle. Each type has characteristic locomotor actions and limitations, some promoting and others decreasing speed.

Bodily proportions, other than the functional length of the limb segments, have already been considered; but it may be mentioned again in this chapter that the center of gravity in limbed reptiles is usually closer to the rear than to the front legs, while in mammals the reverse holds true. In thoroughbred horses the weight over the forequarters as compared to that over the hindquarters is about as 9 is to 7, the proportion being a little narrower for geldings and mares.

Some thought should also be given here to bodily posture as a whole. It is obvious that an animal with arched lumbar region and with hind limbs tucked under the body will occupy a better position for springing forward than one otherwise disposed. It follows, then, that an animal with angular limb segments should be better fitted for leaping than one with columnar limbs; and it is true that an elephant cannot leap but can only glide forward.

As already stated, it is hardly feasible to express, in percentage of body length, what might be regarded as constituting an average length of limb. A "longer" limb may merely indicate a shorter body, or vice versa. In the generalized condition it is probable, however, that the length of limb is relatively that encountered in small animals of the bodily proportions of a rat.

It is the functional, rather than the over-all, length of each limb segment that is of interest in the present connection. The measurement between the terminal articular surfaces is satisfactory in the case of propodial and epipodial, but the functional length of manus and pes is more difficult. It probably should be considered as from the wrist or ankle joint to a point, varying in different kinds of mammals, somewhere between the distal ends of the metapodials in plantigrades to the ends of the toes in unguligrades. The difficulty is increased when endeavoring to measure quantities of skeletons with disarticulated foot bones. Hence, as a compromise, the length of the longest metapodial has been taken.

The measurements of about three hundred individual animals are herein considered, most of them taken by myself; but those of fetal and other horses published by Ewart (1894) and of titanotheres and other mammals by Osborn, as well as additional scattered measurements of the larger extinct reptiles, have been utilized. It is thus seen that there has been no effort to gather as large a series of measurements as possible, but merely sufficient to detect trends. In the case of highly cursorial species, as many specimens were measured as were available; and I should like to have had many more individuals and species of other swift animals than I have been able to examine. The inevitable result of these facts is the danger accompanying all restricted sampling, that the individual considered may represent an extreme. This is all the more unfortunate in that occasionally the variation within a small group (such as Arab horses) is wider than in all the other living forms of the genus examined.

In this work a great variety of measurements of various parts of the body have been taken and scrutinized; but it was eventually decided that only those of propodials, epipodials, and metapodials would prove truly useful. For comparing these the following indices were employed:

$$\text{Humeroradial or brachial index} = \frac{\text{Radius}}{\text{Humerus}} \times 100 \,,$$

$$\text{Humerometacarpal index} = \frac{\text{Metacarpus}}{\text{Humerus}} \times 100 \,,$$

$$\text{Intermembral index} = \frac{\text{Humerus} + \text{Radius}}{\text{Femur} + \text{Tibia}} \times 100 \,,$$

$$\text{Femorotibial or crural index} = \frac{\text{Tibia}}{\text{Femur}} \times 100 \,,$$

$$\text{Tibioradial index} = \frac{\text{Radius}}{\text{Tibia}} \times 100 \,,$$

$$\text{Femorometatarsal index} = \frac{\text{Metatarsus}}{\text{Femur}} \times 100 \,.$$

An index similar to the intermembral, but with lengths of metacarpus and metatarsus added to the other segments, was considered and investigated but was found not to differ from the intermembral index to a worth-while degree.

Finally, for each limb in all specimens measured, the sum of the lengths of propodial, epipodial, and metapodial was reduced to 100 and the percentage of each segment in terms of par was calculated, with the slide rule, to the nearest full number (hence the sum total may be either 99 or 101 in the tables).

The different indices have different significance for any one factor. Thus development of hind limb is more diagnostic for judging degree of cursorial adaptation than that of the pectoral member, and of metatarsus than of femur, while the humeroradial index may reflect influences very different from cursorial.

In the generalized mammal the hind limb is used for little else than locomotion, but the fore limb has frequent other uses, such as that of a tool or in feeding. So it responds in different degree to cursorial stimuli. If the latter were uncomplicated, it is likely that the thoracic member would be a trifle the shorter in mammals at least, because it has less propulsive action—but only a trifle, for otherwise it would function clumsily. For an animal using the manus in bringing food to the mouth the relative length of humerus and radius is determined largely by size of head and length of neck. In the generalized condition these two are approximately equal in length. If the neck lengthens or the whole arm becomes smaller, the humerus will be relatively shorter than the radius, in order that the hand may still reach the mouth while holding food. Thus in most saltatorial rodents and kangaroos the radius is much longer than the humerus. On the other hand, the bipedal dinosaurs probably did not use the manus as a true hand to any considerable extent; but the upper arm provided anchorage for important shoulder musculature, so the forearm was the segment chiefly reduced, and their humeroradial index dropped as low as 45 (according to figures in the literature for Albertosaurus). So it is seen that change in this index may be due to influences other than cursorial and hence that it is not so indicative a character as some others. But relative decrease in humeral length does occur regularly in highly cursorial quadrupeds. Of more critical importance, however—and a more reliable index—is relative increase in the length of the metacarpals.

It has for many years been recognized that in cursorial specialization there is increase in the length of metapodials and decrease in the relative length of propodials. In saltatorial specialization this statement applies to the hind limb. Considering limb proportions as concerned particularly with titanotheres, Gregory (in Osborn, 1929) has summarized what was then known, and it will be useful to quote him. He divided quadrupeds into four locomotor types: (1) ambulatory—small, primitive, subplantigrade, running clumsily, such as skunks and shrews; (2) mediportal—largely digitigrade, such as tapirs; (3) graviportal—ponderous, columnar limbs and erect metapodials, such as elephants; and (4) cursorial—unguligrade, such as horses. Gregory noted that the tibia lengthens in cursorial and shortens in graviportal specialization. The radius either stays the same or shortens less than the tibia in graviportals, but it lengthens as much as the tibia in cursorials. In graviportals the radius is not abbreviated step by step with the tibia but may actually lengthen. Some primitive condylarths and perissodactyls, however, had high-speed tibial and radial ratios and low-speed metapodial ratios. In mediportal mammals the propodial is equal to or longer than the epipodial; in graviportals it is longer and in cursorial forms, shorter.

In the generalized animal, as in man, but two segments intervene between the shoulder or hip and the ground. Why there is a tendency to increase the metapodial and decrease the propodial segment in cursorial species appears to be a question not readily answered mathematically; but the evidence that this change promotes speed is incontrovertible. Very possibly it is not a matter solely of the mechanics of bones, but of the tetrapod muscular equipment's being such that it functions better for speed with this arrangement. Resulting favorable facts are that the center of gravity is raised and the distal limb lightened. With three functional segments the limb as a whole can be flexed and extended more easily and quickly than with two.

HUMERORADIAL INDEX

In the generalized condition the functional lengths of humerus and radius are about the same, and the humeroradial index is thus about 100. Among bipedal reptiles it is subject to much variation, from 45 in some (saurischian) theropods to 74 in others, and from 59 to 120 in trachodonts. With the latter exception, the radius always appears to be shorter than the humerus in tetrapod reptiles (ratio, 68 to 82 in lacertilians).

Among living mammals the lowest ratio encountered is 68 in hippos (Osborn) (71 in the hyrax), while it rises to 167 in the giraffe. In Pyrotherium—the bizarre Oligocene graviportal notoungulate of South America—Gaudry's figures, copied widely, show a ratio of about 40.

In essentially bipedal saltators the index rises to 133 in elephant shrews and to 141 in the red kangaroo (greater than 100 in all kangaroos), while in leaping rodents it is 120 in Dipodomys, 119–38 in Dipodidae, 136 in Dolichotis, but 100 or less in the average run of rodents. It is less than 100 in rabbits and usually more in hares (117 in L. callotis), but the latter are quite variable.

The speedier carnivores are conservative in this respect, and the index is about 100 in hyenas and most dogs, dropping to 92 in some foxes (Vulpes) and rising to 108 only in one individual of the long-legged Chrysocyon. It is interesting to find that the bush dog, Icticyon, with its very short legs, has a ratio (86) that parallels that of that genetic freak, the dachshund (88). The condition in cats is not what one might expect, for in spite of the high speed of some of them in a short dash the index (90–99) rises to par only in the cheetah (99, 100,102).

Among perissodactyls the radius is considerably shorter (ratio, 81 to 88) in tapirs but, curiously, still shorter in the little, extinct Helaletes, supposedly cursorial, and also in rhinos (about 90); the ratio is increased to 105 in the extinct cursorial Hyracodon. In fossil horses there was a general decrease in the length of the humerus in step with their progressive development, varying with type, to 130 in the lightly built Neohipparion and dropping to 102 in the regressive Hippidium. In wild living Equidae there is great variability, the ratio being from 112 in some Prezewalsky horses and Grevy zebras to 133 in the wild ass E. hemionus. In domesticated horses the extremes encountered (107–27) occur in Arabs. During prenatal development the percentage rises (Ewart) from somewhere near 70 to as high as 135 before birth (very variable but averaging about 116 in the adult).

In elephant, hyrax, and hippo the humeroradial index is in the low seventies, the low eighties in pigs, and the high eighties in Tragulina and Moschus. In the other artiodactyls studied it is less than 100 only in one muntjac (98, 106), a bison (94), and in one duiker (Cephalophus, 94, 108) and the klipspringer (Oreotragus, 91, 94), both of which have habits not essentially cursorial in character. My one mountain goat (Oreamnos) has a ratio of 100. In all other artiodactyls measured, the humerus is shorter than the radius.

In North American deer the index varies from 102 to 120, and in the prongbuck from 111 to 122. In African antelopes the ratio progresses from Ourebia (105) through Kobus (114, 117), Saiga (118), and Hippotragus (120) to the more lightly built forms, mostly gazelles, above 130 (G. laevipes, Litocranius, Aepyceros), as well as in Damaliscus, and even to 141 (G. thompsoni, Antidorcas); there is

much individual variation (two G. dorcas, 112 and 135). Camels are
in the middle range (117–26); giraffes with extreme development
(Okapi, 143; Giraffa, up to 167).

The relative length of the humerus may also be examined in terms
of its percentage of the sum of humerus, radius, and metacarpus
(= 100). This index rises above 50 in numerous dinosaurs (Albertosaurus, 58); but in mammals it exceeds this figure only in hippo, elephant, and hyrax, with the maximum (53) occurring in the extinct
Uintatherium. In generalized mammals it is in the middle forties; and
among nonungulate mammals it drops below 40 only in the thylacine
(39, 40), some kangaroos, elephant shrews (37, 40), some jerboas
(38), Dolichotis (37), Chrysocyon (39), and Hyaena (39). The figure
is below 40 in practically all horses (below 30 in Neohipparion) and
some foals of living horses. It is in the middle thirties in cattle (but
39 in Bison); the low thirties and very high twenties in camels, deer,
and heavier antelopes; the middle twenties in gazelles (Antidorcas;
Litocranius; Aepyceros, 25); and as low as 23 in Giraffa (Okapi, 28).

In the same light—in percentage of the sum of humerus, radius,
and metacarpus—the radius is a stable element. It drops to a rather
low figure in some dinosaurs (Albertosaurus, 26); but in the generalized mammal it is most often in the middle forties. The percentage
rises to the very high forties and low fifties only in saltatorial forms
(kangaroos, elephant shrews, kangaroo rats, jerboas, Patagonian
cavy); and in mammals without ungulate affinities it drops below 40
(39), among those measured, only in a cavy, dachshund, and some
cats. Among perissodactyls the percentage drops to the high thirties
in tapirs (35, 37), rhinos (39), and horses (36–40), the figure not varying with specialization, being the same, with individual variation,
from the Eocene to the present. Other ungulates, as well as the hyrax, have the radius in the middle thirties, there being little or no variation with specialization.

HUMEROMETACARPAL INDEX

As a rule in bipedal reptiles the metacarpus was not much elongated, and the considerable variation in this index (15–66 in trachodonts) is due more to relative difference in humeral than in metacarpal length.

In generalized mammals the longest metacarpal tends, very rough-
ly, to be one-quarter to one-third the humeral length. The extremes

encountered are in Elephas (14) and in the antelope Litocranius (169).

The only definite trend in marsupials away from the average is in Thylacinus (44). The metacarpus in elephant shrews is not affected. In saltatorial rodents (but not in kangaroos) there is some shortening (Dipodomys, 20; Pedetes, 16). Hares are not affected.

In a restoration of an ancestral canid (Cynodictis) this index is 23; but it rises through domestic dogs (39–43) to 45 in Chrysocyon and

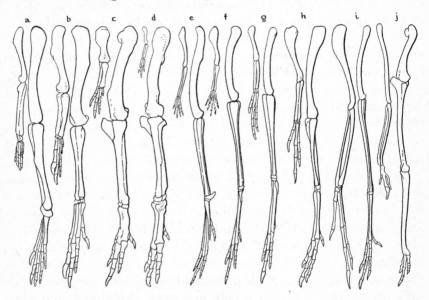

Fig. 31.—Proportions of forelimbs and hind limbs, the latter reduced to the same length, of bipedal reptiles and of birds. *b–d*, showing diminution of fore limb in theropodous dinosaurs; *e–h*, the increase in length of fore limb in coelurosaurs. *a*, Ornithosuchus; *b*, Anchisaurus; *c*, Ceratosaurus; *d*, Tyrannosaurus; *e*, Saltoposuchus; *f*, Procompsognathus; *g*, Compsognathus; *h*, Ornitholestes; *i*, Archaeornis; *j*, Rhea. Redrawn from Heilmann.

the dachshund and to 46 in one Lycaon. Unexpectedly, the percentage is still higher (48) in hyenas, with their heavy forequarters; but in cats there is definite elongation only in the cheetah (41).

In tapirs (47–53) the index shows more change than in rhinos (39). In fossil horses it rises from Orohippus (42) to Hypohippus (99) and Neohipparion (116) but recedes in the stockier Hippidium (70). In wild horses it is quite variable, the extremes being met in a single species (E. grevyi, 81–90), except that E. hemionus (98.7) surpasses all others. In domestic horses the extremes (72 and 89) occur among Arabs. In fetal horses the index rises from 43 (20-mm. embryo) to 113

(730-mm.), according to Ewart (1894), and as high as 131 in a Preze-walsky foal.

In the generalized condition the longest metacarpal appears to average about 12 per cent of the sum of humerus, radius, and metacarpal. The extremes that I have encountered in dinosaurs occur in trachodonts, from 8 to 23, and are due in large part to variation in the length of humerus.

In mammals there is reduction in relative metacarpal length in saltatorial forms, such as marsupials (as low as 8 in Thylogale) and leaping rodents (8–11), but not in elephant shrews or hares. The percentage increases only slightly in dogs (16–19) and cats, even in the cheetah (17), the maximum in these two groups occurring in Hyaena (20).

In rhinos (17, 19) the figure is less than in tapirs (20, 22); and horses show surprisingly slight change in this respect throughout their history, the percentage being persistently in the twenties and rising, in adults, above 30 only in the extinct Merychippus (31.4) and Neohipparion (33).

As expected, the very lowest figures are encountered in the elephant (7.5), hyrax (12.7), and hippo (13.7). In artiodactyls the percentage rises from Tragulina (23) to the high twenties in sheep and goats (but Oreamnos, 22; Ovibos, 22; Bison, 24); to the low thirties in deer and camels (but Rangifer, 28); the middle and high thirties in pronghorn, most antelopes (but klipspringer, 28), and giraffes; to culminate above 40 in the lightest antelopes (Gazella dorcas, 41; Antidorcas, 40; Aepyceros, 41; Litocranius, 42).

INTERMEMBRAL INDEX

Scrutiny of this index indicates that it is entirely worthless for indicating either speed or the lack of it, except that a relatively long hind leg often points to leaping ability.

In reptiles this ratio drops as low as 22 in the theropod Albertosaurus and rises to 83 in the sauropod Camarasaurus but is in the fifties for most of the orthopod dinosaurs. It is in the eighties in the lacertilians measured.

I judge that in mammals the generalized condition involves an intermembral index in the vicinity of 75. Only very rarely in quadrupeds does it rise above 100, in brachiating primates (apes and spider monkey), with maximum of 155 in the orang (Mollison, 1910); in sloths (up to 178 in Bradypus, according to Straus and Wislocki [1932]); some hyenas; the Pleistocene forest horse Hippidium (106); and the giraffe (107).

In some kangaroos (Aepyprymnus) the intermembral index drops to 38 and in others (Macropus rufus) rises to 66, but it is low in saltators. Thus it is no greater than 50 in selected Tarsius (Straus, manuscript), 48 in Dipodomys, 41 in Pedetes, 35 in some jerboas. It rises definitely above the average in Dolichotis (87, 94), but not in elephant shrews and only slightly in hares.

The ratio is high in dogs (83–94), but the maximum is in the short-legged Icticyon. In cats it is a trifle lower (80–90) and of all carnivores is highest in hyenas (96, 102).

Tapirs show a very slight rise, more pronounced in living rhinos (91, 92; but 74 in the extinct cursorial Hyrachyus). No increase in this index is encountered among extinct horses until the Upper Miocene, and then chiefly in the slower forest horses (Hypohippus, 84; Hippidium, 106). The increase is moderate in living horses, but there is considerable variability (82–91).

As might be expected, the index is high in the elephant (94), with its columnar legs. It is also high in camels (96), but not markedly so in llamas or much above average in most artiodactyls (but 94 in the moose).

In the course of this study I made a real effort to correlate the preacetabular as compared with the postacetabular measurement of the innominate bone. A long ischium provides better leverage for the crural flexors, and this should be of prime importance to all leapers. But there are other very complicated factors involved, associated with the need in leaping for firm anchorage and hence a long ilium. Thus in frogs the preacetabular may be three times the postacetabular measurement, and it was found in mammals that this index varies irrespective of cursorial specialization.

FEMOROHUMERAL INDEX

This index (Humerus/Femur × 100) is not very useful, as it largely follows the intermembral index; but it is distorted even more by a disproportionate shortening of the humerus in some saltators. Thus it is an indication of saltatorial specialization. In the generalized condition this index may be regarded as being somewhere near 80; but in jerboas and some kangaroos (Aepyprymnus) it may reach 40 and in

Tarsius 56, while it definitely surpasses 100 in brachiating primates (to 147 in orang and 152 in siamang [Mollison]) and reaches 179 in the three-toed sloth (Straus, manuscript). The only mammals that I have measured in which functional length of humerus and femur are practically equal are individuals of the anteater Tamandua; the bush dog Icticyon; and the Patagonian cavy Dolichotis.

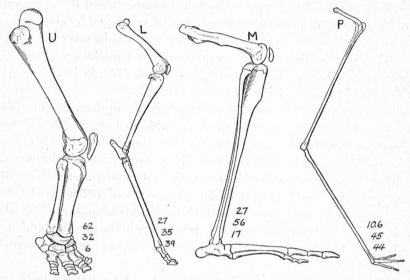

Fig. 32.—Hind-limb skeletons, showing the extreme of relative segment development: *U*, the graviportal Uintatherium; *L*, Litocranius, the gerenuk; *M*, Macropus, the kangaroo; and *P*, Phoenicopterus, the flamingo. The upper numbers represent the percentage of the functional length of the humerus, the middle numbers of the tibia, and the lower numbers of the longest metatarsus, on the basis of the sum of the three bones equaling 100.

FEMOROTIBIAL OR CRURAL INDEX

Among saurischian theropods the femur is usually longer than the tibia in the large, carnivorous types, while the reverse is the case in smaller, lighter sorts. In sauropods the femur is much the longer (index, 60–64). Among ornithischians, trachodonts usually have the femur somewhat the longer (index, 80–90), but occasionally in orthopods it is shorter. In stegosaurs and ceratopsians it is much longer (index, 65). In lacertilians the femur is longer (index, 73–88).

Invariably in birds the femur is much shorter than the tibia, the lowest indices (Chordeiles, 141) being in goatsuckers and penguins. Figures over 200 are encountered in some of the moas (up to 219), Sagittarius (to 276), Cariama (262), Jacana (286), Himantopus (360), Ereunetes (218) and doubtless some other small shore birds,

Grus (253), and the flamingo (Phoenicopterus) to the extreme of 427. Those with the higher figures are overspecialized in the cursorial direction for other purposes besides swiftness in locomotion.

Among the marsupials measured, this index drops below 100 only in Thylacinus; and it is only rarely in kangaroos and wallabies that it exceeds 200 (M. rufus, 208), usually being from about 130 to 160. In elephant shrews it rises above 140, but does not exceed 100 in Tarsius, probably in relation to the unusual manner employed by that animal in leaping. It is low in sloths, particularly in Choloepus (84).

The index is high in the leaping rodents Dipodomys (145), Pedetes (136), jerboas (Allactaga, 144; Jaculus, 175), in Dolichotis (to 155), and to a lesser degree in hares (108–23).

The percentage has not altered significantly in dogs but drops to 100 or below in selected individuals, notably in Lycaon (95, 99), and even lower in the aberrant Icticyon (86) and dachshund (76). It is below 100 in most cats and down to 77 in some lions and in hyenas.

The femorotibial ratio is low in tapirs (80) and rhinos (about 68; but 83 in Hyracodon). It is within five points of 102 in most fossil horses but, curiously, rises in both the swift Neohipparion (117) and the short-legged Hippidium (128). In living wild horses the tendency has been downward (77–92), but a little higher in domesticated horses (87–97).

This index tends to be low in graviportals (hippo, 63; elephant, 54; mastodon, 69; uintathere, 53; but Procavia, 97). It is low in living camels (82, 84) and somewhat higher in llamas (90, 103), both of which are poor jumpers. It is about the same figure (113) in giraffe, okapi, and the more primitive deer (Tragulus, Moschus) but quite variable in most deer, being lowest in the wapiti (107) and highest in that accomplished leaper, the mule deer (Odocoileus hemionus, 127). It is up only slightly in the prongbuck, reputedly a poor jumper. With very few exceptions (a Taurotragus, a Cephalophus), this index in sheep, goats, and antelopes exceeds 100 in variable amount but is over 120 only in the chamois and in every one of the gazelles and lighter antelopes, the extremes being in G. dorcas (137), G. arabica (131), and, curiously enough, the clumsy-looking Saiga (130), but not in Aepyceros (121, 126). The figure appears to be low in cattle (Bison, 92; Ovibos, 91).

It is worth while to consider the length of the femur in terms of its percentage of the sum of the functional length of femur, tibia, and longest metatarsal (= 100) only in the most notable cases, for this index for the most part reflects the development of tibia or metatarsus.

In saurischian dinosaurs the figure is well below 50 in theropods (35–45) but not in sauropods (51); in ornithischians, below 50 in orthopods (36–46) but not in stegosaurs or triceratopsians (52, 57).

In birds the femoral percentage is almost always below 30, excepting goatsuckers, penguins, and a very few others probably, and drops below 20 in the, for the most part, long-legged forms mentioned above, culminating in the figure 10.6 in Phoenicopterus.

This ratio is an indication of leaping ability; and only in those least proficient in this action—graviportals and three-toed sloth—does it reach 50 (Bradypus, 50; rhinos, 50; hippo, 52; Elephas, 61; Mastodon, 55; Uintatherium, 62; some titanotheres, 55). Consequently, the femoral figure is short in the good jumpers, partly because of relative reduction in this segment and partly because of metatarsal elongation.

The index is below 40 in all kangaroos and below 30 in a few (M. rufus, 27; M. gigas, 28). It is low in elephant shrews (32–33), in saltatorial rodents (from 35 in Pedetes to 24 in Jaculus), and in Dolichotis (31, 34), but to only a minor extent in hares (37–40). There has been a very slight reduction in this index throughout the history of the Equidae, culminating in Neohipparion (31) and Hippidium (31.3), and not in the modern Arab (37–39). In the horse there is a constant developmental reduction from 48 in the fetus of 20 mm. to about 30 at 900 mm.

There is a reduction to the low thirties in most artiodactyls (but Bison, 39; Ovibos, 42), reaching 30 or just below only in the lighter antelopes and gazelles and giraffes (minimum 28.6 in Gazella dorcas).

TIBIORADIAL INDEX

This index can be used for judging the degree of saltatorial specialization when this is pronounced, but it is useless for indicating cursorial ability. It does not merit very full discussion, but particular points are of some interest. I judge that in the most generalized condition the radius is about two-thirds to three-quarters the length of the tibia.

The extreme minimum for tetrapods is reached by some of the theropod dinosaurs, doubtless less than my figure of 13.8 for Albertosaurus. It was below 50 for perhaps most dinosaurs but rose in the less bipedal forms to as much as 85 in the sauropod Camarasaurus.

The ratio is low in kangaroos but variable, from 32.5 (Aepyprymnus) to 58 (M. rufus). It is very high in sloths (Bradypus, 172) and in brachiating primates, with maximum of 180 in gibbon (Mollison, 1910). It exceeds 100 also in baboons.

The figure is over 80 in dogs, reaching 97 in Lycaon and 100 in the dachshund. It is still more variable in cats (75–98), and it is particularly high in hyenas (112, 120; but 98 in Proteles). In saltatorial rodents it is low (Dipodomys, 44; Pedetes, 34; Jaculus, 32) but high in

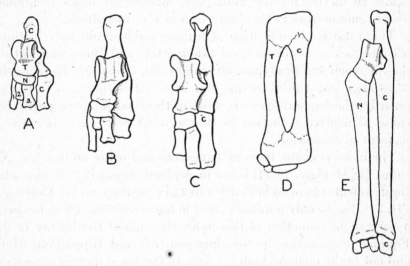

FIG. 33.—The left tarsus of selected vertebrates illustrating elongation, reduced to a uniform width. *A*, generalized mammalian type, the hedgehog: *C*, calcaneus; *T*, talus; *N*, navicular, 1, 2, 3 cuneiform; *C*, cuboid. *B*, kangaroo rat, narrowed, resulting in relative elongation of proximal part. *C*, elephant shrew, with elongation of both proximal and distal parts. *D*, frog, with elongation of talus (tibiale) and calcaneus (fibulare). *E*, tarsier, with elongation of calcaneus and navicular.

Dolichotis (86, 90). In hares the best runners are slightly high (over 80), such leapers as the snowshoe (68–74) are unchanged, and the rabbits rather low (60–63).

Among perissodactyls, rhinos (but not tapirs) are very high (109; but the extinct cursorial Hyrachyus, 76), and there is a tendency toward increase in the later fossil horses (91–96) except Neohipparion (83), continued progressively in living wild horses (92–98) and domesticated horses, practically all of which reach 100—Shetland pony, draft horse, and thoroughbred alike.

Artiodactyls are extremely variable. In the low sixties are Moschus, Tragulus, and some Muntiacus; in the nineties are llamas, Ovibos, and an occasional heavy antelope (Taurotragus, 92). Those exceeding 100 are living camels (the extinct Altocamelus, 138), giraffe (129), and okapi (117), as well as the elephant (115). The lighter deer and antelopes have this index but little altered, although showing considerable variation.

An additional way of scrutinizing epipodial development is by comparing the percentage of the tibia to hind-leg length (femur, tibia, and metatarsal = 100) to that of the radius to foreleg length (humerus, radius, and metacarpal = 100).

In dinosaurs the difference in the percentages as of tibia and radius varies, usually in favor of the tibia, from not more than 1.4 in sauropods to 12 in theropods; 4.5 in orthopods; 0.4 in Triceratops; and 2 in Stegosaurus.

In mammals, also, these percentages are, on the whole, surprisingly similar, differences usually being less than 2 in nonungulates, the larger percentage almost always, but not invariably, being for the tibia. In a few specific instances the difference is more (Hyaena, 5; jerboas, up to 10; Cavia, 6).

In ungulates the percentage for the radius is usually, but not invariably, larger; and the difference is often 5 or 6 for rhinos and living (but not fossil) horses. In artiodactyls the figure rises to 7 in camels, giraffes, and Moschus (tibial percentage the larger), but is usually 3 or less.

FEMOROMETATARSAL INDEX

For dinosaurs this index is low in sauropods (12–16) but higher in theropods, particularly in the more birdlike forms (Struthiomimus, 77). Among orthopods it is quite high (58) in some of the slender examples presumably arboreal (like Thescelosaurus), but lower (27–33) in trachodonts, ceratopsians, and particularly in Stegosaurus (11).

The index exhibits enormous variability in birds. In weak-footed forms (nighthawk, 56; swift, 70; tern, 40) and some others (penguin, 44; scoter, 85; the most robust of the moas, 72–74) it does not exceed 100 or may actually be less than 50. In perhaps the majority of birds, however, it varies from 100 to 150, exceeding the latter figure in such groups as some living ostriches (161), cassowaries (137–56), rheas (160); 200 in the screamer (230), jacana (201), and crane (225); 300 in the stilt; and the astonishing maximum of 408 in the flamingo. As with the crural index, a ratio in the middle ranges indicates for birds a definite degree of cursorial ability; but the higher figures reflect an over-specialization in this regard, developed for wading or other particular purposes.

The extremes of the femorometatarsal index in mammals were encountered in the elephant (9.8), Bradypus (9.1), and giraffe (137) and jerboa (136). It may well have dropped below this minimum in some examples of uintatheres (10). It is perhaps from 35 to 45 in the average generalized small mammal. It rises above 40 in kangaroos, with a maximum of 68 (M. gigas), and also in elephant shrews (65). Tarsius is not quite comparable in this regard, as the elongation is in tarsus rather than in metatarsus.

The index in most dogs is in the low forties, the highest being in Vulpes (48–49) and Cerdocyon (51; but Chrysocyon, 47; the metatarsus of Icticyon was not measurable). In cats it averages slightly lower, dropping below 40 in one lion (36) and a hyena (but Proteles, 48).

In saltatorial rodents this ratio varies from Pedetes (50) through Dipodomys (60–66) to the jerboas (110–36) and is high also in Dolichotis (60–64). In both rabbits and hares it is in the low or middle forties, rising above 50 only in the snowshoes.

It is only among extinct cursorial forms that this figure rises at all in tapirs (Helaletes, 48) and probably in rhinos (the metatarsal lengths for cursorial rhinos are not available to me). It exceeded 50 in even the earliest-known horses and gradually increased throughout the history of this family, to culminate in the swift Neohipparion (101), although it was very high also in the retrogressive Hippidium (90) because of its relatively short femur.

In adult living wild horses the ratio varies from 70 to 77, except in E. hemionus, in which it is 85. In domesticated horses there is a slightly greater range (69–78), the minimal figure occurring in a work horse and a trotter and the maximal in Arabs. A very interesting condition is encountered in fetal horses. Ewart's (1894) data show that this index rises without a break from 43 in an embryo of 20 mm. to 113 in one of 730 mm. In the 900-mm. size it is down to 109, but it rises to 130 in a National Museum Prezewalsky foal and is still 87 in a yearling Arab.

In Artiodactyla this index may be subject to a considerable degree of variation. At least, the variation exhibited by two individuals in each of two species is quite extreme (Cephalophus, 71–104; sheep, 68–84). It is, of course, not impossible that this is due to the inadvertent mixing of the skeletons of two individuals.

At any rate, my measurements show that in even-toed ungulates the femorometatarsal index rises from a minimum in the hippo (29, and also in the hyrax), through Sus (39) to Oreamnos (47) and to Ovibos (50) and Bison (61). In the high sixties and low seventies occur goats (66–68) and probably sheep, Tragulus (63–73), and the remarkable little klipspringer, Oreotragus (61–67), as well as the camel (67–72; but an extinct cursorial camel, Stenomylus, 94). In the high seventies and low eighties are chamois (75), Muntiacus (76, 79),

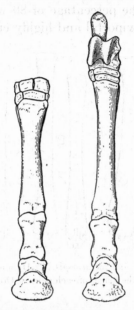

FIG. 34.—The right manus (*left*) and pes (*right*) of a Morgan horse, drawn from a photograph by H. C. Raven of articulated podials in American Museum of Natural History.

Moschus (77, 81), and such rather stocky antelopes as Hippotragus (77) and Kobus (80), as well as llamas (74, 77). Between the high seventies and 100 occur almost all of the deer, the Irish stag and one mule deer (103) surpassing the latter figure. Above 100 are found most prongbucks, okapi (108), giraffes (134, 137), and almost all of the lighter antelopes and gazelles (up to 121 in Antidorcas).

As already stated, I know no way of readily distinguishing metacarpal from metatarsal bones in disarticulated skeletons. There are slight differences that hold in part. In some groups, as in sheep, goats, cattle, and camels, the metacarpus is heavier, broader, and shorter; or the metatarsus is more heavily grooved or with a better-defined process caudoproximally. In this study I have taken particular care to verify, by one means or another, my identifications of metapodials. If I felt any doubt, I have not included the measurements; yet it is not impossible that an error or two has crept into the list of antelopes.

It is certain that in generalized, as in the great majority of, mammals, the metacarpals are shorter than the metatarsals; but it is difficult to say to what degree, because of variability between different groups. Perhaps the percentage of 80 would not be far wrong. Curiously, in both graviportal and highly cursorial forms there is a

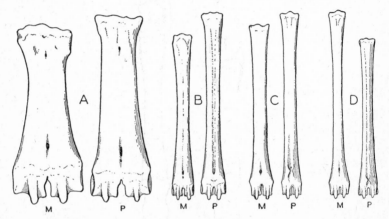

FIG. 35.—Metacarpals (*M*) and metatarsals (*P*) III and IV of several artiodactyls, reduced to a uniform length for the longer of each pair. *A*, Oreamnos; *B*, Odocoileus; *C*, Aepyceros; *D*, Litocranius.

trend toward obliteration of the difference and an increase in the good jumpers.

The latter attribute is accentuated in kangaroos, the maximum difference being in Thylogale, in which the metacarpal is but 19 per cent of the metatarsal length. It is even more pronounced in saltatorial rodents, 17 per cent in Pedetes and Dipodomys and as low in the jerboas as 7 per cent. It is also low in hares (about 60, and 65 in rabbits), and in Dolichotis (55). Cats should perhaps also be considered as a trifle low (70–75; but dogs about 85–90), as well as squirrels, tree shrews, and other good climbers.

The metacarpal is greater than the metatarsal measurement in sauropod (but not in other) dinosaurs, true hyenas (112; but not in Proteles), some pigs (variable), elephant (120), mastodon (141), uintathere (166; but Bradypus, 170), and doubtless in a number of titanotheres and other graviportals for which I do not have the meta-carpal measurement.

Metacarpal and metatarsal lengths are essentially equal in tapirs, camels and llamas, and giraffes (but not okapis), and almost so in pronghorns. The metatarsal is always longer in deer, but either equal in antelopes or else the metatarsal is slightly greater (except much greater in Saiga, 85, and to 116 in Litocranius).

The percentage of the longest metatarsal to the sum of femur, tibia, and metatarsal (= 100) bears a general similarity to the comparable item in the forelimb.

In dinosaurs the smallest figures are for the retrogressively quadrupedal sauropods (7–9) and stegosaur (6.4), and the largest (27) in the birdlike Struthiomimus. In birds there is not so much variation as one might expect. The minima are encountered in those least fitted for walking (nighthawk, 19; penguins, 13–15), and the maxima in waders or other long-legged types, exceeding 40 in secretary bird (43), stilt (42), and flamingo (42–44).

In placental mammals the generalized condition should probably be considered as involving a metatarsus in the neighborhood of 15 per cent (12 for metacarpus) of the sum of femur, tibia, and metatarsus, but somewhat below this figure in marsupials (Marmosa, 11; Thylacinus, 13–14; Perameles, 14). Minima occur in Bradypus (4.5), elephant (6), and uintathere (6.2), and the maximum in giraffes (40).

In kangaroos this percentage is increased only slightly (16–20), because although the metatarsus is lengthened, so is the tibia. The percentage has increased somewhat in elephant shrews (21). In most dogs the figure is from 16 to 18, with maxima in dachshund (19.7), because of the shortness of its tibia, and in Cerdocyon (20). My greatest percentage in carnivores occurs in the hyena (21).

Among saltatorial rodents the figure increases from Dipodomys and Dolichotis (20–21) to the jerboas (30–33). In hares it reaches 20 only in the snowshoes.

In tapirs and rhinos it has increased but little, but it rose in fossil horses from Orohippus (21) to Neohipparion (32). The latter figure is approached among living horses only by E. hemionus (30), one E. prezewalski (29), and one Arab (29). Others, both wild and domesticated, fall between 26.5 and 28.5. In embryos and foals the figure rises to as high as 38.8 for a Prezewalsky foal.

As previously stated, the figure in the elephant is 6 and in the hyrax 12.8. In artiodactyls the lowest figures are for hippo (15) and pig (18); but with the exception of these more primitive forms my lowest percentage is for the mountain goat (Oreamnos, 19). Cattle, sheep, and goats are all in the low or middle twenties (Ovibos, 21). In deer the lowest are the musk deer (26) and muntjac (27), as expected, with the others mostly from 29 to 31. In antelopes my minimum is for the little klipspringer (22.5), rising through the stockier forms (Kobus, 26) to culminate in the lighter antelopes (Litocranius, 34; Antidorcas, 35). The pronghorn is from 30 to 33. Llamas and camels are in the middle range (27–29), and the giraffe, highest of all mammals (39.7).

Additional attention should be directed to the fact that very young ungulates have greater cursorial specialization, in the proportions of their limb segments, than have adults. The propodials are relatively much shorter and the metapodials much longer, as are the entire limbs. But these features are not altogether uniform throughout the Ungulata. Thus newborn antelopes, moose, and horses have legs that are disproportionately long, while those of a calf are not pronouncedly so. The young foal cannot reach the ground with its muzzle much better than can a giraffe without spreading its front legs. Ewart's measurements of fetal horses and my figures for foals indicate relative shortening of propodials and lengthening of metapodials increasing steadily throughout gestation and culminating at or shortly after birth, after which there is a diminution of the discrepancies, owing to the more rapid growth of other parts.

The fact that the newborn ungulate is more specialized cursorially than its parent is very remarkable. Such an attribute might be interpreted as indicating descent from a fleeter ancestor; but there is no evidence that this is so, at least in most cases or to a degree sufficient to explain the phenomenon.

The proper explanation would seem to lie in the field of natural selection. Ungulates are born in a very advanced state, without the protection afforded by a den, they are largely gregarious, and their chief defense is in flight. Very shortly after birth the young must keep up with the herd and outrun a pursuing enemy or else perish; and the slower individuals have done the latter for untold generations. But, nevertheless, the fact of this difference, between newborn and adult ungulate, is very remarkable.

CHAPTER X

Gaits

LOCOMOTION means literally the act of moving from place to place. In its simplest form it involves merely the displacement of the center of gravity; in more complicated form it comprises both shifting the center of gravity and at the same time maintaining equilibrium. This is all there is to it, whether the animal swims, runs, walks, climbs, or flies. There is great variation in the methods by which locomotion is attained, but with very few exceptions (such as gliding by a flying squirrel) it is accomplished by a summation of body actions each of which is essentially rotary. Ideal locomotion requires uniform support of the center of gravity and continuous propulsion. The wheel would be the best instrument for producing linear movement, but it is unsuited to the fundamentals of vertebrate anatomy. Animal mechanics have made as much use of the principles of the wheel as they have been able to do, however, and every action involves a partial rotation around an articulation, each in one direction, followed by recovery in the opposite direction. These rotary movements must be translated by the body into linear motion, during locomotion, just as surely as must the pedalling of a bicycle be translated into forward motion. In its simplest terms this is done by alternating the hubs of moving limbs. First, the limb is rotated about the hip or shoulder to move the foot forward. Then the limb is rotated about the foot to move the hip forward. The distance gained is the product of the limb length times the sine of the angle of rotation. Such principles are discussed in a number of books and papers (Steindler, 1935; Manter, 1938) more fully than is thought necessary here.

As locomotion is an effort on the part of an animal to keep its body from falling while it shifts its center of gravity, there are concerned a vertical and a horizontal factor. When standing, the body is propelled only upward, the propulsion then equaling the gravitational pull (= weight). As an animal starts slowly forward, the horizontal factor (H) is added to the vertical (V), which inclines the line of force diagonally (D) from the vertical in proportion to the speed attained. Then $D^2 = H^2 - V^2$. Taking the angle between D and H as ϕ, then $H = D \cos \phi$. But these formulas are nothing but theoretical, for they ignore wind resistance, friction, and the adroitness necessary to handle a rapidly shifting center of gravity. It is these factors, particularly friction of moving parts, that severely limit speed and endurance.

To the above simple principles must be added certain other basic details, in order that locomotion may be accomplished by tetrapods. A limb must both pull and push the body forward while contributing to the maintenance of equilibrium and must effect recovery after a stride, at the same time co-ordinating with the other limbs.

"Gait" is considered to be the particular manner used by an animal in its progression, as the walk or trot; a "cycle" is one completed action by all of the feet employed; a "stride" is the completed action by a single limb; the "swing" of any limb is the completed advancement or retardation of a single limb; and a "phase" or "instant" is any particular point, with one or more limbs concerned, in the locomotor cycle.

In reality each stride consists of four periods in quadrupedal locomotion. The limb, after advancement, at first pulls the body forward until the foot is below the shoulder or hip, after which it pushes the body upward and forward. In recovery the limb is first pulled forward and bent, so as to clear the ground, and then pushed forward to its utmost extent. These four phases are fundamental but differ to a considerable degree with the kind of animal and its habitual posture. The pull-push ratios of the first two phases differ with the muscular equipment and its disposition, as well as with the velocity. Pull seems greater for the forelimbs and push for the hind. Primitive reptiles probably did more pulling with the forelimbs, and living mammals do more pushing with the hind.

The propulsive-support ratio of limb function varies, also, with body type and speed. Providing both pairs of limbs are approximately of the same size, the support role is relatively higher in the pair nearer the center of gravity and the propulsive role in the other pair.

A dog bounds forward and lands on the forelimbs, which support him while he gathers his hindquarters under him for another effort. The hind limbs contribute much more than half of the propulsive effort and the forelegs more than 50 per cent of the effort expended in overcoming gravity. Of course, however, one pair of limbs can increase in relative strength to the degree that it functions exclusively in both support and propulsion, as in the kangaroo.

Manter (1938) investigated the mechanics of the walk in the cat by means of an apparatus indicating stress of a single foot in the downward, backward, and forward direction. He found by this that a negative component is operative—a retarding thrust as each foot meets the ground, which is greater for the forelimb than for the hind limb. This factor undoubtedly varies with the gait, speed, and kind of animal. He also found that during walking approximately three-fifths of the total reaction is distributed in the forelimbs, chiefly because of the nearer center of gravity, and that the greatest upward thrust by the forelimbs occurs when the step is three-fourths completed.

In considering terrestrial locomotion of quadrupedal and bipedal animals, the first part of the chapter on proportions should be read. The items discussed there all have a bearing on gait. Perhaps it is proper to say that gait is determined by three factors in varying degree—fundamental behavior fixations, bodily conformation, and immediate convenience.

The fixation of locomotor patterns involves the establishment of nervous reflex arcs, usually of extreme complexity. The lower in the scale the animal, the more purely reflex are the locomotor movements. The running of a lizard may be compared to the operation of an automobile. The driver may start and stop the car, go fast or slow, and steer, but he cannot change the order of firing of the cylinders; and it is likely that the lizard cannot alter the sequence of limb movement. The latter, as well as the action of the individual segments, has been fixed over a long period of time on the plan best adapted to some ancestral type and permitted by the conformation of the body and by the limitations of the central nervous system, including limitations on ideal co-ordination. Locomotor reflex arcs are already established, in relatively perfect degree, in such precocious young as most ungulates, but not in placental mammals born in a more helpless state. Locomotor reflexes of the forelimbs only, however, are temporarily present in newborn marsupials, in spite of their immaturity. In all animals the reflexes are more easily acquired for some gaits than for others. Most horses have to be taught the running walk (rack). A child quickly learns to walk erect on its legs, but only with great difficulty upon its hands. A sloth cannot be taught to climb with the agility of a monkey or a kangaroo to gallop. The reflex-arc potentialities are probably absent. On the other hand, it is not impossible, although perhaps unlikely, that an elephant or opossum could be taught to gallop.

At low speed the part played by a single leg in maintaining body balance is very simple; at high speed it is complicated. Its timing and the force that it can exert depend upon the weight of the body and hence the speed and degree of shifting of the center of gravity, as well as the facility with which recovery of the member may be accomplished. The latter is probably a very important factor. In addition, in most mammals the forelegs are shorter than the hind, and this can introduce a difficulty that has never before been pointed out. This fact means that if the hind legs accomplish a full stride, the front legs are unable to match it. Hence at high speed in the symmetrical gaits, such as the running walk, trot, and pace, although the front feet meet the ground symmetrically with the hind, they leave the ground before they would were they as long as the hind. Thus in the fast trot, the front foot always leaves the ground before the contralateral hind foot, and, accordingly, the forequarters are free of the ground longer than the hindquarters. This fact probably acts as a decelerating factor, and the implication is clear, as follows: If a stock, such as the reptiles, with a locomotor pattern based on symmetry of action, has the hind legs longer than the front ones and if cursorial ability then improves, the functional accentuation falls increasingly on the hind legs and decreasingly on the other pair. The tendency will then be for the animal to become bipedal, as have so many of the extinct reptiles. If, however, an animal favors the gallop as a speed gait, the shorter front legs need not prove to be a handicap (as in hares), and it need not become bipedal, although it may do so for other reasons (as with jerboas), particularly if it has a heavy tail.

Additional details of bodily conformation determining gait are great weight of head because of antlers, and excessive limb length, as mentioned elsewhere.

The factor of immediate convenience need not be considered at length. For one thing it is impossible to tell what is convenient to an animal at a given time, and, for another, this is determined largely by bodily conformation, already discussed. Possibly here belongs length of stride. Some horses are much faster walkers than others, because their natural stride is longer. I myself, although rather tall, am a slow walker because my stride is naturally shorter than that of many of my friends of lesser stature. I find a longer stride not natural or, in other words, not so comfortable. The reason is obscure, probably dependent upon intangible differences in the muscles or their physiology. This probably has little to do with maximum speed; but high speed has other similar factors of comfort.

I think that in reality locomotion by tetrapods on land should be basically divided into two sorts. One kind was inherited directly from fishes, mainly by contortions of the body with assistance by the limbs and involving action essentially in the horizontal plane and of a character employed by the earliest tetrapods, as well as by modern amphibians. The second, better fitted to land travel, is accomplished mainly by movement of the limbs, with minor assistance by body-bending, having action chiefly in the vertical plane and of a character employed by the higher mammals. They involve two entirely distinct patterns of nervous control.

Gaits may be divided into numberless arbitrary categories according to limb sequence, number of feet upon the ground at different instants, and such points. Some investigators have followed one plan and some another, for it is difficult to reduce complicated action to rule-of-thumb. In watching a horse race, propulsion seems to be the all-important thing. After studying locomotion for a long time, I feel that the elevating of the body above the ground and keeping it there —or, in other words, equilibrium—is the proper base, and the simplest, from which to start. But, first, for convenience one should divide terrestrial locomotion by limbed vertebrates into quadrupedal and bipedal gaits, although the former progresses more or less insensibly into the latter. And symbols will be needed for the designation of individual limbs and the order in which they operate. The most obvious is the best plan, and they will consist of LF (left front), RF (right front), LR (left rear), and RR (right rear).

It will be helpful to explain the different gaits in graphic manner. The most interesting is by a series of sketches for a single cycle. This is productive of variable results, for with slow-motion pictures one has a large number of choices for the few positions illustrated in each cycle. In making such a selection, however, an effort has been made to choose frames in which the critical leg was in one of five positions—fully advanced, fully retarded, vertical, or the two intermediate positions, according to which appeared to be most desirable for the purpose in mind.

Each gait has eight important periods, one for each of the four foot-falls, and one for each period that a foot is suspended. This, basically, is the most important detail of gaits to illustrate. If two footfalls oc-cur or if two feet leave the ground at the same instant, the series of eight will be shortened or telescoped. A defect is that the impression given is that the interval between each phase depicted is equal, when as a matter of fact it is not. Also the personal equation enters into this and any other comparable scheme, for it is frequently difficult to decide whether or not the weight has actually been removed from one foot (i.e., whether it has theoretically left the ground) before some other footfall occurs.

The series of devices termed the "support formula" is useful in re-cording the number of feet upon the ground at each change of this factor and for illustrating any phase that may have been omitted or slurred over, in the case discussed, from the basic plan for that gait.

Finally, most of the figures illustrating the gaits are, for uniformi-ty, those of the horse, because this is the animal in which most gaits can be readily observed. The series of gait pictures could be greatly expanded; for instance, I have slow-motion pictures of sixteen differ-ent transverse-gallop formulas of the horse. But a few of each basic variety of a gait should prove entirely adequate. With the exceptions noted, all these figures have been traced, by means of a projection ap-paratus, from selected frames of slow-motion pictures (64 frames per second) taken by myself. In studying gaits, however, I have also free-ly used not only the figures published, notably by Muybridge, Still-man, and Hayes, but a series of photographs that for years I have accumulated.

Muybridge (1877) said that a hind foot always begins the walk, while Hayes (1922), Lamb (1935), and others have affirmed that it starts with a front foot. As a matter of fact, it is probably not feasible to designate the foot with which an animal initiates locomotion, be-cause the first foot to move appears to be determined by the body posture of the moment. It is convenient, however, and in the interest of uniformity, to select a particular phase as initiating a cycle. For the symmetrical gaits I have arbitrarily chosen the instant of left-front-foot suspension as the starting detail, and for the gallop the in-stant of the first footfall following total suspension.

QUADRUPEDAL GAITS

It is most logical, I am convinced, to divide the quadrupedal gaits into three main groups, two of them symmetrical and one asymmetrical in rhythm. In each of them there occurs one sequence termed "diagonal" and another called "lateral." In discussing them, accentuation will again be placed upon the horse, for practical reasons.

SYMMETRICAL GAITS

Basic characteristics of symmetrical gaits are that such bending of the axial skeleton as occurs is in the horizontal plane, the intervals between footfalls are evenly spaced, the support pattern is basically repetitively symmetrical, and each action is counterbalanced or damped by the antagonistic movements of a corresponding member. One may divide symmetrical gaits into two categories: (1) those in which each foot is placed at an instant separate from the rest (the walk) and (2) those in which two feet are placed at the same instant (the trot and pace). So the former is fundamentally a four-time, and the latter a two-time, gait. They will be treated under these headings.

In the case of a symmetrical gait the distance between the two front footfalls and between the two hind footfalls must be the same, of course. At slow tempo, when the animal is not extended, this offers no difficulty. In an animal such as the horse, however, with hind legs longer than the front legs, the maximum stride of the former is longer than the anterior appendages can easily stretch. This difficulty is overcome at high speed in the trot and the pace by the lagging front foot leaving the ground before the corresponding lagging hind foot. This is shown for the trot in Figure 38 and for the pace in the last detail of Figure 39. This fact has not been explained before, and it is the reason that there must be greater vertical deflection of the forequarters than of the hindquarters at speed in the symmetrical gaits, because the former are longer unsupported.

The two-time symmetrical division of quadrupedal locomotion is divisible into a diagonal-support gait, termed the "trot," and a lateral-support gait, termed the "pace." In them the support formula is shortened from the theoretical eight phases to four, because of the feet being synchronized by pairs.

Diagonal-support gait, or the trot.—In this gait, support is furnished by alternation of diagonal pairs of limbs; and propulsion, accordingly, is by the opposing pair of diagonals, the two footfalls of each pair being in unison. At slow tempo—the walking trot—the support formula is 4–2–4–2, and in the true trot, 0–2–0–2.

The earliest tetrapods, when they emerged from an aquatic habitat, must have progressed much as does a salamander today. The left front foot and contralateral rear foot were advanced while the body was bent to the right, and the step was taken by both as the body bent in the opposite direction. By this means shoulder and hip were advanced as the corresponding limbs reached forward. This mode of locomotion, sometimes slightly modified, is the one now followed by limbed amphibians and reptiles, particularly those of broad beam, like tortoises and alligators. In it support alternates from one diagonal to the other, while the opposite diagonal limbs are stepping in unison. Some reptiles (such as lizards), however, exhibit a slight modification of this gait; and I have often noted a tendency toward the sequence of the true walk and that the advancement of a hind foot tends to follow, rather than to match, the action of the contralateral forefoot.

Fig. 36.—The footfall formula of the walking trot. The particular feet upon the ground during each of the four phases are indicated by circles. Direction of progress from left to right.

Of course, in the lizard, with its limbs sprawled to the side, the action of the individual legs is very different from anything encountered in mammals. But, aside from that, it is not often that one observes the walking trot in mammals. It does occur in such instances as old and decrepit horses and donkeys, as mentioned by Magne de la Croix (1936), and in an infirm cow and some caged primates observed by myself. During progression at this gait the number of feet upon the ground at one time alternates between two and four.

The true trot (Fig. 37) has the rhythm of the walking trot but at an increased rate. Diagonal footfalls match perfectly, and support alternates between diagonals, the tempo being such that there are either two or no feet upon the ground at once. At this gait equilibrium is easy of attainment, and hence, in the case of the horse at least, it is the least tiring method of traveling at a fair rate of speed. As in all symmetrical gaits, the animal is incapable of utilizing to the full its powerful body musculature in the vertical plane. It does, however, make partial use of this in the horizontal plane, for at each step by the hind feet the hips are swung to that side. The deflection is less than one might think, and S. H. Chubb (in a letter to author) stated that he had found, by some very ingenious photography, that it amounted to but $1\frac{1}{4}$ inches for a side, or a total horizontal oscillation of $2\frac{1}{2}$ inches. In this way each stride is lengthened a fraction of an inch.

Unlike the pace, there is danger of interference in the trot; and, accordingly, at speed the hind feet must be spread so that, when advanced, each by-passes the ipselateral front foot. This has some decelerating influence. The trotting advantage is with a long-bodied horse; but the stride, and hence the time during which the body is unsupported (twice during each cycle), is limited by the law of falling bodies, as explained under the gallop.

The true trot is probably the speed gait of lizards; but I have been unable to prove this, for their action is too quick for the eye to follow

Fig. 37.—The four phases of the true trot, with its footfall formula below. By a five-gaited saddle horse.

and I have seen no illustrative. slow-motion pictures. It is also the gait at medium speed of the great majority of cursorial mammals, but not usually of others. I have never observed anteaters or squirrels to trot. Most ungulates, cats, and dogs do so. It is not a gait suited to small, light mammals whose limb rhythm must be very quick; and that is why a toy dog appears ridiculous when mincing along at the trot.

Table 3 (p. 242) shows that the maximum official record for the trot is at the rate of 31.4 miles per hour for 1 mile. The half-mile record is at an even lower speed (30.8), so it is indicated that a well-trained horse does not tire appreciably for the distance of a mile. After that his speed drops as the distance increases. The maximum distance for the cycle is about 20 feet.

Lateral-support gait, or the pace.—This two-time gait resembles the trot in that support and propulsion are furnished by two limbs in unison; but, whereas in the trot the limbs concerned are diagonals, in the pace they are laterals. Hence support is more precarious, because of the side-to-side shift in the center of gravity, and the gait is a special-ized one.

The walking pace, with support formula 4–2–4–2, is probably never encountered in pure form, for support by the lateral limbs means that the tendency of the body to fall to the opposite side must be overcome by strong muscular effort, in other respects wasted.

At a faster tempo, with support formula 0–2–0–2, this gait be-comes the true pace, sometimes called "rack" or "amble" (Fig. 39). A disadvantage still is that there is a strong side-to-side swing, as the rider of a speedily pacing horse can abundantly testify; but in the case of the horse the body has enough inertia and the rhythm of limb action can be sufficiently rapid for this swing to be partially damped. The lateral oscillations of the hips appear to be a trifle less in the pace than in the trot; and the former gait is undoubtedly the more awk-

Fig. 38.—Another frame from the motion pictures of the trotting horse shown in Figure 37, to picture the fact that in the fast trot the front foot leaves the ground before the contralateral hind foot.

ward of accomplishment, hence more tiring, as can perhaps be dem-onstrated by a human walker swinging his arms in pace rather than in trot rhythm. Probably the greatest advantage of the pace is that there can be no interference between rear and front feet, and there-fore no spreading of the former is necessary. Accordingly, the rear legs can act more truly vertical to the center of gravity, and greater or more efficient propulsive force should result. A longer stride theo-retically is feasible in the pace than in the trot, and the cycle of the famous pacer, Dan Patch, is said to have been as much as 21 feet.

As in the case of the trot, in the fast pace the forequarters are long-er unsupported than the hindquarters, because of length of limb; and there is greater vertical deflection of the forequarters.

Pacing is a gait well suited only to very long-legged animals, most prone to interfere at the trot and with center of gravity high above the ground. A small proportion of dogs, usually of rather large size and mostly setters, take to it naturally, and occasional horses. The latter are easily taught to pace by means of a special harness that discourages spreading, fore and aft, of the legs on the same side. At harness races there are always a number of horses entered in both trotting and (with restrictive harness) pacing races. The only wild-animal group that appears regularly to travel at the pace comprises camels (they gallop, too). I have seen it claimed that the giraffe does so, but this is denied by others; and it is not unlikely that its legs are too long for anything but the walk and the gallop. Whether all of the South American camels pace I do not know.

Probably most horsemen believe that the pace is a trifle faster than the trot but that it is more fatiguing. The figures in Table 3 (p. 242) tend in this direction. The half-mile record is faster for the pace than for the trot, and at a faster rate than for the mile, which is not the case for the trot. The speed drops more rapidly with distance, too,

Fig. 39.—The four phases of the fast pace, with its footfall formula. By a standard-bred horse.

but to an insignificant amount. It is also possible that the figures are misleading, for there are more trotting than pacing races and hence more opportunities for making records in the former gait.

The four-time symmetrical gait, or walk.—The walk is a combined diagonal- and lateral-support gait, and the support tends to alternate between diagonal and lateral limbs, the footfalls are all separate and evenly spaced, and at all speeds there is always at least one foot on the ground. Hence this gait most nearly meets the ideal of the most effective locomotion, which is that deviation from the horizontal should be minimal, with support and propulsion both uniform and continuous. Because of the phase of lateral support, this gait is not suited to a sluggish, broad-bodied animal, such as a tortoise or an alligator; but for the average mammal, at least, it is undoubtedly the least fatiguing low-speed gait.

Study of the different tempos of the walk indicates a basic fact of symmetrical-gait progression by tetrapods. Comparison of the crawl with the slow walk shows that in the phases of even number (second, fourth, sixth) the number of feet upon the ground drops from four to two in the second and sixth, but not in the fourth and eighth, as tempo gradually increases. At a faster walk all phases of even number drop to a two-foot support, where they remain no matter how fast the speed. The reduction is from four to two, rather than to three, because in progressing from the first to the third phase—in Figure 43, for instance—the second front footfall does not occur until after the second hind foot has left the ground. Thus all eight-phase gaits (not the trot or the pace) pass through a stage, as tempo increases, in which support is not uniform for all even-numbered phases but fluctuates between two and four for the walk, but between one and three for the gallop.

The odd-number phases in the support formulas for the walk of different tempos also fluctuate, but differently. They are at first all in threes, then every other (third, seventh) drops to one, and finally all odd-numbered phases are reduced to one for the fastest running walk.

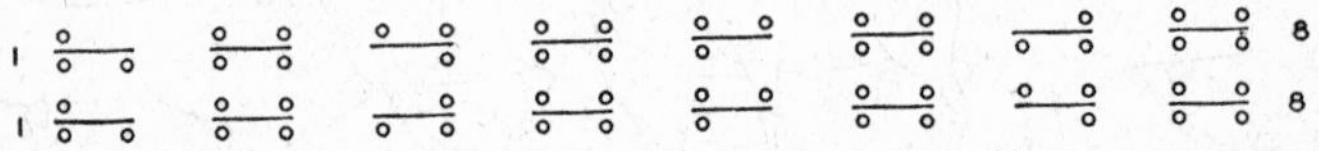

FIG. 40.—The support formula of the crawl, or slowest walk, the transverse-, above, and the lateral-support formula below.

Two sequences are possible for the walk, as in other basic gaits. In one, action is LF–RR–RF–LR, and in the other, LF–LR–RF–RR. The only difference between the two is that one is a mirror image of the other. It is convenient to distinguish between these two sequences; hence, based on the second footfall, the first will be called the "diagonal" and the other the "lateral" walk. As they are so similar, one would naturally expect them to be used almost indiscriminately by particular mammals, but the fact remains that the lateral walk is extremely rare. So it is the diagonal walk to which the mammalian locomotor control has become geared in the vast majority of cases.

The simplest type of walk is here termed the "crawl" (Fig. 40). It is distinguished by its slow tempo and the fact that in typical form no fewer than three feet are on the ground at once. Its support formula is 4–3–4–3–4–3–4–3. The three-point support is shifted, with the help of intermediate four-point suspension, first diagonally (for the diagonal crawl), then laterally, then to the other diagonal and to the other lateral, to complete a cycle of eight different phases. For the sake of completeness the support formulas of both diagonal (Fig. 40, *upper*) and lateral (Fig. 40, *lower*) are given. The support is more solid than in any other gait, and the diagonal crawl constitutes the mode of tottering progression of very young puppies and kittens. Slightly accelerated, this type passes into the next.

The true walk resembles the crawl at a faster tempo. Three speeds are usually recognized: slow, in which the imprint of the hind foot does not reach that of the ipselateral forefoot; medium, in which the

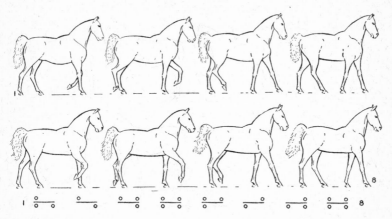

Fig. 41.—The eight phases of the slow diagonal walk (left to right) with its footfall formula. By a five-gaited saddle horse under tight rein.

two imprints coincide; and fast, in which the former exceeds the latter. This is not altogether satisfactory, for it does not take into consideration other differences of greater importance. For practical purposes it seems better to classify them merely as the slow and the fast walk, with variations of each. Support is by never less than two feet.

The slow walk next in sequence to the crawl has support that is only slightly less secure, two diagonals being substituted for two of the four four-point supports in each cycle of the crawl. The support for the slow diagonal walk is, accordingly, 3–2–3–4–3–2–3–4 (Fig. 41). This walk may regularly be observed when a horse is kept at a

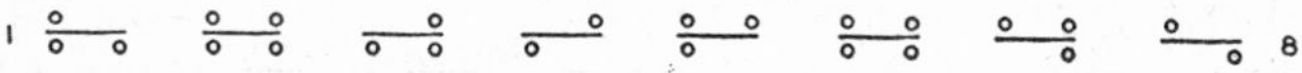

Fig. 42.—The footfall formula of the lateral slow walk

very slow walk. I think I have noted it in infirm animals. The lateral variety (Fig. 42) has the same support formula, of course, but with a different foot sequence. The latter formula was taken from Magne de la Croix's (1936) illustration of a walking opossum, but I have never observed it myself. It will be noted that in the slow walk the security of the four-point support is relinquished through a three- to a two-point diagonal support, and then back through a three- to a four-point support.

The slow walk passes to a faster tempo so insensibly that it is frequently impossible to decide the instant when a leg ceases to furnish support; and so occasionally it is uncertain whether the pictures of a single cycle should be allocated to the slow or to the fast walk.

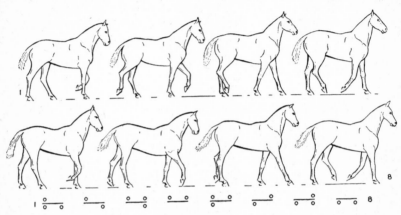

FIG. 43.—The eight phases of the diagonal walk, at a tempo slightly faster than in Figure 41, with its footfall formula. By a thoroughbred hunter.

In the fast walk four-point suspension is abandoned and a lateral two-point suspension substituted. Thus the eight phases of each cycle are composed of four three-point and four two-point suspension instants, the latter alternating between diagonals and laterals. So the relative instability of a two-point suspension is always followed by a three-point instant, during which any defects of equilibrium may be corrected. The fast diagonal walk is regularly employed by nearly all mammals. I have not myself detected the fast lateral walk, and it is not here illustrated, although the proper footfall sequence is given (Fig. 44).

FIG. 44.—The footfall formula of the lateral walk, of the same tempo as in Figure 43

There are a number of factors that may disturb the rhythm of the walk, such as temporary lameness and later fixation of the habit of arhythmical walking, a heavy load, extreme width of body, and what may be termed individuality of preference. At times the second and fourth footfalls of the diagonal walk will be slightly accelerated, tending toward the walking trot (armadillo, most baboons); or, if the second and fourth footfalls be decelerated, the approach is toward the walking pace (as in one dog observed that trots at greater speed, and some racoons). It should be mentioned, perhaps, that it is extremely difficult for an observer to detect minute variations in the symmetry of the footfalls of a small mammal; and it is probable that many kinds approach this walking trot in some degree.

One variation of the walk is encountered in draft horses which are pulling a heavy load. Under this condition the important factor is traction. Even equilibrium is secondary because the harness traces anchored on the load provide much of the balancing influence. The phases of a single cycle then tend to match the crawl, but with all instants of the four-point suspension eliminated so that the pattern is more nearly that of all four arrangements of three-point support. In other words, it is the crawl telescoped, one footfall taking place at the same time that another foot (of the other pair) is raised from the ground. In this way the load is always being advanced by two feet solidly placed, with the other two in transition, one to and the other away from a footfall.

The running walk.—This term is preferable to those of "single-foot," "fox trot," "rack," or "amble." The last two are sometimes used to designate the pace. As the name indicates, it is an accelerated walk, in which the time that each foot spends upon the ground is reduced.

Stillman (1882) asserted that at this gait both front feet but not both hind feet can be clear of the ground at once. This statement holds for only moderate speeds, at a precise rate when a maximum anchored stride by the longer hind legs can be matched by the shorter front legs only by one leaving the ground before the other falls. At still higher running-walk speeds the weight is withdrawn from one hind foot before the other falls, for otherwise the speed attainable would be very moderate indeed.

Theoretically, the running walk is the ideal speed gait, as it provides the most continuous support with the minimum of horizontal deflection and propulsion by one limb after the other, evenly spaced. Actually, it has certain disadvantages. For one thing it appears to require an undue amount of energy to move all four limbs in different manner at the same time with celerity; it is impossible at this gait to utilize the trunk musculature to the full; also straddling of the hind limbs is necessary to prevent interference with the front feet. Hence it proves not quite so fast as, and more fatiguing than, the trot or pace.

The running walk comes natural to very few animals. In diagonal sequence it is the exclusive speed gait of the elephant, as it probably was of many of the larger extinct graviportal mammals. In lateral sequence it is the intermediate gait (between walk and gallop) of some baboons. At least it has been so illustrated by both Magne de la Croix and Muybridge (support pattern, Fig. 45); but the baboons I have watched have done nothing but the diagonal walk, the walking trot or close to it, and the gallop. The diagonal pattern appears to be the one that is always used by horses.

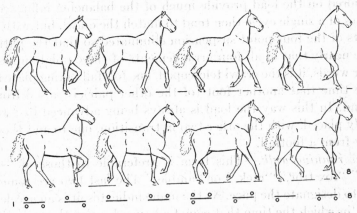

Fig. 45.—The eight phases of the diagonal slow running walk, with its footfall formula. By a five-gaited saddle mare.

As speed is gradually increased from the fast walk, the support pattern of the latter (3–2–3–2–3–2–3–2) is modified, first, by the fact that both front feet, but not both rear, may leave the ground at once, giving a formula of 3–2–1–2–3–2–1–2 (Fig. 45), and, finally, in the fast running walk, the formula 2–1–2–1–2–1–2–1 (Fig. 47). The latter is more easily understood when it is pointed out that it differs from that of the slow walk in that each three-point phase of the latter resembles the corresponding one-point phase of the former with one pair of limbs free of the ground during a long stride.

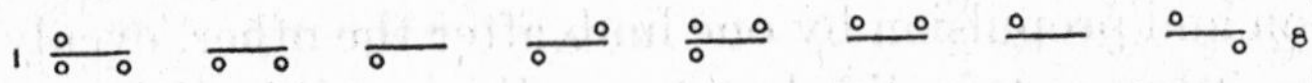

Fig. 46.—The footfall formula of the lateral slow running walk

There is no standing speed "record" for the running walk in the horse. It is a cultivated gait by which considerable distance may be covered more speedily than at a walk and with less fatigue to the rider than at a trot. It is not a gait for racing, and owners of fine saddle horses are not interested in the maximum possible.

Basic characteristics of asymmetrical gaits include pronounced bending in the vertical plane of the axial skeleton; uneven spacing of the intervals between footfalls; asymmetry of the support pattern and the presence of only one such pattern in each locomotor cycle; the fact that each limb action is not damped by specific action of a corresponding member and that typically there is but one period of suspension during each cycle. The propulsive thrusts, incidence of support, movements of recovery, and maintenance of equilibrium are not evenly distributed throughout the locomotor cycle but are

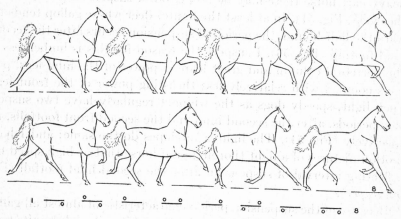

FIG. 47.—The eight phases of the diagonal fast running walk, with its footfall formula. By a five-gaited saddle gelding of high class and particularly spirited action.

grouped in sequential phases. Or it may be said that in symmetrical gaits the primary impulse strokes by the hind feet are equal and symmetrical, while in asymmetrical gaits they are unequal and asymmetrical and are followed by a relatively long interval for recovery of equilibrium.

The basic plan for the gallop is as follows: After a recovery period the animal places one (either) hind foot upon the ground, strides forward with the other and, while thrusting forward with the hind feet, shifts the weight to either the contralateral (diagonal or transverse gallop) or the ipselateral (lateral or rotogallop) front foot, followed by the second front foot widely spaced, both front feet, particularly the second, giving a powerful upward thrust, after which the body is gathered together in preparation for the next cycle.

Either very slow or very high speed does various things to this typical arrangement. At a slow canter the first front footfall may occur before the second hind footfall. At all speeds most horses and cursorial mammals of comparable weight have a period of total suspension after the second front footfall. It is accomplished by a powerful upthrust of the leading front leg and is necessary for recovery of equilibrium, apparently, in a speedy but somewhat heavy animal whose weight precludes a vertebral column of great limberness. In other words, animals of great limberness can gather their hind legs under them without such a strong upthrust by the front legs with consequent period of suspension. Hence in most deer there is no suspension at this period of the cycle of the gallop. And in the labored canter of a heavy cart horse there may be no period of suspension anywhere in the cycle (Fig. 51). In at least the lighter deer whose gallop tends toward the half-bound, the period of suspension occurs after the second hind footfall (Fig. 53). I suspect the reason for this is limberness of the vertebral column and great leaping power of the hind legs, perhaps coupled with relatively less thrusting power of the front legs. Such light, speedy dogs as the whippet regularly have two suspension periods, after the second hind and the second front footfalls, respectively (Fig. 54). The lighter antelopes do the same; and I have motion pictures of a light thoroughbred horse that at high speed has a fleeting interval of suspension after the second hind footfall (Fig. 52, *upper*).

Because of the suspension period characteristic of almost all gallop tempos it is somewhat difficult to decide, arbitrarily, what is its typical support formula. Chiefly for the reason that most interest attaches to the horse, I will select the horse, rather than deer or whippet, as galloping in basic fashion. The fourth detail of this formula also offers difficulty. In theory it might be considered as having four-foot suspension. In practice, however, the third foot leaves the ground before the fourth footfall, so it has only two-foot suspension. The former formula would be 1–2–3–4–3–2–1–0; the latter, 1–2–3–2–3–2–1–0.

Aside from modification of the support formula of the asymmetrical gaits, or varieties of the gallop, incident to the rate of speed, they occur in a much larger variety of patterns than the symmetrical gaits. Because the intervals between footfalls are equal and neither hind foot can be said to "lead," the two-time symmetrical gait occurs in but two varieties—the diagonal trot and the lateral pace; and the four-time symmetrical gait also in two, comprising the diagonal walk and the lateral walk. But, because the intervals between hind footfalls are not all equal in the gallop, at this gait an animal may lead with either the right or the left hind foot, and with either employ the diagonal or lateral sequence. Hence four patterns are possible for the typical gallop. In the asymmetrical gaits a cycle is considered, for convenience, to start with the first hind footfall, and in the typical gallop the two hind footfalls are in immediate sequence. In a slow canter, however, either the second rear and first front footfall may coincide, making a three-time gallop, or the latter may actually precede the former, either in diagonal or in lateral pattern. This makes four more possible kinds of gallop. The interval of suspension may follow either the second hind footfall or the second front footfall, or there may be both or none, making four more kinds. Finally, there are several varieties of the half-bound and bound or other combinations in which various pairs of footfalls are synchronous. It hardly seems worth while to illustrate every one of these possible varieties or even to describe in great detail more than the major sequences.

There are probably several reasons why more speed can be attained at the gallop than at any other gait. One of these is that the body and hind-limb muscles are able to act more as a unit in catapulting the animal forward, and there is a longer interval for complete recovery. The closer together the hind limbs, the more efficient their action in this respect, but the shorter their effective period of support and their equilibrial influence. So the extent of the stride between the two hind footfalls does not vary with absolute speed and is often, even with maximum locomotor effort, not so great as length of limb permits. On the other hand, the extent of the stride between the two front feet is close to maximum, except at slow speed, in order to prolong the support by these members for the greatest possible lineal distance.

Another reason for the speed advantage of the gallop is that only at this gait can the long and powerful neck muscles of the ungulates operate to full advantage. In these the brachiocephalic muscle passes from head to humerus, the rhythm of the gallop is properly timed for the natural rhythm of the length of neck and weight of head of the animal concerned, and the upward swing of the head helps advance the front leg. The rhythm of the other gaits is too fast for the swing of the head to be of help. The part that this muscle plays in the gallop can clearly be seen near the end of a race when the horses are tiring, and then they place great reliance on the up-and-down swing of the head and neck to help them to the finish.

A feature of the gallop is that, except at highest tempo, the leading hind foot (the second hind footfall) is on the ground longer and appears in a larger number of the eight phases of the support formula of the gallop than the lagging hind foot, for the reason that the former not only probably has a larger support function but gives the more powerful thrust, with a certain degree of "follow through," before leaving the ground. If one front footfall appears in fewer phases of the gallop than the other, it is always the leading foot, because the latter gives the more powerful upthrust and expends a smaller proportion of its energy in merely keeping the body from falling.

I doubt if the length of the period of suspension has anything to do with the advantages of the gallop, except that because of the sequences of this gait an animal whose suspension comes after the second front footfall has a better opportunity for gathering his legs under him for the next cycle. As a matter of fact, it seems probable that the suspension interval is shorter in the gallop than in a fast trot. The period of suspension is limited at all gaits by the law of falling bodies. Thus an unsupported body will fall 1 foot in $\frac{1}{4}$ second, but 4 feet in $\frac{1}{2}$ second and 16 feet in 1 second. However, the body falls only from the highest point to which it is projected by the limbs; but the horizontal deflection of a race horse is remarkably little, and it can afford to be unsupported for only a small fraction of a second at a time. Some mammals, such as some of the African gazelles, do spring about with a remarkable degree of horizontal deflection, but they pay for it in rate of speed.

It seems impossible to tell why some animals prefer the transverse, and others the lateral, gallop. Preferring the former are horse, rhino, goat, sheep, cattle, camel, and cat. Favoring the lateral gallop are dog, deer, pronghorn, antelopes, and giraffe. But a change from one form to the other is occasionally indulged in by some. There are naturally "right-handed" and "left-handed" horses; but a horse will lead with one foot for a while and then change to the other, usually so smoothly that close attention is necessary to detect it. This is seemingly done to rest tired muscles, just as a man will shift his weight from one foot to the other while standing; but at times the change is probably made just for a whim, as I have seen a horse change its lead every 100 feet or so.

Of 100 horses passing me consecutively at a race track during early-morning exercise, 52 led with the right foot and 48 with the left when I first noted them, but some changed from one to the other while I was watching. Of these, 2 were following the lateral gallop, leading with the left front foot, but 1 of them changed to the transverse gallop before my eyes.

Gregarious animals usually exhibit a group synchronization in gaits, doubtless akin to the stimulus that causes a flock of starlings to wheel in unison. It has been my experience that in a particular race a large majority of the horses will be leading with the same foot. Averaging my observations of a considerable number of such groups of horses, from 5 to 13 individuals, closely bunched and running at speed, the proportions of those leading with the same foot versus the others have been as 9 is to 2. This trait seems to obtain even more in the wild, to the extent that often every individual of a considerable herd is leading with the same foot. I remember being struck with the fact that in one of Martin Johnson's movies of giraffes there was utter lack of synchronism to their gaits; and inquiry elicited the information that these animals had been startled by a rifle shot, apparently thus disrupting their group synchronization for the time being.

It comes natural to most horses to lead, at the canter, with the inside front foot when moving around a curve, as in a show ring. If it does not come natural to an individual horse, he is easily taught. In such cases, if he is leading with the foot less natural to him and something disturbs the animal, such as the whirr of a motion-picture camera, he is very likely to break his stride and return to the lead to which he is more addicted.

The canter, sometimes termed the "lope," is largely a decelerated gallop, but because of the exigencies of equilibrium it is not quite the same. It has been cultivated in saddle horses, for the comfort of the rider, to the point where it is often at a considerably slower tempo than would naturally occur and than is economical of effort. For the latter reason support looms larger in the picture of the canter than in that of the gallop, just as it requires more effort by the bicycle rider at very slow speed than at a faster rate. Whereas in the gallop support fairly alternates between both front and both hind feet, lateral support in the canter has a more important place, and the first front footfall tends to be in unison with the last hind footfall.

It is not improbable that no canter is slow enough to include the four-point support formula already given, so that actually the formula is 1–2–3–2–3–2–1–0. This is illustrated (Fig. 48) for the normal transverse four-time canter, which is actually a slow gallop. The footfall pattern for the four-time lateral canter or slow rotogallop is also given (Fig. 49). The three-time canter, however, differs from the true gallop in that the second hind foot and first front foot strike the ground in unison, thus omitting or really telescoping the second detail of the typical support formula, which then becomes 1–3–2–3–2–1–0. A later phase in this support formula can be similarly telescoped.

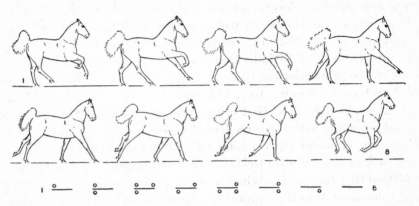

Fig. 48.—The eight phases of the transverse four-time canter in typical gallop sequence, with its footfall formula. By a spirited five-gaited saddle mare. Right hind foot leading.

Another slow canter is that in which the first front foot meets the ground before the second hind foot (Fig. 50). This is frequently encountered but is not merely a slow gallop and so may be termed the "atypical" type. It may vary so closely toward the three-time canter that it is impossible to decide between the two. The support formula is the same as the basic one for the gallop, 1–2–3–2–3–2–1–0, but the footfall pattern is different.

Fig. 49.—The footfall formula of the lateral four-time canter

Still another variation of the canter occurs in the case of the labored action of a heavy draft horse, as illustrated by both Muybridge and Lamb. In this there is no period of total suspension because the second hind foot strikes the ground before the lagging front foot leaves it (detail 8, Fig. 51). Other variations of the canter may be detected, but those included here are sufficient to indicate the possibilities. Transition from canter to gallop is gradual.

As most canters are merely slow gallops, there may be no way to distinguish between the two except arbitrarily. Or it may be said that the gallop is the asymmetrical gait of a tempo sufficiently fast that no more than two feet are upon the ground at the same time. This rule may not apply to particular styles of gallops, as in deer or hares. The true transverse gallop of the horse, then, is shown in the lower series of figures in Figure 52, with support formula of 1–2–1–2–1–2–1–0.

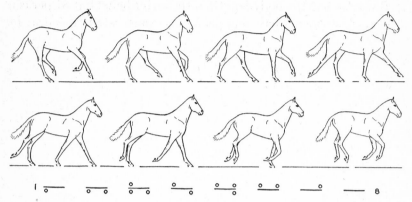

Fig. 50.—The eight phases of the transverse four-time canter in atypical gallop sequence, with its footfall formula. By a thoroughbred gelding. Left hind foot leading.

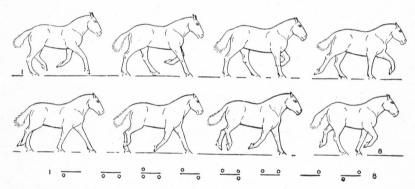

Fig. 51.—The eight phases of the transverse canter as executed by a heavy draft horse, having no period of suspension. Redrawn from Muybridge.

In this series the near (left) hind foot is leading, with support alternating between one and two feet, in each phase, the suspension interval following the second front footfall. In the upper series of this figure is shown a lighter horse, traveling at slightly less speed but with more springy action, whose second hind foot left the ground before the first front footfall, thus having a second interval of suspension, although a very fleeting one, in the middle of the cycle. This is the only instance of this sort among my moving pictures of a large number of galloping horses.

The series of phases in Figure 52 well illustrates the change in body length that takes place between the centripetal (with legs gathered together) and the centrifugal (with legs widely spread) phases of a single cycle. This is particularly noteworthy between phases 4 and 8 of the lower series, the body length in the latter being but 81 per cent of that in the former. Phase 4 appeared so exaggerated after drawing

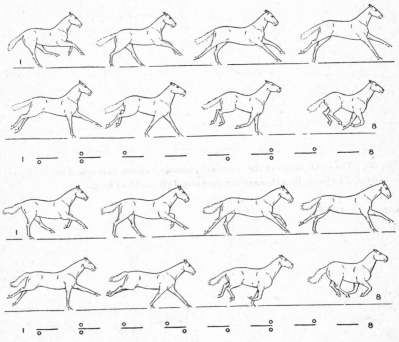

FIG. 52.—Two series, with footfall formulas, showing the transverse fast gallop, left hind foot leading. The lower series is the more typical, of an excellent thoroughbred of fair weight at high speed. The upper series, of a lighter horse with very springy action, is at a transverse gallop of a sort more atypical for the horse, in which there is a very short period of suspension in the middle of the cycle, as well as the longer one at the end.

that I verified the length of body, by means of a photo enlarger, and found that it is as accurate as I could make it. The difference is more pronounced in the lower than in the upper series because the speed was greater in the former.

The period of suspension in the gallop by the horse and many other rather heavy animals with longish legs follows the upward thrust by the leading front leg. In the case of perhaps most of the really lightly built cursorial mammals with slender legs, a curved rump, and tucked-in hindquarters suited to leaping—which includes hares, swifter antelopes, and deer—the period of suspension comes at an entirely different time in the cycle, after the forward thrust by the leading hind leg. Theoretically, this is a more efficient procedure than that followed by the horse, but for its accomplishment the conformation of the animal must be suitable and its weight not too great. Most mammals of these specifications favor the lateral or rotogallop. Seven of the eight phases of this, redrawn from Stillman's pictures of a deer in action, with the footfall pattern, are shown in Figure 53.

The distance covered in a single cycle at the fast gallop varies all the way from 22 feet by a good race horse, through 23 by a very good one, 24 by one of the latter with a long stride, to an exceptional 25 feet, which is the distance given by Chubb (1931) for Man o' War.

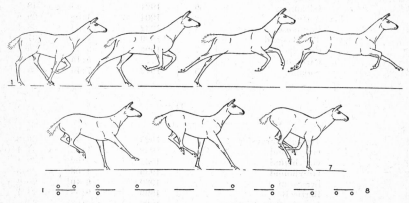

Fig. 53.—Seven phases of the lateral gallop, with its eight-phase footfall formula, of a deer. Redrawn from Stillman.

Some of the swifter antelopes are said to cover as much as 40 feet by exceptional bounds while galloping.

The official speed records for horses are shown in Table 3. Calumet Evelyn in 1933 paced a mile in $1:59\frac{1}{4}$ (30.19 m.p.h.) and in 1936 trotted a mile in $1:59\frac{1}{2}$ (30.12 m.p.h.). All these records are from the *World Almanac* for 1941.

A third pattern of suspension is encountered in such speedy dogs as the whippet and the greyhound, undoubtedly the cheetah, and in some of the lightest, fleetest gazelles, with two suspension periods in each cycle. One of these is after the leading front foot, and the other after the leading rear foot, has left the ground. After the former the legs will be bunched in centripetal suspension (detail 4, Fig. 54), and after the latter they will be extended in centrifugal suspension (detail 8, Fig. 54). To employ this method of locomotion an animal must be built just right, with hindquarters fitted for leaping, a limber back, powerful forequarters for thrusting upward, and a strong neck and brachiocephalic muscles. If the body is heavy, this variety of gallop

TABLE 3
WORLD RECORDS FOR THE HORSE

MILES	HORSE	AGE (YEARS)	YEAR	TIME (SECONDS)	RATE (M.P.H.)
		Running			
$\frac{1}{4}$	Bob Wade	4	1890	$21\frac{1}{4}$	42.3
$\frac{3}{8}$	Galley Slave	2	1938	32	42.3
$\frac{1}{2}$	Gloaming	6	1921	45	40
$\frac{3}{4}$	Artful	2	1904	1:08	39.6
1	Equipoise	4	1932	1:34	38.1
$1\frac{1}{2}$	The Bastard	3	1929	2:23	37.8
2	Pradella	7	1906	3:19	36.2
3	Farragut	5	....	5:15	34.3
4	Sotema	5	1912	7:10	33.4
		Trotting			
$\frac{1}{2}$	Temple Harvester	....	1925	$58\frac{1}{4}$	30.8
1	Greyhound	....	1938	$1:55\frac{1}{4}$	31.1
$1\frac{1}{2}$	Greyhound	....	1937	$3:02\frac{1}{2}$	29.1
2	Greyhound	....	1939	4:06	29.3
3	Lee Stout	....	1939	$6:49\frac{1}{4}$	26.4
4	Bertie R	....	1899	9:58	24.1
5	Imogene Constantine	....	1893	$12:08\frac{1}{4}$	24.7
10	Controller	....	1878	$27:23\frac{1}{4}$	21.9
20	Capt. McGowan	....	1865	58:25	20.5
30	Gen. Taylor	....	1857	1:47:59	16.6
50	Ariel	....	1846	$3:55:40\frac{1}{2}$	12.3
100	Conqueror	....	1853	8:58:53	11.2
		Pacing			
$\frac{1}{2}$	Directum	....	1916	$55\frac{3}{4}$	32.3
1	Billy Direct	....	1938	1:55	31.3
2	Dan Patch	....	1903	4:17	28
3	Elastic Pointer	....	1909	$7:31\frac{1}{2}$	24
4	Joe Jefferson	....	1891	10:10	23.6
5	Angus Peter	....	1933	11:54	25.1

is rarely encountered. I have seen it approached by one race horse, as previously mentioned (Fig. 52).

The mule deer's usual "gallop"—unique as far as I know—is accomplished by all four feet spurning the ground in unison, this being followed by a relatively long period of suspension. This style is not productive of any increase in speed over the regular gallop—rather does the reverse seem to obtain—but it is very effective in mounting a steep slope, and the animal appears to float upward with astonishing ease. The footfall pattern is so simple that it is not illustrated. This animal also uses the lateral gallop.

The bound is really a symmetrical rendition of the asymmetrical gallop. In it an animal leaps from both hind legs together and lands upon both front feet together. In its pure form it is rarely encountered, and then not at speed. A small dog may use it in traveling through deep, soft snow. Its disadvantage lies in the fact that if an animal endeavors to progress at considerable speed and lands on both

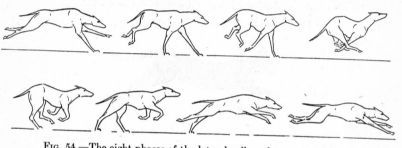

Fig. 54.—The eight phases of the lateral gallop of a speedy whippet

front feet close together, there is a decelerating influence applied that is extremely difficult to overcome. It is just as easy, and much more effective, for the individual to progress at what I have termed the "half-bound."

The half-bound is the gait whereby an animal springs from both hind feet at once and lands first on one front foot, immediately shifting its weight to the other, which has stepped ahead, as in the gallop. In fact the gallop merges insensibly into the half-bound in rather small mammals that are speedy for their size, good leapers, and yet with fairly short legs, such as the house cat, weasels, squirrels, rabbits, and hares. One probable advantage is that during the long leap the animal has a better opportunity for gathering its hindquarters in position for another impulse than it could at the regular gallop. The procedure involved is illustrated by a running cat (Fig. 55).

BIPEDAL GAITS

Bipedal gaits comprise the two-time walk and run and the one-time hop or ricochet by both hind feet in unison. Both are very specialized types of locomotion and are of corresponding interest.

BIPEDAL WALK AND RUN

This gait developed from the quadrupedal trot or walk probably in two fashions, one at slow speed and the other at high speed. Man is not a cursorial mammal, and it is likely that a very helpful and perhaps critical influence in the trend of his ancestors toward bipedalism was the fact that they had other things to do with their hands than keep them on the ground. Their hands were occupied as tools or for carrying articles, when standing around or walking. At first they probably walked either in the quadrupedal or in the bipedal posture, with little or no merging of one into the other.

The other probable manner in which the bipedal two-time gait developed was from a trot. The procedure is illustrated in existing lizards. As locomotional ability increased, the hind limbs developed ascendency over the forelimbs, very possibly because of architectural

Fig. 55.—The half-bound, as executed by a cat

speed limitations in the latter, until the point at which the front legs were an actual hindrance in fast running. At speed the animal then merely rose gradually upon its hind legs and continued thus, easily balanced by its heavy tail; but after a sprint the animal at once becomes quadrupedal. A few particularly fleet lizards, notably the basilisk, now travel in this fashion with amazing celerity; and it seems certainly to have been the manner in which the ancestors of the dinosaurs became bipedal. In this case, then, bipedalism was first developed gradually at the fast trot, which must have been the quadrupedal gait of the early reptiles.

In the bipedal walk and run, progression is much facilitated by action of all four limbs at the trot sequence, and so we really move at a quadrupedal gait with only the two hind feet upon the ground, which furnish all the propulsion and most of the equilibrial effort. At a slow walk a man may progress comfortably with his hands in his pockets, but at a fast walk he is much more at ease, and has more endurance, when swinging each arm in time with the contralateral leg. This is even more so when he runs. The reason is that at a slow walk not a great deal of muscular effort is necessary, and the leg muscles alone accomplish this. At greater speed the body muscles help, by swinging the hips, and this swing must be damped by a counterswing of the shoulders, in order to prevent undue and exhausting shifting of the center of gravity. Also at the run the swing of the arms contributes a very important degree of springiness to the step, thus tending to distribute the effort over many, instead of fewer, muscles.

The terrestrial progression of most birds is at the bipedal walk rather than the hop. The counterbalancing effort by them is not usually by the forelimbs but by a back-and-forth movement of the head and long neck, aided materially by the fact that the legs of the conventional bird (not penguins or loons) are set relatively farther forward than in any mammal. It is true that at speed some of the more highly cursorial birds, such as the ostrich, spread the wings; but apparently the wings either are held stationary to act as sails or stabilizers or are flapped in unison as an aid to speed.

With the exception of a few lizards and most birds, then, man is the only living vertebrate that regularly travels at the bipedal two-time gait, if we exclude the arboreal gibbon, which walks and runs when upon the ground, at the same time holding its long arms aloft as stabilizers. No speed figures are available, except for man and for the ostrich, undoubtedly the fastest avian runner, which can attain 50 miles per hour for a half-mile, according to the late Martin Johnson (manuscript). As listed in the record table (Table 1), the human maximum of 22 miles per hour is a rather poor showing.

BIPEDAL HOP

This, termed by Muybridge the "ricochet," is the saltatory mode of bipedal progression, involving the simultaneous extension of both hind feet as a single unit, without any help by the front feet. It is a sort of bipedal gallop. It can be developed in high degree only by those tetrapods having a long or rather heavy tail to act as rudder or equilibrator. The frog has no tail, but it is fitted for one mighty leap into the depths of a pool or into leafy retreats. If pursued over level ground, the frog's only advantage is the erratic course of its progress. Some hares travel for a short distance in this fashion; but their leaping ability was developed as quadrupeds, and it is doubtful whether they will ever become habitual bipeds.

There appear to be two ways in which bipedal saltation probably developed, both necessitating rather light body weight.

When the reptilian ancestors of birds took to the trees, they were probably already quite highly cursorial and partly bipedal. In the trees they found it convenient to hop from branch to branch; and this is the pattern in which the nervous mechanism operates for terrestrial locomotion in many birds that spend much of their time in trees, but not for most of those feeding exclusively on the ground. Arboreal bipedal reptiles thus probably hopped, but not the exclusively terrestrial bipedal ones.

A deer mouse (Peromyscus) is quadrupedal, but when hurrying over rough terrain it often becomes saltatorial and to some extent bipedal. Its legs are not long enough to step, one at a time, over slight obstructions, so it must leap, and it is sufficiently light to do this with ease. It is on the right road to becoming a saltatorial biped, as is the jerboa. In the latter the reflexes for this mode of progression may well have been so firmly fixed that if, in future millenniums, its descendents should become as large as a beaver they might very well travel by saltation. It is thus likely that the initiation of bipedal saltation in mammals took place in a plains habitat, where a small mammal needed to cover considerable distances for food and where the ground had sufficient grass or other low herbage for it to have to leap over low obstruction in order to progress at the required speed.

On the other hand, if a larger quadruped, of the size of a pointer dog, should gradually become bipedal, it could easily step over low obstructions, and it would find saltation a very jarring and fatiguing mode of locomotion to initiate. So if a bipedal animal saltates, the chances are that its ancestors were small forms. Thus the ancestors of kangaroos were doubtless smaller than a rabbit when they began to leap with both feet in unison. If a bipedal animal travels with feet alternating, its ancestors were probably of considerable size. Thus, if man's ancestors had been as small as a marmoset when they first became terrestrial (rather than arboreal), we might be hopping like kangaroos at present.

It has been suggested by a number of people that saltation was initiated not to increase speed, but for the purpose of dodging pursuers. I think that both these possibilities are unlikely. It was probably started by the ancestors of its possessors because it was the most convenient way of locomotion by a small mammal over the terrain of its habitat. Any definite increase in potential speed came only after it was well along in development. That the ability could be utilized to advantage in dodging pursuers was a favorable factor operating for the survival of its possessor.

Only by the development of saltation for speed and dodging ability is a small mammal enabled to range far from its burrow in an open habitat. Certainly, a jerboa is far swifter than if it were unable to leap. In the case of a larger animal, such as a kangaroo, it is doubtful whether it is sufficiently effective at locomotion to justify the evolutional effort put into it, if I may be permitted the expression. A kangaroo is an amazingly specialized animal, but its method of traveling by saltation was hardly begun for the purpose of ultimate speed. Rather has it built speed into the locomotor pattern that was already established, probably for some other purpose.

The actual speed of small mammals is difficult to evaluate and to compare with that of larger forms; and there appear to be no reliable, or at least consistent, figures for the large kangaroos. They are said to be able to cover as great a distance as 25 feet at a stride, but they do not do so each time. Rather do all saltators take one or two short hops in order to gather themselves properly for a greater effort.

Conclusions

UNDENIABLY a final brief chapter of conclusions is useful, and this usually proves to be the most exasperating part to prepare. The difficulty lies, I think, in the necessity for omitting the qualifications and the cautious circumlocutions of statement so dear to the heart of the scientific worker. This entire book is a résumé of the subject, and further to condense into a few sentences some of the more complicated details hardly seems altogether satisfactory. Particularly is this so where qualification is essential.

An attempt has been made to keep this chapter as brief as is feasible and to include in it only details that are deemed to have a direct bearing on the development, both early and late, for speed.

The development of locomotor ability has been the most important factor in the evolution of body form.

Mere rate of speed, or even speed relative to size, is not an indication of cursorial specialization; a mouse can run faster than a horse, relatively.

Evolution of form, from lowest to highest vertebrates, has been not in a straight line but in a series of zigzags, to fit the organism for the different environments encountered.

The basic body form of mammals has been highly influenced by heritage from their fish ancestry.

The primary locomotor apparatus of fish has always been the body. The chief use of the pectoral fins was originally as stilts, and of the pelvics, as props; in the free-swimming stage both are fundamentally equilibrators.

The amphibian posture involved proximal limb bones directed laterally so that elevation of the body above the ground required the expenditure of considerable muscular effort. The same statement applies to living reptiles, but not to most dinosaurs and mammal-like reptiles.

At first, the forelimbs were used chiefly for pulling the animal forward; the hind limbs chiefly for support. This was so largely because of the heavy tail, characteristic of most amphibians and reptiles.

Shoulder and hip joints of a character necessitating divergent

248

limbs proved extremely difficult for reptiles to relinquish. Dinosaurs overcame the latter, but only mammal-like reptiles overcame both.

No living reptile is highly adapted for running or hopping, although some are speedy by virtue of their celerity of movement, and at high speed several use the hind limbs only.

Among fossil reptiles, only dinosaurs developed forms that had skeletons definitely modified for a bipedal life. These were in great variety and some, as among theropods, were more completely bipedal than any mammal.

Therapsids developed an essentially mammalian posture, basically fitted for a more efficient type of sustained locomotion than is the typical reptilian posture. This culminated in the Theriodontia. The elbow began to be directed backward and the knee forward.

Birds developed from an archosaur stock. Their immediate ancestors must have been small, active, essentially bipedal, and partly cursorial forms.

The skeletons of all birds are basically highly adapted for running, reflecting ancestral modification. Ninety per cent of birds have legs of higher cursorial modification than all mammals but those most highly fitted for speed. This is so even of such as goatsuckers, that can hardly walk. But those with longest legs have become overspecialized, for wading, for counterbalancing a heavy head during flight, or for some such purpose. Both their extensor and their flexor muscles of the hip have particularly favorable angles of leverage, there is great development of caudofemoralis and a powerful iliofibularis (= tenuissimus), and the vasti are better developed for running than in any mammal.

The earliest mammals must have been small and partly arboreal, at home either in the trees or on the ground.

The only marsupials well specialized for speed are the pouched mice, kangaroos, marsupial wolf, and bandicoots. The first two are chiefly bipedal.

An arid-plains habitat is the best environment for the development of speedy mammals. Different groups of mammals have reacted dissimilarly to such stimuli; and it is impossible to escape the conviction that this has involved, among other things, differences in their ability so to react.

Cursorial and saltatorial types have been developed in the following orders of placentals: Insectivora, elephant shrews; Primates, tarsier; Rodentia, the only speedy cursorial forms are some of the cavies, while other speedy forms are saltatorial, chiefly the Cape jumping hare, kangaroo rats, Australian pouched mouse, jumping mice, jerboas; Lagomorpha, hares and rabbits; Carnivora, dogs and cats; Perissodactyla, horses particularly; Artiodactyla, all but hippos and, to a lesser degree, swine.

For speed, muscles are lightened in the distal part of the limbs and hence made quicker, chiefly by elongation of the tendinous part. There is also a tendency toward distal migration of some muscles, and they are fitted for action in the sagittal plane. Some of the muscular adaptations for speed occur in other mammals needing strong retraction of the limbs, as diggers and climbers. There is a slight tendency for the contraction of the brachial nerve plexus to four roots, probably due to a simplification of the kinds of movements.

Muscles of the back and lumbar region must be strong in mammals that arch the back in running; of the pelvis in those with very strong hind legs; and of the tail base in good leapers.

Trapezius fuses with deltoid to form a cephalohumeral muscle in carnivores and ungulates. This in itself is not a cursorial character but results from the suppression of the clavicle in mammals using the forelimb chiefly for support. It does, however, help much in running.

The latissimus dorsi inserts more distally in artiodactyls, the fibers frequently continuing into pectoralis or dorsiepitrochlearis; in carnivores at times into panniculus. The deltoid often inserts very low, even into the forearm fascia.

The low insertion of pectoral may be characteristic of ungulate stock but, nevertheless, adds power in running. The supraspinatus is more a protractor and less a rotator in cursorial forms.

There is a tendency in ungulates, but not in carnivores, for a lengthening and splitting of the long triceps.

There is reduction of the medial head of the brachialis, lessening rotation; reduction of biceps to a single head, inserting either on radius (perissodactyls, carnivores) or on both radius and ulna (artiodactyls).

There is a tendency for simplification of forearm extensors, suppression of brachioradialis and of a second head of extensor carpi radialis. Origin of extensor digitorum communis shifts distally in ungulates, sometimes with increase in the number of insertional tendons and development of a lateral proper extensor.

The deep antebrachial extensors are suppressed in ungulates but not in hares or carnivores.

Pronator teres is usually decadent (although large in dogs), accompanying reduction in rotation; and marginal forearm flexors are weak.

In ungulates the flexor digitorum sublimis often forms a tubular sheath for the profundus tendons, and the distal tendons split into a number of branches.

Pronator quadratus is absent in ungulates (except at times in tapir), and the short flexors of the manus are much reduced.

The iliopsoas is unusually large only in hares, the Patagonian cavy, and perhaps kangaroos.

The long gluteus inserts on the patella and is particularly effective in cats and saltators, including kangaroos.

The ventral hip muscles are specialized for speed by acting more exclusively in the sagittal plane, being inhibited for rotational action largely by conformation of the joints and ligaments.

Adductors tend to comprise a closely knit mass in runners but not in leapers. The obturator externus has increased in length by migrating through the obturator foramen in artiodactyls. Quadratus femoris is very long in some ungulates, and in that order the gracilis tends to have a fascial extension to the ankle.

Added effectiveness in running is afforded by insertion of the hamstring muscles onto the sheath of the tendo calcaneus in ungulates, saltators, dogs, and cats (and some diggers); but the condition also occurs in many other mammals. In kangaroos the semimembranosus ends in a long tendon.

The tibialis anterior is unusually large in some leapers. A femoral origin of the extensor digitorum longus is a primitive character; but it occurs in ungulates, carnivores, and most rodents and should add to their speed. In artiodactyls it is likely to divide into several heads.

The peronei are progressively degenerate as digits become reduced in specialization for high speed.

The triceps surae tends to be robust, at times with an extra head that may arise from the patella in some leapers. The soleus is often reduced (ungulates), fused, or lacking (kangaroos, dogs).

There is drastic reduction in the short plantar flexors accompanying decreased motility of the individual toes. The flexor brevis is retained, however.

The fusiform shape required by efficient fish has shaped the vertebral column of all higher vertebrates. This chanced to be excellently arranged for transformation into a cantilever bridge plan, highly suitable for the support of terrestrial vertebrates.

High vertebral spines indicate powerful back musculature locally, for controlling particularly strong adjacent weight or stresses and a heavy, antlered head. This necessitates particular strength of the quarters concerned. If in forequarters, it aids turning agility but reduces sustained speed; if in rear, it indicates either seesawing ability (Stegosaurus) or saltation (kangaroo). Bipeds may have seesaw support with heavy tail (kangaroo); or if without tail weight, then the body must be upended on legs (man).

Locomotion of even the highest mammals is definitely aided by vertebral movements.

Conformation of the head and neck has a great influence on speed and gait.

A heavy head is largely supported by the nuchal ligament.

The largest ears are found in desert mammals. Their size may be partly for better hearing but also probably to increase the body surface in relation to mass so as to facilitate radiation of body heat. Size of external ear is irrespective of size of auditory or mastoid bullae. Many desert rodents have bullae of phenomenal size; and these are believed to have a particular sensory function, such as perception of vibrations caused by footfalls.

Length of neck is probably influenced chiefly by feeding habits in relation to length of leg, but also very definitely by locomotional requirements. Or, in some, length of neck and weight of head determine gait. Saltation in rodents is accompanied by a shortening of the neck and often by fusion of some of the cervical vertebrae. The long neck of ungulates is used constantly to shift the center of gravity while running. If the head is very heavy, the animal usually favors a symmetrical gait, like the trot. The long neck of the giraffe is adapted to swing with the long legs in a gallop of slow tempo, and not the trot or pace.

A long body is an aid to speed in animals with short legs and a short body in those with long legs. But action of the trunk during locomotion is correlated, also, with length of neck and weight of tail.

Slope of spinous processes denotes direction and degree of muscular stress. Pronounced slope is characteristic of agile mammals and of some of the heavier ungulates but is absent in clumsier kinds and is not encountered in reptiles. In mammals with heavy forequarters the anticlinal center tends to move backward.

Spinous processes are long in grazers with heavy heads but short in browsers. They average longer in artiodactyls than in perissodactyls. Lumbar spines are longer and more slender in saltators.

Bipedal reptiles had an increased number of sacral vertebrae (up to 9).

The cursorial characteristics of the avian limb have increased the number of sacral vertebrae (11–20).

Sacral declivity is pronounced in graviportal mammals with columnar limbs and in small cursorial types (agouti, mouse deer), that hold the legs considerably flexed.

Bipedal reptiles usually had heavy tails. The tail base in this class functioned more as an anchorage for muscles important in running than is the case in mammals.

The character of the reduction of the caudal vertebrae common to all birds is an indication that the ostrich-like and flying birds were derived from a common ancestor.

Leaping (and climbing) mammals have a tail fitted for equilibration, robust in the large forms (kangaroo) and long in the small ones, with a black and white tip in the case of the more gifted rodents. In saltators the relative effectiveness of tail (length or hairiness) increases with the relative hind-foot length. In running mammals the head and neck act as an equilibrator.

Chevron bones are best developed in mammals with powerful tails, such as leapers.

Absence of the clavicle, perhaps, is of cursorial advantage, but many noncursorial groups lack it.

In adaptation to high speed the following are common to both pairs of limbs: reduction of lateral movement, lengthening and distal lightening, relative reduction in length of the proximal segment and increase of epipodials and metapodials, reduction in number of digits, and change from plantigrade to digitigrade and then to an unguligrade condition.

Fins, first used as an aid to locomotion over the bottom, developed along the branchiocloacal line. They became equilibrators in the free-swimming stage.

A progressive step toward more efficient locomotion was the freeing of the amphibian shoulder girdle from the axial skeleton. In reptiles there was also posterior migration of the shoulder and simplification of the girdle, as the number of bony elements dwindled. The paraglenoid ossification developed sutures in response to stresses of diverse muscle groups. Shape of girdle was altered drastically by the change in posture of the limb, from being held sprawled to the side to a position more beneath the body, permitting change in direction of the glenoid and a lightening of the limb skeleton. The change in posture was accompanied by migration of some of the muscles, notably of the procoracoid matrix to form a pectoralis major and spinati, resulting in formation of a scapular spine, practical elimination of procoracoid, and great reduction of coracoid.

Shape of scapular blade in mammals is determined chiefly by functional requirements of muscles along the vertebral border of the scapula and subscapularis. The border is broad in graviportals and narrow in lighter, agile ungulates.

Reduction of clavicle allows shrinkage of scapular spine, and this accompanies cursorial specialization.

Relative size of supraspinous and infraspinous fossae is no indication of the size and power of the two muscles concerned.

In ponderous mammals the head of the humerus tends to be less offset. In specialization for speed the shape of the head becomes more cylindrical and the tuberosities lower in lighter forms, with a more proximal deltoid crest. The distal articular surface becomes flatter and with altered shape, with expansion of the radial and reduction of the ulnar articulation, the latter moving rearward. Cursorial modification involves increasing restriction of action to one plane, and only much later is there fusion of the forearm bones, the latter character varying much. The distal ulna is reduced and, finally, also the proximal radius, while its distal part broadens. The wrist joint changes from a modified ball-and-socket to a hinge joint.

The typical reptile foot is asymmetrical in respect to toe length. Leg and foot action in the sagittal plane was made possible by a shortening and an elimination of some of the phalanges, so that the digits became more nearly of equal length.

Reduction in the number of digits is encountered among mammals of different habits, but most frequently in those adapted for speed, the forelimb usually being more conservative in this respect than the hind. Digit 1 is the first to be raised above the ground and to lose its function as the foot lengthens. The fifth is usually the next to follow.

In horses digits 2 and 4 are represented only by metacarpal vestiges.

Among artiodactyls cursorial adaptation has progressed farther in the Bovidae than in the Cervidae, the extreme being found in pronghorn, giraffe, and camel, in which all parts of the lateral digits (2 and 5) have been lost.

As a rule, the smaller the foot or, rather, the smaller its area of contact with the ground, the higher the adaptation for speed. In a non-arid environment foot size also varies considerably with the character of the terrain, whether with hard or soft surface. The forefoot of ungulates is always larger than the hind foot.

To improve the posture of the hind limb for efficient locomotion, reptiles had to bring the knee beneath the body. This was necessary in bipedal kinds and was a requisite in the mammal-like group.

Alteration in limb posture changed the slope of the ilium from vertical to posterior and finally to anterior and caused the dorsal migration of the ilium.

Bipedal dinosaurs had pelves of both triradiate and tetraradiate patterns.

A tilt in the innominate axis away from the horizontal is characteristic of heavy mammals and in those light runners that have tucked-in hindquarters (like mouse deer).

Length of the mammalian ilium is not readily correlated with speed. The forked form of ilium occurs largely in forms with a bounding type of gallop. A long ischium increases the effectiveness of the retractor muscles of thigh and crus; a pronounced tuber ischii makes more effective the hamstring muscles; a projected ascending ramus of the ischium helps the quadratus femoris and deeper adductors and occurs in leapers and runners. The pubis is weak in most speedy mammals because of the unimportance to them of adduction of the thigh.

In man the erect posture has reduced the effectiveness of the muscles of the hip, and as a result the innominate is tending toward reversion to the quadrupedal position in respect to the thigh.

In speedy mammals the acetabulum tends to face more downward.

Increased locomotional efficiency in dinosaurs and mammal-like reptiles involved lightening the femur and developing a somewhat offset, spherical head, instead of an elliptical one at the end of the shaft. The trochanters have changed with the alterations in posture and are not strictly comparable in the different classes.

The spherical character of the femoral head is reduced in some mammals in which lateral motility of the limb is decreased, as in ungulates. The head is less offset in heavy forms.

A high greater trochanter is characteristic of good runners and leapers but is found also in other mammals with powerful legs. The lesser trochanter is poorly developed in graviportals.

In bipedal reptiles the tibia progressively took a greater part in weight-bearing at the ankle. In most mammals it carries the whole load.

In speedy mammals the torsion angles of the tibia tend to be zero.

The fibula is reduced in speedy mammals and tends toward distal fusion as rotation of the crus disappears; but this is also found in slow forms with other habits.

In most reptiles and in birds the ankle-joint is between the proximal and the distal tarsal bones. Pelycosaurs first developed the joint between crus and tarsus that is found in mammals.

A posterior calcaneal process, so necessary in the mammalian mode of progression, occurred in known reptiles only in theriodont bauriamorphs.

Elongation of the proximal tarsal bones for leaping is a seemingly useful specialization, but in mammals it has occurred in marked degree only in some lemuroid primates. This is probably correlated with leaping only in a form that uses its feet also for grasping. Limited elongation of the distal tarsals occurs only in elephant shrews.

In cursorial forms motility of the tarsus is reduced. Particularly in artiodactyls is there a tendency toward consolidation and simplification of the distal tarsus, probably not actually related to speed but to the degree of restriction of ankle movement to one plane.

Pedal developments have been much as in the manus, with reduction of toes in the digitigrade posture. The first to be lost in reptiles is the fifth, the first being lost only in a few dinosaurs. Metatarsal elongation was most pronounced in ornithischian dinosaurs.

The fifth metatarsal is always absent in birds; the first is reduced but unfused; and the others are fused, and with the distal tarsalia they become the tarsometatarsus.

Raising the heel in speed specialization is probably the chief stimulus for progressive reduction of the digits.

There is reduction of the hallux in didactyl marsupials. In syndactylous ones the second and third are bound together, and these with the fifth form a symmetrical pair bordering the dominant fourth. In the more saltatorial forms the pes is much compressed laterally.

In leaping rodents there is a tendency toward fusion of the dominant metatarsals into a birdlike "tarsal bone." In them the pes in high specialization becomes tridactyl; but the toes are held together, and together with the hairy plantar pad they function as a monodactyl entity. In hystricomorph rodents the trend is toward a dominant middle toe.

In ungulates the central toe (perissodactyls) or pair of toes (artiodactyls) become dominant, the others receding and disappearing in higher specialization.

Shortening of the limb muscles increases speed but reduces strength. Lengthening the limb increases stride but reduces power. Decreasing the distal weight of limb quickens stride and reduces energy output. A short leg moved rapidly can give as much speed as a long one with slow action, but the former is exhausting and less efficient.

For speed there must be an optimum weight for size, or vice versa, and an optimum leg length for musculature and body weight.

Development of the hind limb is of more significance than of the forelimb, and of metapodial than of propodial.

Relative length of humerus and radius is largely determined by size of head and length of neck in forms using the manus in feeding. In speedy forms this restriction does not operate.

The tibia lengthens in cursorial and shortens in graviportal specialization. The radius either remains the same or shortens less than the tibia in graviportals but lengthens as much as the tibia in cursorials.

In the generalized condition the humeroradial index is about 100. From 68 in hippos it rises well above par in speedy rodents (but not in most dogs and cats), rises through horses (below 100 in most other perissodactyls; 130 in Neohipparion) and reaches the 130's in some gazelles and an extreme of 167 in giraffes.

If the sum of the three arm segments be reduced to 100, the humerus exceeds a value of 50 only in hippo, elephant, and hyrax. In generalized kinds it is in the middle forties, dropping below this figure in mammals specialized for speed and culminating in gazelles and giraffes (23). The radius, so considered, has a rather stable value and rises into the high forties and low fifties only in saltators, dropping to the high thirties in perissodactyls and the low thirties in some artiodactyls.

In generalized mammals the longest metacarpal tends to be one-quarter to one-third the length of the humerus. The extremes are encountered in elephant (14) and gerenuk (169). It rises in dogs and throughout the speedy ungulates, and among the latter it is higher in the small young than the adult.

In relation to effective arm length there is relative reduction of metacarpal length in saltators. The lowest figure occurs in elephant (7.5), hyrax, and hippo but rises in more specialized ungulates from 23 in Tragulina to 40–42 in the lighter gazelles.

Intermembral index is worthless for indicating cursorial ability, but it does denote degree of development of the hind leg in saltators. It drops below 50 in many kangaroos and reaches 35 in some jerboas. The femorohumeral largely follows the intermembral index and is not very useful.

Among saurischian dinosaurs the femur is usually longer than the tibia in the large, carnivorous theropods and the reverse in lighter kinds. The former is also usually the case in ornithischians, but it is shorter in some orthopods.

The femur is much the shorter in birds, the lowest indices (141) being in goatsuckers and penguins. Ratios of over 200 are encountered in many of the longer-legged forms, culminating in the flamingo (427). The latter are overspecialized, for purposes other than running.

The femorotibial index in marsupials rises above 200 only in a few kangaroos. In Tarsius it is below 100. It is high (175) in the most gifted leaping rodents but not in hares (108–23), and it is low in dogs (about 100). It drops below par (to 68 in rhinos) in the least specialized ungulates and in camels and is highest in the mule deer, in a few of the gazelles, and in the saiga.

The tibioradial index can be used for judging the degree of saltatorial specialization, but it is useless for measuring cursorial ability. In the generalized condition the radius is about two-thirds to three-quarters the length of the tibia, and in leapers this difference increases.

The femorometatarsal index has considerable leverage, as it reflects both increase of metatarsal and decrease of femoral length. The index is low (to 12) in sauropods but higher (to 77) in birdlike theropods. It is enormously variable in birds, averaging 100–150 in most but dropping in weak-footed forms (to 40 in terns) and rising through the longer-legged sorts to 408 in the flamingo.

In mammals the extremes are encountered in elephant and sloth (9), and in giraffe (137) and jerboa (136), with a generalized average of 35–45. It does not rise much in either hares or dogs.

Metacarpals are usually shorter than metatarsals. In both graviportal and cursorial forms there is a trend toward obliteration of this difference and toward accentuation in saltators. The metacarpal is the longer in sauropod dinosaurs, hyenas, the clumsier graviportals, and some pigs. The two are essentially equal in tapirs, camels, giraffes, and pronghorns.

In ungulate foals the shortness of propodials and length of metapodials is accentuated, as well as the relative limb length.

Locomotion comprises displacement of the center of gravity and the maintenance of equilibrium.

Gait is determined by behavior habit, conformation, and convenience.

As hind legs increase in relative power in forms with symmetrical gaits, the tendency will be toward bipedalism (reptiles). If the asymmetrical gallop be favored, bipedalism need not be predicated (hares), although those with heavy tails frequently become bipedal.

Each locomotor cycle in quadrupeds has eight periods, one for each footfall and one for each foot suspension. The interval of each varies with speed and gait.

Progression by tetrapods may be quadrupedal or bipedal. Gaits of the former should be divided into symmetrical (walk, trot, pace) and asymmetrical (gallop, bound) groups. Each has two basic foot sequences, termed "diagonal" and "lateral."

Symmetrical gaits involve bending the skeleton in the horizontal plane, the intervals between footfalls are evenly spaced, support pattern is repetitively symmetrical, and each movement is damped by another limb. There is a two-time and a four-time group.

In the two-time symmetrical gait the normal eight phases are compressed into four, because the legs move in pairs, in the diagonal variety (the trot) by diagonal members, and in the lateral (the pace) by ipselateral ones. The camels comprise the only group regularly favoring the latter. The former is the gait best suited to large mammals with very heavy heads.

The four-time symmetrical gait—the walk—has the footfalls all separate and evenly spaced, and at all speeds there is at least one foot on the ground.

There is but one truly asymmetrical gait, the gallop. This involves bending the axial skeleton in the vertical plane, uneven spacing of the intervals between footfalls, asymmetry of the support pattern occurring but once in each cycle, while the action of each limb is not damped by another. It is the most effective of the fast gaits for most speedy mammals, probably because it allows of maximum participation by the body musculature. By strong leapers it is subject to modification, which makes it secondarily symmetrical, in the bound and half-bound and in the mule deer's spring. There are many variations of the gallop, involving different sequences of footfalls.

Bipedal gaits comprise the two-time walk and run and the one-time hop or ricochet. The former is really a bipedal trot, and the latter more in the nature of a bipedal gallop or bound.

In the comparisons of the bodily proportions of pertinent animals, measurements have been utilized of the following genera. Those marked with an asterisk have been taken from the literature; the remainder were made by myself.

REPTILIA

Parapsida
  Squamata
    Lacertilia
      Cyclura (iguana) 2
      Conolophus (iguana) 1
      Iguana 1
      Varanus (monitor) 2
Diapsida
  Dinosauria (extinct)
    Saurischia
      Theropoda
        Albertosaurus 1*
        Gorgosaurus 1*
        Tyrannosaurus 2*
        Allosaurus 1*
        Ceratosaurus 1*
        Struthiomimus 2*
        Ornitholestes 1*
      Sauropoda
        Apatosaurus 2*
        Camarasaurus 2*
    Ornithischia
      Orthopoda
        Hypsilophodon 1*
        Thescelosaurus 2*
        Camptosaurus 1
        Kritosaurus 1*
        Claosaurus 1*
        Edmontosaurus 2*
        Trachodon 3*
        Hypacrosaurus 1*
        Saurolophus 1*
        Corythosaurus 1*
    Stegosauria
      Stegosaurus 1
    Ceratopsia
      Triceratops 1

AVES

Palaeognathae
  Struthio (ostrich) 1
  Rhea (rhea) 1
  Casuarius (cassowary) 1
  Dinornis (extinct moas) 4*
  Megalapteryx (extinct moa) 1*
  Euryapteryx (extinct moa) 2*
Impennes
  Aptenodytes (penguin) 1
  Spheniscus (penguin) 2
Neognathae
  Ciconiiformes
    Phoenicopterus (flamingo) 2
  Anseriformes
    Cariama (screamer) 1
    Oidemia (scoter) 1
  Falconiformes
    Sagittarius (secretary bird) 2
  Galliformes
    Meleagris (turkey) 1
    Callipepla (quail) 1
  Gruiformes
    Grus (crane) 2
  Charadriiformes
    Jacana (jacana) 1
    Himantopus (stilt) 1
    Ereunetes (sandpiper) 1

Caprimulgiformes
 Chordeiles (nighthawk) 1
 Nyctidromus (parauque) 1
Micropodiformes (swift) 1

MAMMALIA

METATHERIA

Marsupialia
 Didelphiidae
  Marmosa (opossum) 1
 Dasyuridae
  Thylacinus (thylacine) 2
 Peramelidae
  Perameles (bandicoot) 1
 Macropodidae
  Hypsiprymnus (rat kangaroo) 1
  Aepyprymnus (rat kangaroo) 1
  Bettongia (rat kangaroo) 1
  Potorous (rat kangaroo) 1
  Petrogale (rock wallaby) 1
  Onychogale (nail-tailed wallaby) 1
  Thylogale (scrub wallaby) 1
  Wallabia (Grey's wallaby) 1
  Macropus (kangaroo) 5

EUTHERIA

Insectivora
 Tupaia (tree shrew) 1
 Cercoctinus (elephant shrew) 1
 Elephantulus (elephant shrew) 1
 Erinaceus (hedgehog) 1
Primates
 Macaca (macaque) 1
 Tarsius (tarsier) 2
Edentata
 Bradypus (three-toed sloth) 1
 Choloepus (two-toed sloth) 1
Rodentia
 Sciuromorpha
  Citellus (ground squirrel) 1
  Tamasciurus (chickaree) 1
  Thomomys (pocket gopher) 1
  Dipodomys (kangaroo rat) 2
  Pedetes (Cape jumping hare) 1
 Myomorpha
  Neotoma (wood rat) 2
  Allactaga (jerboa) 1

Scirtopoda (jerboa) 1
Jaculus (jerboa) 1
Hystricomorpha
 Proechimys (spiny rat) 1
 Cavia (cavy) 1
 Dolichotis (Patagonian cavy) 2
Lagomorpha
 Ochotona (pika) 1
 Pronolagus (South African rabbit) 1
 Sylvilagus (cottontail rabbit) 1
 Sylvilagus (marsh rabbit) 1
 Lepus (hare) 8
Carnivora
 Canidae
  Cynodictis (fossil ancestral canid) 1
  Canis (dogs, coyote, wolf) 8
  Chrysocyon (maned wolf) 2
  Cerdocyon (South American fox) 1
  Dusicyon (Falkland fox) 1
  Icticyon (bush dog) 1
  Urocyon (gray fox) 1
  Vulpes (red fox) 2
  Lycaon (African hunting dog) 3
 Hyaenidae
  Hyaena (brown hyena) 1
  Crocuta (spotted hyena) 1
  Proteles (aard wolf) 1
 Felidae
  Acinonyx (cheetah) 3
  Felis (cat, lion, leopard) 5
Dinocerata (extinct)
 Uintatherium 1*
Notoungulata (extinct)
 Homalodontotherium 1*
Proboscidea
 Mastodon (extinct) 1*
 Elaphas (Indian elephant) 2
 Loxodonta (African elephant) 1*
Hyracoidea
 Procavia (hyrax) 1
Perissodactyla
 Equidae
  Eohippus (extinct) 1
  Orohippus (extinct) 1
  Mesohippus (extinct) 2
  Miohippus (extinct) 1

Merychippus (extinct) 1
Hypohippus (extinct) 1*
Pliohippus (extinct) 1
Neohipparion (extinct) 1*
Hippidium (extinct) 1
Equus (wild asses) 2
Equus (Prezewalsky horse) 3
Equus (zebras) 10
Equus (domestic horses) 14

Brontotheridae (extinct)
   Brontotherium and other titano-
      theres 10*

Chalicotheridae (extinct)
   Moropus 3*

Tapiridae
   Acrocodia (Indian tapir) 1
   Tapirus (American tapir) 3
   Helaletes (extinct tapir) 1

Hyracodontidae (extinct rhinos)
   Hyracodon 2
   Hyrachyus 1

Rhinocerotidae
   Diceros (rhino) 2

Artiodactyla
   Hyodonta
      Sus (pig) 1
      Phacochoerus (wart hog) 1
      Hylochoerus (forest hog) 1
      Hippopotamus 2
   Tylopoda
      Alticamelus (extinct giraffe-camel) 1
      Stenomylus (extinct small camel) 1
      Camelus (dromedary) 3
      Llama 3

Tragulina
   Tragulus (mouse deer or chevro-
      tain) 2
Pecora
   Okapia 1
   Giraffa 3
   Moschus (musk deer) 2
   Muntiacus (muntjac) 3
   Cervus (wapiti, European deer) 4
   Rangifer (caribou) 1
   Alces (moose) 1
   Odocoileus (American deer) 5
   Hydropotes (water deer) 1
   Antilocapra (prongbuck) 8
   Taurotragus (oryx) 1
   Hippotragus (sable antelope) 1
   Antilope (black buck) 2
   Gazella (gazelle) 6
   Antidorcas (springbuck) 1
   Litocranius (gerenuk) 2
   Saiga (saiga) 1
   Aepyceros (impala) 2
   Redunca (reedbuck) 1
   Kobus (waterbuck) 2
   Ourebia (oribi) 1
   Oreotragus (klipspringer) 2
   Cephalophus (duiker) 2
   Damaliscus (hartebeest) 1
   Gorgon (gnu) 1
   Rupricapra (chamois) 1
   Oreamnos (mountain goat) 2
   Capra (goat) 2
   Ovis (sheep) 2
   Ovibos (musk ox) 1
   Bison (bison) 2
   Bos (cattle) 3

Literature Cited

ALSTON, E. R. 1880. On Antechinomys and its allies. Proc. Zoöl. Soc., London, pp. 454–61.

AKELEY, MARY J. 1929. Carl Akeley's Africa. New York: Dodd, Mead & Co. Pp. 321.

ANDREWS, R. C. 1924. Living animals of the Gobi Desert. Nat. Hist., 24:150–59.

———. 1933. The Mongolian wild ass. *Ibid.*, 33:3–16.

———. 1937. Wings win. *Ibid.*, 40:559–65.

ANTONIUS, O. 1938. On the geographical distribution, in former times and today, of the Recent Equidae. Proc. Zoöl. Soc., London, pp. 557–64.

ASH, E. C. 1929. Dogs: their history and development. 2 vols. New York: Houghton Mifflin Co.

BENSLEY, B. A. 1901. A theory of the origin and evolution of the Australian Marsupialia. Am. Nat., 35:245–69.

———. 1903. On the evolution of the Australian Marsupialia with remarks on the relationship of the marsupials in general. Tr. Linn. Soc., London, 9:83–214.

BÖKER, HANS. 1935. Einführung in die vergleichende biologische Anatomie der Wirbeltiere, Vol. 1. Jena: G. Fischer. Pp. 228.

BONFIELD, A. W. 1930. Roan antelope does 40 m.p.h. East Africa.

BORELLI, ALPHONSI. 1681. De motu animalium. Rome. Pp. 520.

BREDER, C. M., JR. 1926. The locomotion of fishes. Zoologica, 4:159–297.

BROOKE, V. 1874. On Sclater's muntjac and other species of the genus Cervulus. Proc. Zoöl. Soc., London, pp. 33–42.

———. 1878. On the classification of the Cervidae with a synopsis of the existing species. *Ibid.*, pp. 883–928.

CAMP, C. L., and BORELL, A. E. 1937. Skeletal and muscular differences in the hind limbs of Lepus, Sylvilagus, and Ochotona. J. Mamm., 18:315–26.

CAMPBELL, BERRY. 1936. The comparative myology of the forelimb of the hippopotamus, pig, and tapir. Am. J. Anat., 59:201–47.

CHUBB, S. H. 1931. "Man o' War" and "Gallant Fox." Nat. Hist., 31:318–27.

COTTAM, C. 1937. Speed of the gray fox. J. Mamm., 18:240–41.

COUSTÉ, H. 1916. Mechanics applied to the horse. Translation from the French, 1914 ed., by E. B. CASSATT. New York. Pp. 80.

CUTTING, C. S. 1938. The fastest hunt in the world. Nat. Hist., 41:179–89.

DOLLO, L. 1899. Les Ancêtres des Marsupiaux étaient-ils arboricoles? Trav. Stat. Zool. Wimereus, 7:188–203.

DUCHENNE, G. B. 1867. Physiologie des mouvements. Paris. Pp. 872.

ELFTMAN, H. O. 1929. Functional adaptations of the pelvis in marsupials. Bull. Am. Mus. Nat. Hist., 58:189–232.

———. 1939. The function of the muscles in locomotion. Am. J. Physiol., 125:357–66.

ELFTMAN, H. O., and MANTER, J. 1935. Chimpanzee and human feet in bipedal walking. Am. J. Phys. Anthrop., **20**:69–79.

EWART, J. C. 1894. The development of the skeleton of the limbs of the horse, with observations on polydactyly. J. Anat., **28**:236–56, 342–69.

FENIUK, B. K., and KAZANTZEVA, J. M. 1937. The ecology of Dipus sagitta. J. Mamm., **18**:409–26.

FLOWER, W. H. 1876. An introduction to the osteology of the Mammalia. London: Macmillan & Co., Ltd. Pp. 344.

FLOWER, W. H., and LYDEKKER, R. 1891. An introduction to the study of mammals, living and extinct. London: A. & C. Black. Pp. 763.

GADOW, H. F. 1933. The evolution of the vertebral column. London: Cambridge University Press. Pp. 356.

GAMGEE, JOSEPH. 1869. On the action of the horse. J. Anat. Physiol., **3**:370–76.

GOLDSCHMIDT, S. G. 1933. An eye for a horse. New York: Charles Scribner's Sons. Pp. 133.

GORDON, SETH. 1933. A fast goat. Field & Stream, p. 80.

GREGORY, W. K. 1910. The orders of mammals. Bull. Am. Mus. Nat. Hist., **27**: 1–524.

———. 1912. Notes on the principles of quadrupedal locomotion and on the mechanism of the limbs in hoofed animals. Ann. New York Acad. Sc., **22**:267–92.

———. 1935. The pelvis from fish to man: a study in paleomorphology. Am. Nat., **69**:193–210.

———. 1935. Further observations on the pectoral girdle and fin of Sauripterus taylori Hall, a crossopterygian fish from the Upper Devonian of Pennsylvania, with special reference to the origin of the pentadactylate extremities of Tetrapoda. Proc. Am. Phil. Soc., **75**:673–90.

———. 1937. The bridge-that-walks. Nat. Hist., **39**:33–48.

GREGORY, W. K.; MINER, R. W.; and NOBLE. G. K. 1923. The carpus of Eryops and the structure of the primitive chiropterygium. Bull. Am. Mus. Nat. Hist., **48**: 279–88.

GREGORY, W. K., and RAVEN, H. C. 1941. Studies on the origin and early evolution of paired fins and limbs. Ann. New York Acad. Sc., **42**:273–360.

HARRIS, J. A. 1937. The fetal growth of sheep. J. Anat. Physiol., **71**:516–727.

HATT, R. T. 1932. The vertebral columns of ricochetal rodents. Bull. Am. Mus. Nat. Hist., **63**:599–738.

HAYCRAFT, J. B. 1900. Animal mechanics. In Text-book of physiology, ed. E. A. SCHAFER. Edinburgh & London. Pp. 1365.

HAYES, M. H. 1922. Points of the horse. 4th ed. London: Hurst & Blackett. Pp. 595.

HEILMANN, G. 1927. The origin of birds. New York: D. Appleton. Pp. 210.

HOWELL, A. B. 1930. Acquatic mammals. Springfield, Ill.: C. C. Thomas. Pp. 338.

———. 1932. The saltatorial rodent Dipodomys: functional and comparative anatomy of its muscular and osseous systems. Proc. Am. Acad. Arts & Sc., **67**:377–536.

———. 1933a. Morphogenesis of the shoulder architecture, Part I: General considerations. Quart. Rev. Biol., **8**:247–59.

———. 1933b. Morphogenesis of the shoulder architecture, Part II: Pisces. Ibid., pp. 434–56.

————. 1935a. The primitive carpus. J. Morphol., **57**:105–12.

————. 1935b. Morphogenesis of the shoulder architecture, Part III: Amphibia. Quart. Rev. Biol., **10**:397–431.

————. 1936a. Morphogenesis of the shoulder architecture, Part IV: Reptilia. *Ibid.*, **11**:183–208.

————. 1936b. Phylogeny of the distal musculature of the pectoral appendage. J. Morphol., **60**:287–315.

————. 1937. Morphogenesis of the shoulder architecture, Part VI: Therian Mammalia. Quart. Rev. Biol., **12**:440–63.

————. 1938a. Muscles of the avian hip and thigh. Auk, **55**:71–81.

————. 1938b. Morphogenesis of the architecture of hip and thigh. J. Morphol., **62**:177–218.

————. 1941. The femoral trochanters. Field Mus. Nat. Hist., Zoöl. Ser., **27**:279–91.

HUXLEY, T. H. 1880. On the application of the laws of evolution to the arrangement of the Vertebrata and more particularly of the Mammalia. Proc. Zoöl. Soc., London, pp. 649–62.

KINGSLEY, J. S. 1925. The vertebrate skeleton. Philadelphia: Blakiston. Pp. 337.

KOWALEVSKY, W. 1873. Monographie der Gattung Anthracotherium Cuv. und Versuch einer natürlichen Classification der fossilen Hufthiere. Palaeontographica, **22**:131–46.

JONES, F. WOOD. 1923–25. The mammals of South Australia. Adelaide: Government Printer. Pp. 458.

LAMB, A. J. R. 1935. Horse facts. New York: Greenberg. Pp. 127.

LECHNER, W. 1933. Die Schulterextremität einger Wiederkäuer: Beitrag zur vergleichenden Anatomie der Selenodontier, I Teil. Ztschr. f. Anat. u. Entwcklngsgesch., **99**:735–804.

LeSOUEF, A. S., BURRELL, H., and TROUGHTON, E. LeG. 1926. The wild animals of Australia. London: G. G. Harrofi & Co. Pp. 388.

LEWIS, G. C. 1939. Notes on a pair of tarsiers from Mindanao. J. Mamm., **20**:57–61.

LULL, R. S. 1904. Adaptations to aquatic, arboreal, fossorial, and cursorial habits in mammals, IV: Cursorial adaptations. Am. Nat., **38**:1–11.

LYDEKKER, R. 1913–16. Catalogue of the ungulate mammals in the British Museum (Natural History). 5 vols. London: British Museum.

MAGNE DE LA CROIX, P. 1929. Filogenia de la locomociones cuadrupedal y bipedal en los vertebrados. An. Soc. cient. Argentina, **8**:383.

————. 1936. The evolution of locomotion in mammals. J. Mamm. **17**:51–54.

MANNICHE, A. L. V. 1910. The terrestrial mammals and birds of north-east Greenland. Meddelelser om Gronland, **45**:1–200.

MANTER, J. T. 1938. The dynamics of quadrupedal walking. J. Exper. Biol., **15**:522–40.

MAREY, E. J. 1879. Animal mechanism: a treatise on terrestrial and aerial locomotion. "International Science Series." New York: Appleton. Pp. 283.

MARSH, G. P. 1856. The camel: his organization, habits, and uses. Boston. Pp. 224.

MARTIN, RUDOLF. 1928. Lehrbuch der Anthropologie in Septemascher Darstellung. Jena: G. Fischer. 2d ed. 3 vols. Pp. 1816.

MAXWELL, MARIUS. 1924. Stalking big game with a camera in Equatorial Africa. New York: Century Co. Pp. 313.

MINER, R. W. 1925. The pectoral limb of Eryops and other primitive tetrapods. Bull. Am. Mus. Nat. Hist., **51**:145–312.

MOLLISON, T. 1911. Die Körperproportionem der Primaten. Morphol. Jahrb., **42**:79–304.

MORTON, D. J. 1935. The human foot: its evolution, physiology, and functional disorders. New York: Columbia University Press. Pp. 244.

MUYBRIDGE, E. 1877. Animal locomotion. Philadelphia. Pls. 131.

NEWSOM, W. M. 1937. Mammals on Anticosti Island. J. Mamm., **18**:435–42.

NOBLE, G. K. 1931. Biology of the Amphibia. New York: McGraw-Hill Book Co. Pp. 577.

OLIVER, W. R. B. 1930. New Zealand birds. Wellington, N.Z. Pp. 541.

OSBORN, H. F. 1900. The angulation of the limbs of Proboscidea, Dinocerata, and other quadrupeds, in adaptation to weight. Am. Nat., **34**:89–94.

———. 1929. The Titanotheres of ancient Wyoming, Dakota, and Nebraska. U.S. Geol. Surv., Mono. 55. 2 vols. Pp. 953.

OWEN, RICHARD. 1866–68. The anatomy of vertebrates. 3 vols. London: Longmans, Green & Co.

PACK, R. C. 1933. Speed of gray fox. Field & Stream, p. 69.

PALMGREN, AXEL. 1928. Die Insertion des M. biceps brachii und des M. brachialis bei den Huftieren im Lichte der vergleichenden Anatomie. Acta zool., **9**:331–64.

PARKER, T. S., and HASWELL, W. A. 1910. A textbook of zoölogy, Vol. 2. London: Macmillan & Co., Ltd. Pp. 728.

PARSONS, F. G. 1903. On the obturator tertius muscle of ungulates. J. Anat. Physiol., **37**:41–42.

PETTIGREW, J. B. 1885. Animal locomotion. "International Science Series," No. 8. New York: Appleton. Pp. 264.

POCOCK, R. I. 1922. On the external characters of some hystricomorph rodents. Proc. Zoöl. Soc., London, pp. 365–427.

REYNOLDS, S. H. 1913. The vertebrate skeleton. 2d ed. London: Cambridge University Press. Pp. 535.

RIDGEWAY, W. 1905. The origin and influence of the thoroughbred horse. London: Cambridge University Press. Pp. 538.

ROMER, A. S. 1922. The locomotor apparatus of certain primitive and mammal-like reptiles. Bull. Am. Mus. Nat. Hist., **46**:517–606.

———. 1924. The lesser trochanter of the mammalian femur. Anat. Rec., **28**:95–102.

———. 1933. Vertebrate paleontology. Chicago: University of Chicago Press. Pp. 491.

———. 1939. Notes on branchiosaurs. Am. J. Sc., **237**:748–61.

ROMER, A. S., and BYRNE, F. 1931. The pes of Diadectes: notes on the primitive tetrapod limb. Palaeobiologica, **4**:25–48.

SCHAEFFER, BOBB. 1941. The morphological and functional evolution of the tarsus in amphibians and reptiles. Bull. Am. Mus. Nat. Hist., **78**:395–472.

SCHMALHAUSEN, I. 1917. On the extremities of Ranidens sibiricus. Rev. zool. russe, **2**:129–35.

SCHRENKEISEN, R. 1932. The speed of a fox. Field & Stream, October, p. 77.

SCHULTZ, A. H. 1926. Fetal growth of man and other primates. Quart. Rev. Biol., **1**:465–521.

———. 1937. Proportions, variability, and asymmetries of the long bones of the limbs and the clavicles in man and apes. Human Biol., **9**:281–328.

SCLATER, P. L., and THOMAS, O. 1894–1900. The book of antelopes. 4 vols. London: British Museum.

SCOTT, W. B. 1937. A history of land mammals in the Western Hemisphere. 2d ed. New York: Macmillan Co. Pp. 786.

SELOUS, F. C. 1908. African nature notes and reminiscences. London: Macmillan & Co., Ltd. Pp. 356.

SETON, E. T. 1929. Lives of game animals. 4 vols. New York: Doubleday, Doran.

SIMPSON, G. G. 1931. A new classification of mammals. Bull. Am. Mus. Nat. Hist., **59**:259–93.

———. 1934. Attending marvels. New York: Macmillan Co. Pp. 295.

STEINDLER, ARTHUR. 1935. Mechanics of normal and pathological locomotion in man. Springfield, Ill.: C. C. Thomas. Pp. 424.

STEWART, D. 1937. Variations from normal gait after muscle section in rabbits. J. Anat., **72**:101–8.

STILLMAN, J. D. 1882. The horse in motion. Boston. Pp. 127.

STIRTON, R. A. 1940. Phylogeny of North American Equidae. Univ. California Pub., Bull. Dept. Geol. Sc., **25**:165–98.

STRAUS, W. L., JR. 1926. The nature and inheritance of webbed toes in man. J. Morph. Physiol., **41**:427–39.

———. 1927. Growth of the human foot and its evolutionary significance. Contr. Embryol., Carnegie Inst. Washington, **19**: No. 101, 95–134.

———. 1942. The homologies of the forearm flexors: urodeles, lizards, mammals. Am. J. Anat., **70**:281–316.

STRAUS, W. L., JR., and WISLOCKI, G. B. 1932. On certain similarities between sloths and slow lemurs. Bull. Mus. Comp. Zoöl., **74**:45–56.

SWARTH, H. S. 1929. The faunal areas of southern Arizona: a study in animal distribution. Proc. Calif. Acad. Sc., 4th ser., **18**:267–383.

TERRES, J. K. 1941. Speed of the varying hare. J. Mamm., **22**:453–54.

THOMPSON, D'ARCY W. 1917. On growth and form. London: Cambridge University Press. Pp. 793.

THOMSON, J. A. 1923. The biology of birds. New York: Macmillan Co. Pp. 436.

VINOGRADOV, B. S. 1937. Faune de l'U.R.S.S., Vol. III: Mammifères. Acad. Sc. U.R.S.S. Pp. 196.

VIRCHOW, HANS. 1928. Anatomie und Mechanik des Hasenfusses. Ztschr. f. Saugetierkunde, **3**:98–171.

WALMSLEY, THOMAS. 1918. The reduction of the mammalian fibula. J. Anat., **52**:326–31.

WATSON, D. M. S. 1918. The evolution of the tetrapod shoulder girdle and forelimb. J. Anat., **52**:1–95.

WILLISTON, S. W. 1925. The osteology of the reptiles. Cambridge: Harvard University Press. Pp. 300.

WINDLE, B. C. A. 1890. The flexors of the digits of the hand, I: The muscular masses in the forearm. J. Anat. Physiol., **24**:72–84.

———. 1897. Myology of Dolichotis patagonica and Dasyprocta isthmica. *Ibid.*, **31**:343–53.

Windle, B. C. A., and Parsons, F. G. 1897–98. On the myology of the terrestrial Carnivora. Proc. Zoöl. Soc., London, Part I, 1897, pp. 370–409; Part II, 1898, pp. 152–86.

———. 1901–3. On the muscles of the Ungulata. *Ibid.*, Part I, 1901, pp. 656–704; Part II, 1903, pp. 261–98.

Zittel, K. A. von. 1932. Text book of palaeontology. 2d ed., rev. by A. S. Woodward. London: Macmillan & Co., Ltd., Pp. 464.

Index

[PRINTED
IN U·S·A]